The Charlton Standard Catalogue of

CHINTZ

Second Edition

By
Linda Eberle
and
Susan Scott

W.K. Cross
Publisher

Birmingham, Michigan ● Toronto, Ontario

COPYRIGHT AND TRADEMARK NOTICE

Canadian Cataloguing In Publication Data

Eberle, Linda
The Charlton standard catalogue of Chintz
2nd ed.
Includes index.
ISBN 0-88969-188-0

1. Chintzware - Catalogues. I. Scott, Susan, 1948-
II. Title.

NK4085.B23 1997 738.2'7 C97-930497-0

Printed in Canada
in the Province of Manitoba

EDITORIAL

Editor Nicola Leedham
Graphic Technician Davina Rowan

ACKNOWLEDGEMENTS

The Charlton Press wishes to thank those who have helped and assisted with the second edition of the *Charlton Standard Catalogue of Chintz*.

CONTRIBUTORS

The Publisher would like to thank the following individuals who graciously supplied photographs or allowed us access to their pieces for photographic purposes. We offer sincere thanks to: Carolyn Evers, Jane Fehrenbacher, Laurie Goldberg, Bill Hogan, Fritz Mueller, Cindy Oliver, Judy Osborne, Bob Ostrowski, David Shestak, Sweet Pea Creations.

A SPECIAL NOTE TO COLLECTORS

The Charlton Press has an ongoing commitment to excellence and completeness in the production of all its reference works. We will consider editorial additions or corrections regarding colourways, varieties, or dating of patterns. Your help in providing new or previously unobtainable data on any aspect of Chintz collecting will be considered for inclusion in subsequent editions. Those providing information will be acknowledged in the contributor's section of this catalogue.

Please send your contributions together with your name, address and phone number to our editorial offices in Toronto:

Editorial Office
2040 Yonge Street, Suite 208
Toronto, ON M4S 1Z9
Phone: 1-800-442-6042 Fax: 1-800-442-1542

GRIMWADES LTD., STOKE-ON-TRENT.

Supplement "C"

All articles on this list can be supplied in decorations illustrated on sheets C/1, C/2, C/3, and any similar styles of decoration.

"ROYAL WINTON" IVORY TABLEWARE.

TABLE OF CONTENTS

ondon Showrooms:
24, THAVIES INN,
HOLBORN CIRCUS, E.C.

"Crown Ducal" Ware.

Canadian Agent:
EMERSON NICHOLLS,
P.O. Box 354,
LONDON, ONTARIO

A. G. RICHARDSON & Co., Ltd.,

(*Directors:* A. G. Richardson, J. Rushton, J. Harrison),

EARTHENWARE MANUFACTURERS,

Gordon Pottery, Pinnox St., **TUNSTALL,** Stoke-on-Trent, England.

SPECIALITIES: Ivory Vellum Decoration, Matt Black Ground styles as A340, 443, & 614, etc., and exclusive Chintz & other designs, as A500 & 601, etc. Victorian Silver Ware.

PREFACE

This has been a remarkable year in the world of chintz. At the beginning of 1996 there were no books on chintz; now there are several. Auction houses were unaware of chintz; now Christie's South Kensington in London has scheduled their first all chintz auction. Factories had no interest in the manufacture of chintz; now several companies have begun to reproduce traditional chintz dishes and fabric. Few people knew what chintz was when you asked for it; now there are magazine stories, radio interviews and pages of chintz for sale on the Internet. Who can predict what this year will bring?

As many of you already know we met more than four years ago via the telephone and the hours spent chatting California to Toronto resulted in a warm friendship, a first meeting in England followed by a trip to the Chintz Convention in California, and ultimately, the first edition of the *Charlton Standard Catalogue of Chintz*. Linda is still an avid chintz collector although she has slowed down from the days when she collected fifty tea pots and coffee pots in one year. Susan is still a free lance writer who specializes in twentieth century collectibles and now writes a monthly 'hot collectible' column for *Canadian House & Home.* Linda is still out there looking for chintz while Susan is searching the archives and libraries for any new piece of information she can find.

We would never have been able to write this second book without the help of a long line of people. First and foremost we want to thank our husbands once again — Gene Eberle and Douglas Scott — who were left behind while we went off to England to research and photograph new patterns and shapes. Nicola Leedham, our editor, has a clear eye and a sharp pencil and we are grateful for her guidance. John Klycinski came back to help with new pattern slides. He and Linda spent the day with Shelley collector, Judy Osborne, photographing Shelley chintz patterns and shapes from Judy's own collection as well as pieces from her friend Marie Leenerts. As you know, we were anxious to expand the Shelley section of the book and the National Shelley China Club in the United States, particularly Curt Leiser, have been of great help. Royal Doulton in England kindly allowed us to spend a morning in their archives and photograph pages of Shelley chintz patterns. Members of the Chintz Collector Club have once again been diligent in recording new patterns, shapes, and numbers. In particular, Sonia Moreno, Cindy Oliver and Jane Fehrenbacher from California, Laurie Goldberg from Virginia and Carolyn Evers from Oregon, have helped with photographs, many of which we have used in the shape section. Dave Timney of Vancouver Island allowed Susan into his secret room to photograph rare breakfast sets. Fritz Mueller has once again been fanstastic. He photographed shapes and recorded numbers and when Susan called him in despair, he happened to be in Toronto and came over and spent six hours helping her sort photographs. Yet another desperate call to Bob Ostrowski in Idaho resulted in hours and hours of work for him and a huge stack of photographs as well as information for the book. Tolie Coales, daughter of the Canadian representative for Grimwades for fifty years, once again welcomed Susan into her home and continued the saga of her father's life with Grimwades. Marilyn Sanders, who still doesn't collect chintz — aside from the breakfast set in Evesham she found one day — continued to help Susan with the search through trade catalogues.

The history of chintz is in some ways a history of twentieth century English ceramic export patterns and as we followed the trail of chintz around the world, we had a great deal of help. On our most recent trip to England, there were too many helping hands to name them all. Joy Humphreys once again invited us for dinner and allowed us to photograph anything we needed. Beverley and Beth Adams set up a table outside in Church Street so Susan could photograph pieces which were dragged out of a dozen different boxes on the floor in Beverley's shop. Diana Frost found a Saville tray with what we had thought was **Black Crocus** but which was backstamped **Triumph.** We would like to thank her in particular for this discovery, as well as for her support and friendship. Mark Wilkinson and Michael Jeffery of Christie's South Kensington allowed Susan to help herself to any transparencies she needed. Jocelyn Lukins, our Royal Doulton consultant, once again provided a bed, a better pattern photograph of **Victorian**, and her usual encouragement. Susan's cousin Wendy Watson and her husband Peter continued to feed and house us while we wandered through the fields at Ardingly in search of treasure. Linda's friend, Tony Atkinson, also provided a bed and a memorable dinner while we worked at the British Museum's lending library in the wilds of Yorkshire. Ivy Mayer, secretary to the export director of Grimwades, has become a dear friend and she has continued to seek out information for us on the years at Grimwades. Through Ivy, we met Dora Shaw who worked for Wood & Sons for many years. Dora and Ivy not only fed us, they went to the City Museum on our behalf and recorded the numbers of any chintz patterns they were able to find in the newly discovered A. G. Richardson pattern books. Gerrard Shaw, his manuscript on Crown Ducal complete and enrolled in a master's degree at York, came home for the weekend and he and Alison made us a great lunch and he searched for a slide of **Priscilla** for us. He sent Susan photographs of pages out of the Ducal pattern books to help with a couple of questions about pattern numbers. Dr. Tony Burke of Australia sent us a picture of a marked piece of **Ostria** and we could see that the pattern was identical to our marked piece of **Carnation**. Perhaps the most amazing discovery came from Toni Cardwell of New Zealand. Just before the convention in 1996, she discovered a 1936 Grimwade's export catalogue in Australia and she was permitted to make colour xeroxes of the complete catalogue for the various chintz clubs around the world. We have reproduced a number of these pages in the book since they are of great help in identifying many hitherto unknown shapes.

When Susan went back alone in November 1996, she spent a day with Len Griffin, the author of several books on Clarice Cliff. He suggested she get a tape recorder and preserve some of the interviews she had scheduled with chintz workers. His advice and encouragement are greatly appreciated. Ivy introduced Susan to Norma Waterfall nee Smallwood who worked as a designer at Grimwades with

Gordon Forsyth and Mabel Leigh and she shared her memories of the design room at Grimwades with her. Susan interviewed Mrs. H.E. Cooper who is 85 years old but still "has her memories of when she was working." Jean Heath went to work for Grimwade's when she was 13 years old and the hour long interview with her is a remarkable piece of social history. We would like to thank Mrs. Cooper, Jean Heath, Doreen Donegan, Florrie Dennis, Norma Smallwood, all the women who helped us to put a 'human face on chintz'. Chintzware was relatively cheap and cheerful china meant for everyday use. It was never meant to last. Most of the people we met in the potteries —even those who had worked for Winton and Kent — had very little chintz in their cupboards; they had Royal Doulton figurines. Chintz rarely figured in any of the literature of the day, certainly there was no mention of chintz in any of the design books or *Studio Yearbooks*. Factories opened and closed, were taken over and then taken over again and records were usually discarded. There are remarkably few written records to do with any of the factories which produced chintzware. Royal Winton has absolutely nothing left — no molds, no pattern books, no clipping files. James Kent was sold to Hadida in the late 1980s but it would seem that all the records were destroyed at that time, if not earlier. Nothing of Elijah Cotton has been found. All the Myott records were destroyed in a disastrous fire in 1949. Roy Midwinter made every attempt to find the patterns books for the book on Midwinter but he became convinced they had been destroyed. Gerrard Shaw, through detective work and perseverance, discovered some of the A.G.Richardson pattern books in the City Museum at Hanley but most of the chintz patterns were not included and not one was named.

We have gone through more than forty years of *Pottery Gazette & Glass Trade Review*, an equal number of *The Pottery, Glass & Brass Salesman*, a New York trade catalogue, and the later American publication, *Crockery & Glass Journal*. We have pored over American and Canadian decorating magazines and found very few mentions of chintz in thousands of pages. Yvonne Butorac, a Toronto writer who had started researching chintz, kindly allowed Susan to borrow a number of early Canadian trade catalogues found in the basement of her mother-in-law's gift shop. Inspired by these copies of *The Gift Buyer*, Susan then found a thirty year run in the rare book room at the University of Toronto and much of the new information about the dating of Winton patterns came from the advertisements in this publication. Gail Bardhan of the Rakow Library in the Corning Museum of Glass was very helpful in locating information and Susan spent two happy days sitting at a microfiche reader trying to decipher early copies of the *Crockery & Glass Journal*. Although at times it looked pointless since there was so little recorded about chintz, it all became worthwhile when an advertisement for Wright, Tyndal & van Roden suddenly appeared in a 1933 copy of the magazine along with a short article on the introduction of three new Royal Winton patterns, **Summertime, Somerset,** and **Floral Feast**. Some of the information in the new Royal Winton section on dating and backstamps comes from the library at Corning.

Perhaps even more important than the written records we have found, is the access we have had to hundreds of collectors, each with large or small collections. We have tried to build up a picture of chintz from the empirical evidence of what remains —not unlike archeologists sifting through ancient middens trying to cobble together a working history of a group of people from the artifacts they left behind. Many new collectors have written to us after reading the first edition. The result is a greatly expanded shape section, a much larger Shelley section with nine new patterns, a much larger Crown Ducal section with five new patterns, one new Lord Nelson pattern, two new James Kent patterns, five new Royal Winton patterns, several new manufacturers and dozens of newly identified shapes. We have simply incorporated new information wherever it seemed appropriate so we do hope — if you have already read the first edition — that you will take the time to reread the introduction and particularly the Grimwade's section in order to enjoy our new discoveries.

We hope that you will continue to write to us and to send us any new information. We apologize in advance for any omissions. While we have not included a section devoted to bone china chintz, we have noted, when known,those earthenware patterns which were also reproduced in bone china by companies such as Royal Albert. As the chintz market continues to boom perhaps more collectors will be interested in bone china. When this becomes the case you can be assured that we will research the matter thoroughly.

Linda Eberle

Susan Scott

INTRODUCTION

The History of Chintz

The history of chintz goes back hundreds of years, although the chintz so eagerly sought today is very much a twentieth-century industrial product. Chintz — the Indian word was *chintes* — goes back to the fantastical fabrics imported into England from the India of the late seventeenth century. Richly hued flowers and brightly plumed mythical birds decorated both the persons and the houses of the early 1700s to such an extent that it threatened domestic weavers. Even before 1800 chintz had come to mean homey, cozy, overstuffed furniture and a certain English country house look. An advertisement in *The Pottery Gazette* as late as 1957 describes "the homely rustle of chintz, the warm welcoming design of flowered pattern."

Inevitably the china manufacturers created hand-painted tableware which captured the feel of Indian chintz. The development of the process of transfer printing was very important in the popularizing of chintz ceramics. By the 1820s there were a number of Staffordshire factories producing chintz that was meant for everyday use. This chintz is recognizable by the very Victorian shapes to which it was applied and by the loose patterning and more subtle colouring than the twentieth-century versions.

Around 1912 Royal Doulton produced several versions of an all-over pattern called **Persian,** which remained in production until the second world war and was used mainly on cabinet pieces. However, chintzware was not really produced to any extent by any of the carriage-trade pottery firms. The firms which catered to the middle classes and to the masses were the firms which came to personify chintz. In 1918 A. G. Richardson developed their first chintz — a pattern so far identified only as A500 — but followed with **Rose and Motifs** and **Delhi** in the same year. Most of these early Crown Ducal chintzes were used for vases and trinket boxes, not for dinnerware. In dating chintzware to the 1920s, it is useful to study the patterns produced by Richardson's, since they seem to exemplify that exotic 1920s look. They were particularly popular in America, and a long article in *The Pottery, Glass & Brass Salesman* extols Richardson's work:

. . . there is always a steady demand for the chintz patterns . . . these come in many variations of colour background, and the subdued brilliance of the realistic flowers and plumaged birds makes an ever-delightful note. ***Festival*** *decoration with its intertwined lanterns hanging over blithely frolicsome scenes seems to have the ability to capture the fancy of many who like its vivacity. Crown Ducal ware is a beautiful piece of industrial accomplishment with none of the slight faults of immaturity.*

It is useful to place this tableware against a broader historical background. The 1920s were the Jazz Age, the time of the exotic and art deco. Yet the world had barely survived the war to end all wars and the Russian Revolution. The January 1927 advertisement for the new Crown Ducal chintzes describes them as "bordering on the sensational . . . novel indeed and radically different, but not bolshevik." Chintzes somehow managed to be both different but cozy, exotic but not revolutionary. Books on twentieth-century design never contain references to chintz. They were intended for "seaside cottages and bungalow furnishings," not avant garde houses in New York.

From 1918 through the first half of the 1920s, most of the Crown Ducal chintz pieces were vases and console sets (candle sticks and bowls), as well as toilet sets. A 1929 report pointed out that ten years before, the Crown Ducal Works in England had produced only a few vases of various shapes and some odd pieces of decorative earthenware. "Today a tremendous volume business in dinnerware is theirs — and they serve the American market chiefly, for this ware appeals immensely to the value-loving and thrifty native housewife, in whom more for the money awakens instant response. . . .the early examples of CD ware consisting of chintz all-over pattern vases and similar items gained great favor with all who saw them . . . . " A steady stream of requests for individual breakfast sets to match, for tea sets and salad services flowed into the offices of Maddock & Miller, exclusive agents for Crown Ducal. In 1925 the manufacture of dinner services began "the first specimens were of the popular chintz effects which are still in steady demand especially for subsidiary sets." The Americans calculated that a Crown Ducal dinner service would cost about $100, while a comparable bone-china service would be over $500. After a strange gap of almost ten years, Crown Ducal produced a series of chintzes in the 1930s such as **Primrose**, **Priscilla** and **Pansy** but these have never achieved the popularity with collectors of the earlier patterns.

Other firms that were producing chintz very like the 1920s Crown Ducal were Samuel Ford & Company, Wood & Sons, and A. J. Wilkinson Ltd. all located in Burslem. All these firms were geographically very close together and exhibited at the same trade shows. It is not surprising to find that soon after one firm produced something marketable, the others followed. For most of them, however, these all-over patterns were simply one out of the many lines they produced. In order to have an exclusive pattern, a company would have to buy the complete run which required a sizable capital outlay. Having a "controlled" pattern was expensive not just in money but in space; it meant buying the whole run from the lithographic firm and keeping it on premises. Many factories would simply go to the lithographer and select one of the stock patterns out of their books. Patterns like James Kent's **Mille Fleur** were clearly not 'controlled' patterns; A. G. Richardson had the same pattern in their books as Crown Ducal Pattern Number 5007 and Lord Nelson named this pattern **Marigold**. A. J. Wilkinson introduced a new pattern **Mayflower** in 1925 for which they were commended by the *Pottery Gazette*. Grimwade's used the identical pattern on a cube teapot clearly dating around the same time. The Grimwade's pattern **Rose Du Barry** has been found as James Kent's **Chelsea Rose** and Shelley's **Briar Rose**, and recently a piece of James Kent's **Silverdale** turned up with a Royal Winton backstamp. These factories were all close, and many of the workers were related or acquainted. Inevitably, strange pieces will have been produced.

In fact, this was unusual for Grimwades. Although occasionally they resorted to stock patterns, the company became known for chintz. Their chintz lines were a major part of their business and they tended to use exclusive patterns designed in their own shop. Throughout this early period Grimwades Ltd. was producing a wide range of products; the company was noted for their ewers and basins amongst other lines. At this time their chintzes were closer to the Victorian versions than to the Crown Ducal "fantastical" and seem somewhat old-fashioned in comparison (see Grimwade's **Merton, Carnation,** and **Fernese** for comparison with other mid 1920s chintz patterns). Gradually their patterns changed, and in 1928 Grimwades introduced their first "modern" chintz, **Marguerite**, which was an instant success. The pattern was available on an amazing assortment of articles; it has even been found on a ceramic hot-water bottle.

As the decade ended and the world-wide depression deepened, the production of decorative pieces was replaced more and more with useful items at reasonable prices more suited to the hard economic times. Clearly there were still decorative items made but the prices had to be low. Grimwades is first mentioned in *The Pottery, Glass & Brass Salesman* in March 1933. Ebeling & Reuss, china and glass importers, is praised for importing fancy chintz earthenware baskets, vases, flatware and even short sets. Buyers are urged to look at the cake plates which they should be able to retail for $1.00 or possibly $1.25. The July 1932 *Gazette* discussed the reorganization of Grimwades' lines during recent months — "occasioned no doubt by the fact that certain lines which were at one time very largely manufactured by Grimwades such as ornamentals and toiletware are less in demand than formerly and therefore these have had to be substituted by other creations more in keeping with the demand of the times." In addition, the improvements that had been made in sanitation spelled the end of the broad production of toiletwares for all but a limited market. Tolie Coales, the daughter of the Canadian representative for Grimwades, recalled her father having ewers and basins shipped directly to the Canadian Maritime provinces. He took orders and then sold off the samples since there was little or no market for them in the rest of Canada. In an interview in *The Gift Buyer*, May 1953, George Coales recalled his first trip to Western Canada — it was 1910 and he took almost half a ton of baggage and his excess baggage charges were greater than the original fare. He travelled with his sample cases by train from coast to coast of Canada for more than forty years and was always surprised by the success of his chintz lines.

The first British Industries Fair was held in 1915, and each year firms mounted displays of their newest lines and hoped to capture the attention of the buying public, as well as trade publications. Ceramics designers were forced to come up with hundreds of new patterns every year to keep up with their competitors and attract publicity. The Grimwade's pattern **Summertime** dates to 1932 and is numbered 775, and the pattern **Clyde** is numbered 5637 and probably dates to 1939. Grimwades therefore came up with something close to a thousand patterns a year throughout the 1930s. Obviously most of these were not chintz patterns but it is not surprising that in their constant search for new patterns, Grimwades took patterns such as **Welbeck** (2204) and redid them in different colourways like **Hazel** (2208) and **Spring** (2506). It is said that the first chintz pattern **Marguerite** was copied from a cushion cover embroidered by the wife of Leonard Grimwade, the owner of the factory. Other patterns came from clothing worn by staff, from pictures in books, from anywhere and everywhere. They were known throughout the 1930s and indeed through the 1950s as the "acknowledged pre-eminent house for chintz patterns."

Publicity was eagerly sought by all the Staffordshire firms. In the early 1930s Elijah Cotton supplied dealers who carried a sufficient range of Lord Nelson Ware with a five-foot-tall ceramic Nelson monument like the one in Trafalgar Square, made up of plates, sandwich trays and egg cups drilled and bolted together. Even today you occasionally run across drilled Nelson Ware chintz plates in the street markets around Stoke-on-Trent.

Not only did the factories turn out new patterns on a weekly basis; they attempted to create new and interesting shapes regularly. In 1922 Crown Ducal were lauded in the American press for their chintz "trays and cups" which have come to be known as tennis or hostess sets. In 1923 it was their 12-inch lily bowls with matte black interiors which won approval. By the late 1920s it was Grimwades that were leading the way in innovative chintz designs and shapes. In 1933 it is Grimwades who are noted in the American trade journals for their plates with plain embossed borders and chintz centers (these plates are known to American collectors as Wedgwood plates). The 1932 *Pottery and Glass Record* noted that Grimwades' "latest design among sets is the small tray with a toast rack, sugar, cream and little teapot, all fitted into grooves but detachable. . . this being called the Bed-side set. It is also supplied with an irregular oblong shape and including a little groove for butter."

The square Ascot shape and the deco Norman shape were introduced in 1932. In 1935 the Athena shape was introduced and described in the *Gazette* as "hexagonal sided in rectangular form with a fancy handle." The 1936 Grimwade's Australian Export Catalogue (we have reproduced some of the interesting shape pages) is invaluable in showing which shapes were available in the mid 1930s. In 1940 the whole Rosebud line was introduced to great acclaim, and although initially produced in a solid colour with hand-painted handles and finials, it was not long before chintz was applied to the whole line. Lily and Petunia followed soon after. One of the most popular of the post-war shapes was the Albans with its clean lines and acorn finial. Interestingly the stacking teapot, which is so incredibly popular in North America, never appears to have been mentioned in the British press and has rarely been seen by British dealers. One of the first mentions of the stacker was in an advertisement in the Canadian Birk's catalogue for 1941, where a plain pink, blue and green "three-in-one Breakfast set" is advertised for sale for $2.00. In the same catalogue a Countess Bedside set is offered for $3.50.

By 1940 the British government had imposed restrictions on the decoration and production of pottery and these remained in force for the home market until 1952. As a result, patterns such as **Morning Glory** and **May Festival** often appear in England without hand painting and are presumably pre-1952. By the time the war ended, the Canadian representative alone had two years of back orders, which the factory simply could not supply. Shipments went around the world as fast as they could be packed, but often there were mix-ups and pieces intended for Canada landed in New Zealand or elsewhere. Sheryl Vogt, the founder of the Australian Royal Winton Collectors' Club, heard from a New Zealand dealer that "the US buyers would not accept old or outmoded designs so the newest ware was kept for the Americans and the government insisted on 75% of production being exported, up to 1952 . . . so as much old stock as could be mustered from warehouses was sent out to Australia and New Zealand up until that time. This has turned out to be most fortunate as we still have a good range of pre-war ware from what was essentially a small family pottery."

The wartime production of plain white utility ware created a craving for colour and warmth, which resulted in a tremendous upsurge in the sales of chintzware both at home and abroad throughout the 1950s. Considering the direction of the design movement during this decade, this is quite surprising. Firms like Midwinter Ltd. produced a tremendous amount of chintzware from just after the war until the 1970s, yet a recent book on the company devotes one line to chintz. James Kent Ltd., under the able management of Ruth Kent, exported containers full of **Dubarry**, **Apple Blossom** and **Rosalynde** to North America through the 1950s and the 1960s. Export was so important that Miss Kent, who was the Sales Director after the war, was sent to Canada in 1951 to attempt to understand the Canadian needs; after crossing Canada, she went on to Australia. In *The Gift Buyer* from 1949 to 1953 there were a whole series of advertisements for new Royal Winton chintz patterns. In fact, in a 1953 interview,George Coales was quoted as saying that he was delighted that Grimwade's had been able ***to issue fifteen new chintz patterns in the last year.*** Clearly chintz enjoyed a resurgence at least through the early part of the 1950s. There were suddenly advertisements for **Cottonwood** by Langdale Pottery Company, for **Wild Rose Chintz** by Winterton Pottery, for **Springtime** by John Shaw & Sons Ltd. and for **Summer Flowers** by Myott Son & Company. The prices remained quite low. For example, a Barker Brothers Royal Tudor Ware cake plate and server was advertised in the *Montreal Gazette* in May of 1954 for $2.35, while a Royal Winton chintz stacking teapot is noted in the Christmas 1951 *Canadian House & Home* for $2.50.

Although many of the patterns that we now know were produced after the war are similar to the pre-war patterns, such as **Marion**, **Nantwich** and **Cheadle**, there are others that are very much in the 1950s mold, such as **June Festival**, **Spring Glory** and **Peony**. Suddenly, from being new and fresh, all-over floral prints came to be described very differently in the 1950 *Crockery & Glass Journal*: "Dinner sets with small rosebuds or other tiny all over motifs 'crawling' have lost stature as the stock-in-trade of foreign-made wares. In their stead are larger floral motifs . . . sophisticated stylized versions." Just as the 1920s chintzes have a certain look, so do the 1950s versions. The flowers are much larger and further apart and the ground colours tend to be black, navy and burgundy. Even with these changes chintz could not be made to enhance the look of Scandinavian blond wood furniture and the amoeba shapes of the modern dishes. Gradually the potteries phased out their chintz lines and moved on to a completely different style.

Grimwades was bought by the Howard Group in 1964 and moved their operation to Norfolk Street. At the time of the takeover, Canada was the largest single overseas market with Australia and New Zealand not far behind. Ivy Mayer says that whenever she thinks of chintz she thinks of Canada, and when she thinks of Rosebud she thinks of Australia. After the move there was little room in the new location for the production of chintzware. Although chintz was not produced to any great extent after 1964, Ivy remembers a room with shelves full of sheets of chintz lithographs and she says good customers could still order chintz and if the sheets were available, the factory would fill the orders. We found two invoices from Grimwades to J.L. Bradshaw Ltd. in Stratford, Canada, one dated March 24, 1969, and the other June 5, 1969. The one invoice is for 215 "two tier" Tid Bit sets in **Cheadle**, **Victorian Rose** and **Old Cottage Chintz**. Everything else on the invoice appears to be in later non-chintz patterns, such as **Thistle** 1594. The backstamp used by Royal Winton after 1964 is easily recognizable and the earthenware has a whiter cast than before.

Although MIKASA turned out a complete line of James Kent's **Dubarry** in the mid 1980s, Staffordshire potteries have largely ignored the returning popularity of chintz. Crownford China Company Ltd., with the trade name Queen's China are now manufacturing a fine bone china they call **English Chintz**. When we went to watch the lithographs being applied, we were told that most workers find the transfers too difficult and prefer not to work with chintz. Spouts and handles are left plain since there is no one left with the skills of a Florrie Dennis to do the job. Interestingly, in the last year the manufacture of chintz in the old style has suddenly become economically viable again. There are several companies looking at reproducing old-style chintz ceramics — one of which is Royal Winton!

The Human Face of Chintz

There were no records that we could find to tell us more about chintz ware. Finally we advertised in the *Evening Sentinel* in Stoke-on-Trent. Several letters came in response. One was from Florrie Dennis who worked for Royal Winton from the age of fourteen. "I worked for two weeks and didn't receive any pay until the end of the third week which was five shillings and nine pence a week." They were told "we must always decorate a piece of ware how we would like to buy it . . . perfect."

Florrie wrote a long letter describing the process of applying the lithograph to the pottery. It will be easier to understand her remarks if you think of wall papering around windows and difficult corners and try to imagine how hard it must have been to do toast racks and lamps. Large sheets of patterned paper were kept in a separate room and the girls had to go and get pieces and cut them into the appropriate size for the ware they were decorating.

"We had a pot of size which we then brushed on the piece of ware with a camel haired brush which we had to buy for one shilling old money so of course used to clean them every night. We applied the size onto the piece of ware then wafted it until nice and tacky. In front of us was placed a pattern of whatever piece of ware you were going to practise on. We had to fetch our litho from a little decorating shop. We applied the litho onto the piece of pottery looking closely at the pattern in front of you then we were shown a geyser at the bottom of the shop and given a chamber pot to carry very hot water to the bench and a piece of waste rag and a hard sponge and a soft sponge and a piece of hard yellow soap. When we had applied the litho sprays to the piece of ware we then dipped the hard sponge into the hot water then rubbed the sprays of litho on the ware then a little harder then of course it was very wet then taking the soft sponge which we have rubbed onto the hard soap began to sponge off the wet paper which by now had fastened the floral sprays onto the ware. Then taking the piece of soft cloth gently dabbed the piece of ware to be passed as perfect...the most popular pattern was **Summertime** which consisted of all summer flowers . . . also we did a chintz called **Black Hazel** and a lot of tea ware which was called ajax ware (this was a shape range). We were not allowed to cut into flowers and used a razor blade to decorate round the handles and teapot spouts and cup and cream handles. All the patterns we used were all set out and each had a number."

"...after six months you were expected to go on piece work to earn your wages. The prices then were very low. I worked in my dinner hour many days." When we went to see Florrie she told us much more about her life. She left school at fourteen on a Friday and she started at Royal Winton on the Monday. She started in 1928 and the first pattern she worked on was **Marguerite** the first real all over chintz at Winton. Out of her wages, she gave all but a shilling to her father. One week she worked every lunch hour and made an extra shilling which she hid in the toe of her shoe. When she went to bed she forgot about it and it hit the floor when she took her shoe off. Even at eighty she can remember vividly the beating her father gave her that night.

The decorating manager was a man called Mr. Parry and he could be very unkind to the young girls who worked for him. Florrie told us you always got more for your fittings but only if they were perfect (fittings were pieces like teapots and coffee pots).You had to do the pieces that were assigned to you. She still remembers girls sitting crying over their benches because they could not manage to do the spouts of the teapots or coffee pots and at the end of the day might have nothing to show for their efforts. They didn't get paid as a result and could be beaten when they came home empty handed. She remembers staying late to help girls with their spouts and handles. "I was only small and can remember how difficult it was to handle putting the border on the inside and outside of the large wash basins . . . ."

This year we again asked for help in the *Evening Sentinel* and two more Grimwades workers responded. Jean Heath, nee Edwards, agreed to have Susan come out and talk to her. She had wonderful stories of the kindness of the staff at Grimwade's. When she went to work there she was thirteen years old and her birthday was at Christmas. She can still remember the cake and the gifts that the Grimwades workers gave her. Her sister worked there all her life as a gilder and soon before she left she was asked to work on a white and silver tea set. She was told it was a special order and extra care was needed. This was the tea set which was presented to her upon her retirement from Grimwades. Jean still had a letter which she received in 1946 from The English China Shop Ltd., Importers of Fine English China in Vancouver, British Columbia. When she packed a Royal Winton coffee set she put a letter in the coffee pot. The reply is worth quoting: "The coffee set is now on its way to the United States. I sold it to some American tourists and they were really delighted with it. The Americans come up to Canada just to buy our nice English ware which they can't get down there." It may be fifty years later but the Americans are still coming up over the border in search of Royal Winton!

The other letter was from Mrs. H. Cooper who wrote to say that our plea for help brought back memories of when she worked on the "Potbanks." She is 85 years old but she still remembers being a lithographer "doing the **Balmoral** chintz and sizing and cutting out of the intricate pattern for the pieces of earthenware, especially the toastracks which were the bane of my life." She said that she could remember taking four sheets of pattern with the white border (like wallpaper edges) and sticking them together in order to be able to get more pieces out of each sheet. "You had to be careful and cut around the flower."

Grimwades were considered the pre-eminent producers of chintzware and when you look at the products from the various factories you will begin to understand why. Elijah Cotton simply did not attempt to cover the handles and spouts with the chintz and were therefore able to sell their product at a lower price. Interestingly, a few Lord Nelson stacking teapots have turned up with spout and handles covered in chintz so perhaps an ex-Griwmades employee went to the Cotton factory and did the same work for them. The chintz ware which is produced today also has undecorated spouts and handles even though the slide-off method is now used whereby the transfer is dipped in water and then put on the ware. The method is much easier but spouts and handles are still beyond the skills of most workers.

It was — and is — "hard work for small wages." When you read these letters and talk to these elderly ladies, you get a vivid picture of how young these workers were and how difficult the work was. When you are enjoying your special **Welbeck** coffee pot, think of the fourteen year old who decorated it, and if it isn't perfectly done think of her sitting on her three-legged stool weeping as she tries to achieve perfection with materials that were far from perfect. They did it so well that thousands around the world still seek out and enjoy the "cheap and cheerful" product of their labors.

Advice for Collectors

One of the questions Americans in particular often ask is "What about buying chintz as an investment?" Please don't. Buy chintz because you love the look. Buy it because you are trying to put together a shelf of interesting patterns in your kitchen. Buy it because you have always wanted to collect something and chintz really appeals to you. But don't buy it as an investment. Art and antiques and collectibles can go up or down in price according to the vagaries of fashion and the whim of the collecting public. You would be much wiser to put your retirement money into blue chip stocks and your 'fun' money into chintz.

In the past year we have heard more stories of treasures found and tales of disappointment and we have added to our list of hazards and questions to ask for those who are new to chintz buying or, indeed, for those who are buying over the telephone or the Internet.

The biggest complaint we have heard in the past year is the number of pieces sold as perfect which are restored. When a vase sells for $10 it is not worth spending $30 to restore but when it sells for $325 . . . as the price of chintz goes up and up, there are obviously going to be more restored pieces on the market. Look very closely at the spouts of teapots and coffee pots, since they are the most vulnerable to chips. Always check finials to make sure they haven't been reattached. Look at the plain back and if a piece is crazed all over except for one corner which is smooth, this may be an indication of a restoration. Try to look at a piece in bright sunlight since many repairs become visible in this light. Find out what the return policy is. As long as the piece is marked restored and the price has been adjusted accordingly, if you want the piece buy it by all means — especially if it is for display and you don't have that particular shape or pattern. Do be careful in washing a restored piece. Several collectors discovered a restoration through over-zealous cleaning.

The depth of colour in various patterns and even the shading can greatly affect the price. There are several Winton patterns, in particular **Sweet Pea** and **Julia**, and James Kent **Florita** where pieces can vary tremendously in the depth of colour. Ask how strong the colours are to make sure you will not be disappointed if and when a faded vase arrives. **Sunshine** is a pattern where sometimes the flowers are a deep rich pink and sometimes they are almost orange. As you would imagine, chintz collectors love the pink and do not like the orange.

Both **Summertime** and **Old Cottage Chintz** were made from the early 1930s until well into the 1960s. The lithographs changed over the intervening thirty years. The pinks and reds in **Summertime** and the pinks and blues in **OCC** are quite different, and if you are trying to make up sets it is important to find out which decade you are talking about.

Another new issue is the question of Royal Winton cheese dishes and cheese keeps. Both the 1930s Australian and the 1950s Canadian trade catalogues list the rectangular covered dish as an Ascot cheese dish and the square covered dish as an Ascot butter dish. Americans think of both these dishes as butter dishes and when they imagine cheese dishes they are thinking of the large slope-sided cheese keeps like the Rex and the Dane (refer to the shape section).

One of the most common complaints is still the size of the teapot or coffee pot — what was expected and what arrived. There are many ways of measuring size. Sometimes when you read an advertisement, such as Ebeling & Reuss for James Kent, and see that a teapot 30 is more expensive than a teapot 36 you may be confused. According to Dora Shaw, the number refers to the number of pots which could be loaded into each pannier. The panniers were loaded on to horses who carried the ware down to the barges for shipping out. Obviously, the larger the number the smaller the piece. It is only in the past two years that this system has been abandoned for decimalization. When you are offered a two-cup, or four-cup, or six-cup teapot or coffee pot, be sure that you are clear what that means. Usually a two-cup teapot means two six-ounce cups of tea and four cup means four six-ounce cups; if you are expecting a normal eight-ounce cup measurement you will be disappointed.

Another common complaint is trays which are meant to house various bits and come either incomplete or incorrect. If you are offered a divided tray, make sure it is a divided tray and not simply a tray with indentations for egg cups and salt and pepper which are not in evidence — Linda has first hand experience with this particular problem. A long-time collector was offered a complete breakfast set, but after some discussion discovered that although there was a teapot, toast rack, and cup, there was a salt and pepper in the place of the cream and sugar! A 1938 advertisement in a Toronto newspaper offered a breakfast set for sale with a teapot, cream and sugar, toast rack and **jam pot** although the illustration clearly shows the standard cup. A report in 1946 of a display at a Toronto store recommended the breakfast tray with toast rack, teapot, cup, **marmalade jar** and petit cream jug. It is not surprising that we also get confused. Mistakes are easily made. It is wise to ask very detailed questions if you are buying from another country and you want to be sure of what you are getting.

If you are offered a cruet set, make sure that the mustard has a lid if it ought to have one and that you are sent one pepper and one salt — not two of either one. Sometimes when you are at a show and in a hurry, you will buy what you think is a great bargain and discover that you got what you paid for. Some patterns are very similar and sadly sometimes tops and bottoms do not really go together once you get them into the light of day. The most common mismatch is the various cruet sets. One woman had a **Sunshine** salt and pepper and the rest of her set was **Summertime**. In fifty years she had never noticed that they were two different patterns.

Always ask for the measurements of whatever piece you are buying. If you ever see a plate listed as four-inch nominal, you are talking about a six-inch actual size plate. None of our experts in the potteries were able to give us an answer as to why plates and dishes are listed in trade catalogues in nominal sizes when the actual size is two inches bigger. Royal Winton plates were made in sizes from four-inch actual to ten-inch. It seems to be much easier to find nine-inch plates than ten-inch plates so the ten-inch usually sells for a premium.

Trays came in all shapes and sizes. Cake plates came with and without cutout handles — since the cutout handles cracked more often, the price is usually a little higher. Jugs came in sizes ranging from three to nine inches and every conceivable shape, so make sure of the dimensions and the shape. The prices in this guide are for the more common shapes such as the Royal Winton Globe or Countess. You would expect to pay more for a rarer shape like Duval or Athena.

There are at least ten different cream and sugar shapes in Royal Winton and a variety in all the other makers. The Winton Ascot, the Globe and the Countess cream and sugar came with two versions of the sugar bowl, so if it matters to you, be sure that you are getting the shape you want. The Ascot, the Albans and the Raleigh came in a larger size as well so if you are trying to match other pieces be sure to ask for the measurements.

Midwinter, James Kent and Howard Potteries 'Royal Winton' coffee pots, teapots, cream and sugars and cups and saucers sometimes come with a plain white foot. Some people do not like the look of the white rim; remember to ask.

The most fragile colour in chintz is the blue, and various reactions can cause them to fade quite badly. Relish dishes that have been used for something acidic such as pickles may be very faded where the juices bleached out the colours. When you are buying a bowl look carefully at the edges and the bottom. Sometimes you won't notice with a pattern like **Welbeck** until you look closely and then you will realize that the blue is gone from the bottom of the bowl.

If you buy a teapot and it has a fine white dust inside when you rub your finger over it, it may have been bleached. Whenever something is put in bleach (which we do **not** recommend), it must be neutralized in water for an equal length of time or the chemical reaction will continue indefinitely and could destroy the piece.

People often ask which cup should be on the breakfast sets because they are concerned about having the "right" one. Ivy Mayer, the secretary of Royal Winton's export director, told us that the breakfast sets were always sold with the buyer's "cup of choice," so any cup could be considered correct since who knows what a Philadelphia importer chose forty years ago. The exception to this is the breakfast sets in **Lily, Rosebud** and **Petunia**, where normally you would expect everything on the tray to match.

Sauce boats and jam pots normally come with an under plate, and you should expect to pay less if it is missing. Some of the Royal Winton and the Midwinter jam pots came with chrome lids, some with ceramic. The ceramic lid is inset and the chrome fits over the pot with a protruding rim. Look carefully to make sure that you have the right lid. The Winton Rheims jam pot came in a short and tall version, and the short version usually sells for less because the pattern does not display as well as on the tall pot. Many collectors prefer the all-ceramic jam pots, which usually makes the price higher.

If you are buying a bowl or compote ask if the pattern is on both the inside and the outside of the piece. The tray under the salt and pepper sometimes has pattern on the outside of the tray, sometimes just on the plate. Some salt and pepper collectors care. Some baskets and bowls have a thin strip of pattern on the inside and others don't. Ivy Mayer showed us a Canoe dish with the pattern only on the inside and gilding on the outside and told us it was an experiment to reduce costs after the war. There is always a premium for pieces which are completely covered with the pattern.

Many of the 1930s chintzes were used for what Americans call "Wedgwood" plates. The pattern covers the center of the plate and the rim is white and embossed. The plates came in several sizes — round and square plates in nine and 12 inches. The 1950s versions had no embossing and were available with solid colour bands in maroon, green or yellow in eight and ten inch square plates. Although some collectors don't like these plates over the past year they seem to have become more popular. The 1950s Royal Winton cups with the pattern on the inside of the cup and the center of the saucer seem to be rare in England, Australia and New Zealand. They were advertised in the 1953 Canadian catalogue and turn up in North America quite often. Make sure that the pattern inside the cup matches the pattern in the center of the saucer — again this is a personal experience of Linda's.

Sometimes new collectors become very concerned about the crazing on many of the pieces, especially Royal Winton. This is not fine bone china but earthenware, and often the glaze will become crazed over a number of years. Unless a hairline crack has appeared, this should not greatly effect the value. As chintz is shipped around the world from climate to climate one wonders if this will effect the crazing. An Australian collector recommends that you keep a dish of water in the china cabinet to prevent further crazing. Even if you are paying more for your chintz these days than for Royal Worcester, do not forget that it was cheap and cheerful when it started life. The ill-fitting lid is not necessarily the wrong lid — it may never have fit properly.

Sometimes the lithographs are very badly applied, especially with some of the James Kent and Lord Nelson Ware. The joins are supposed to be invisible and some of the Royal Winton pieces are remarkably well done. If this is important to you, look carefully, especially around awkward corners. Some people like the hominess of the badly done pieces. Susan's Lord Nelson **Rosetime** bud vase looks as though a young girl, thinking about her date on a Friday night, just threw the litho onto the vase — nothing matches, but it has its own peculiar charm.

How to Use This Price Guide

Prices

There have been incredible changes in the chintz world since the publication of the first edition of the chintz guide. Obviously we have tried to track the changes in prices but, as all of you know, this is a very difficult task since prices differ not only from country to country but from one part of the country to another and even from one dealer to the next. Some patterns have gone up in England and down in the United States. Some shapes are more collectible in one country than another.

We have had a number of letters and phone calls to ask about different sizes and shapes. As we are sure you are now aware, the chintz producing companies — especially Royal Winton — covered an incredible variety of shapes and sizes with chintz. We have given the price for three sizes of Royal Winton Globe shaped jugs but there are jugs in Countess, Athena, Duval, Fife, Albans, Wycombe, Ventnor, Raleigh, Dutch, Cambridge, Rosebud, Lily and on and on. Some of these jugs — like Duval — are harder to find and therefore cost more.

We have tried to give a selection of the pieces that are most commonly found by the collector. Some of you have written to ask us about the prices of items like Royal Winton lamps, baskets, wall pockets, spoons, salad sets, music boxes. We have included pictures of some of these rare items in the shape section but we have not attempted to put prices on pieces which only turn up once in a long time. It truly is a question of what one person is asking and another person is willing to pay and there is no consistency which would make a price list of any value.

The majority of collectors used to be American, and several years ago it is fair to say that prices were much higher there than in the rest of the world. In the past year prices have gone up dramatically in England, Australia and New Zealand and stayed the same or gone down in Canada, except for those dealers selling directly into the American market. English prices in some cases now exceed American prices, particularly for Royal Winton chintzes. Christie's South Kensington were amazed when a lot of chintz estimated at £200-300 finally sold for £4800. Other English auction houses have had similar experiences. Estimates on recent chintz lots have been terrifyingly high and it is difficult to predict how the market will react. For the first time Christie's are holding a chintz only sale and this may have an impact on prices, especially in England. Elijah Cotton, James Kent and Crown Ducal, as well as some of the lesser-known manufacturers have continued to be priced lower than Royal Winton and in some cases these prices have gone down from a year ago. Although some new collectors are happy to have a piece of chintz of whatever manufacture, others will only collect Royal Winton and only certain pieces. We have in some cases found that prices are much the same or lower for ordinary items like tea plates or bonbon dishes, while they have gone up dramatically for jugs and bud vases. It is fair to say that most collectors want pieces which will display well and show off the pattern. Coffee pots now sell for more than tea pots and cups and saucers sell better than tennis sets for this reason.

As any of you who have used a price guide know, they are always subject to fierce debate. As we said in the first edition, in the case of something like chintzware, where the collecting field is very new and prices have risen both quickly and dramatically, the debate is very heated indeed. A price guide is exactly that: a guide to recent prices which have been paid for the pieces described. Chintz collecting is so new that many dealers and collectors are unsure what to charge and what to pay. We asked dealers and collectors around the world to let us know which patterns and which pieces had risen or fallen in the last year and we were pleased with the response. Last year we told you about a stacking teapot in **Sweet Pea** bought in Washington State for $125; Linda had a call from a collector last week who bought a stacking teapot in **Summertime** on Staten Island for $45! Another collector called to say they had seen a stacker advertised on the Internet for over $2000! How do you establish a price? The price in any market is what one person asks and another person is willing to pay.

One dealer called and made a point which is worth repeating. If you have a set of chintz and you want to sell it, the price you get will very much depend on the venue. Our prices are average prices paid by a collector not by a dealer. If you want to advertise and find the ultimate collector you may be able to get the same price but it will take time and effort. If you are selling to a dealer, you may only get 40-50% of the book price since that dealer has overheads, carrying costs, and so on, but you will sell quickly. There are advantages and disadvantages to everything and you have to decide whether your time has any monetary value.

In the final analysis Oscar Wilde's trenchant comment about pricing is as true today as it was last year: "A cynic is a man who knows the price of everything and the value of nothing."

In this book we share with you what we know about the prices of chintz, but we also try to talk about its value — as a pleasing collectible, as a part of our shared history and as a product of the ingenuity of the men and women who worked in the potteries in hard times.

Numbering System

The system we have in place enables every piece of chintz to have an exclusive letter and number.

Pattern Name Codes

The letter codes represent the pattern; for example "GT" is **Green Tulip.** We have added several additional Royal Winton patterns. In the case of **Carnation, Fernese, Merton** and **Paisley,** these were patterns which collectors continued to write to us about and although in the first three cases only a few items have been listed, we thought these patterns should be included. We have also included a pattern we are calling **Offley**. This pattern was advertised in Toronto in 1938 and we know that three chintz patterns **Sandon, Meaford** and **Offley** were introduced earlier that year. A description of **Offley** in the *Pottery Gazette* seems to fit this pattern so we decided to call it **Offley** for the moment. Thanks to London dealer and good friend Diana Frost, we were able to change the name of **Black Crocus** to **Triumph** after she found a Saville tray with the backstamp "Triumph". Since most different colourways in Royal Winton have different names, and patterns produced around the second world war like **May Festival** are rarely backstamped, we feel comfortable using this name. A.G. Richardson presented special problems, since there were well over a dozen patterns and we had names for only **Primula** and **Marigold** when we started working on this project. With Gerrard Shaw's guidance, Susan found copies of forty years of the *Pottery Glass & Brass Salesman* and discovered advertisements for a number of the Crown Ducal patterns, including pattern names. We were able to identify **Ascot**, **Blue Chintz**, **Festival**, **Florida** and **Ivory Chintz**. Gerrard was able to give us **Canton** and **Rose & Motifs** from his research in England. In order to make the collector's life easier, we decided to create appropriate names for the other five patterns until we are able to find the actual factory names: **"Grey Fruit," "Ivory Fruit," "Mauve Chintz," "Pink Chintz,"** and **"Purple Chintz."** For the second edition, after letters, calls and photographs from collectors we have been able to add **Delhi, Pansy, Peony, Priscilla** to our Ducal pattern list. We have created a separate page for **"Blue Chintz without Bird"** which we have called **"Spring Blossom"** because several people pointed out that they are valued differently by collectors of the pattern.

Wade **"Butterfly Chintz"** and Myott **"Spring Flower"** are also temporary names until factory names can be found. We were sent dozens of photographs of unknown chintz patterns and we have included a few which were representative of styles of chintz or interesting companies.We have left the patterns unnamed unless we actually know them like Wilkinson's **Mayflower**. We hope once again that collectors will continue to send us information so that we can gradually fill in the missing names.

PATTERN CODES

Barker Brothers Ltd.

Letter Code	Pattern Name
Bab1	Unnamed
Bab2	Unnamed
Bab3	Unnamed
Bab4	Unnamed

Brexton

Letter Code	Pattern Name
Bx1	Unnamed
Bx2	Unnamed

Elijah Cotton Ltd. — Lord Nelson Ware

Letter Code	Pattern Name
AC	Anemone Chintz
BB	Black Beauty
BR	Briar Rose
CL	Country Lane
GT	Green Tulip
He	Heather
MgC	Marigold
Ma	Marina
P	Pansy
R	Rosetime
RB	Royal Brocade
Sk	Skylark

Empire Porcelain Co. Ltd.

Letter Code	Pattern Name
BM	Black Marguerite
LT	Lilac Time
WL	Water Lily

Ford & Sons

Letter Code	Pattern Name
FS	Unnamed

Grimwades Ltd. — Royal Winton

Letter Code	Pattern Name
A	Anemone
Ba	Balmoral
Be	Bedale
Bee	Beeston
Car	Carnation
Chd	Cheadle
Chl	Chelsea
Chz	Chintz
Cl	Clevedon
Cly	Clyde
Co	Cotswold
Cr	Cranstone
Cro	Crocus
Crom	Cromer
De	Delphinium Chintz
Do	Dorset
El	Eleanor
ER	English Rose
Esl	Estelle
Est	Esther
Ev	Evesham
Fer	Fernese
FiB	Fireglow Black
FiW	Fireglow White
FF	Floral Feast
FG	Floral Garden
Fl	Florence
H	Hazel
JL	Joyce-Lynn
J	Julia
JF	June Festival
JR	June Roses
Ke	Kew
Ki	Kinver
Maj	Majestic
Mag	Marguerite
Mar	Marion
May	Mayfair

Letter Code	Pattern Name
Mer	Merton
MF	May Festival
MG	Morning Glory
N	Nantwich
Of	Offley
OC	Old Cottage Chintz
O	Orient
Pa	Paisley
Pe	Pekin
Pel	Pelham (Sampler)
Peo	Peony
QA	Queen Anne
Q	Quilt
Ri	Richmond
RD	Rose Du Barry
Roy	Royalty
Ru	Rutland
Sh	Shrewsbury
So	Somerset
Sp	Spring
SG	Spring Glory
Spt	Springtime
St	Stratford
Su	Summertime
Sun	Sunshine
SN	Sweet Nancy
SP	Sweet Pea
T	Tartans
Tr	Triumph
V	Victorian
VR	Victorian Rose
W	Welbeck
WF	Wild Flowers
Wi	Winifred

Johnson Brothers Ltd.

Letter Code	Pattern Name
RC	Rose Chintz

James Kent, Ltd.

Letter Code	Pattern Name
AB	Apple Blossom
CP	Crazy Paving
D	Dubarry
F	Florita
Ha	Harmony
Hy	(white background) Hydrangea
HyB	(black background) Hydrangea
L	Lichfield
MgK	Marigold
MiF	Mille Fleurs
Pr	Primula
Ra	Rapture
Roc	Rochelle
Ro	Rosalynde
S	Silverdale
Tp	Tapestry

Midwinter

Letter Code	Pattern Name
Br	Brama
C	Coral
LD	Lorna Doone

Myott Son & Co.

Letter Code	Pattern Name
SF	*Spring Flower*
SuF	Summer Flower

A.G. Richardson Ltd. — Crown Ducal

Letter Code	Pattern Name
As	Ascot
BC	Blue Chintz
Ca	Canton
Dh	Delhi
Fe	Festival
Fd	Florida
GF	*Grey Fruit*
IC	Ivory Chintz
IF	*Ivory Fruit*
MgR	Marigold
MC	*Mauve Chintz*
PaR	Pansy
Py	Peony
PC	*Pink Chintz*
PrR	Primula
Ps	Priscilla
PuC	*Purple Chintz*
RM	Rose & Motifs
SB	*Spring Blossom*

Ridgway Potteries Ltd.

Letter Code	Pattern Name
RP	Unnamed

Royal Doulton Ltd.

Letter Code	Pattern Name
Per	Persian

Shelley Potteries Ltd.

Letter Code	Pattern Name
BD	Blue Daisy
Clo	Cloisonne
Cs	Countryside
GD	Green Daisy
MS	Marguerite
Mat	Maytime
Me	Melody
PiC	Pink Clover
Pri	Primrose
RG	Rock Garden
SuG	Summer Glory
TR	Tapestry Rose

Wade & Company

Letter Code	Pattern Name
Bu	*Butterfly Chintz*
Pai	Paisley
Th	Thistle Chintz

Wedgwood & Co. Ltd.

Letter Code	Pattern Name
WC1	Unnamed
WC2	Unnamed

A. J. Wilkinson Ltd.

Letter Code	Pattern Name
Maf	Mayflower
MM	*Modern Mayflower*

Wood & Sons Ltd.

Letter Code	Pattern Name
WS	Unnamed

SHAPE NUMBERS

The number codes represent the shapes and are the same across all the factories for the same item; a round seven-inch plate, for example, is '104' whether it is Lord Nelson Ware or A.G. Richardson. We have left gaps in the numbering system to accommodate the variety of chintz pieces that will inevitably come to light.

Number	Shape
01	Ashtray, small
02	Ashtray, large
04	Bonbon dish
05	Bonbon dish, tab handles
09	Bowl, 5"
10	Bowl, 6"
14	Bowl, 8" soup
15	Bowl, 9"
17	Bowl, lily 12" (matte black interior)
22	Bowl, octagonal, 7"
24	Bowl, octagonal, 8"
23	Breakfast set
28	Butter dish
30	Butter pat
35	Cake plate, open handles
36	Cake plate, tab handles
37	Cake plate, 8" square pedestal
40	Cake stand, 2 tier
41	Cake stand, 3 tier
42	Cake plate, with server
43	Cake stand, chrome handle
44	Cake stand, chrome base
45	Canoe-shaped dish
50	Cheese keep
52	Coaster
53	Coffee pot, 3 cup
55	Coffee pot, 6 cup
60	Compote, footed
65	Condiment set on tray
70	Cream and sugar
71	Cream and sugar on tray
75	Demi-tasse
77	Egg cup, footed
80	Hot water jug
85	Jam pot with liner
90	Jug, 4" round
91	Jug, 4 1/2" round
92	Jug, 5" round
95	Jug, 5" straight-sided
96	Jug, 7" straight-sided
97	Nut dish
103	Plate, 6 1/2" round
104	Plate, 7" round
105	Plate, 8" round
106	Plate, 9" round
107	Plate, 10" round
201	Plate, 4" square
202	Plate, 5" square
203	Plate, 6" square
204	Plate, 7" square
205	Plate, 8" square
206	Plate, 9" square
207	Plate, 10" square
301	Plate, 4" triangular
402	Plate, octagonal, 5"
406	Plate, octagonal, 9"
407	Plate, octagonal, 10"
112	Relish dish, small
115	Salad bowl, chrome rim
117	Salt and pepper
118	Salt and pepper on tray
120	Sandwich tray, 10" x 6"
121	Sandwich tray, 12" x 7"
122	Sandwich tray, 13"x 6"
125	Sauce boat and liner
130	Teacup and saucer
131	Teacup and saucer, oleander shape
135	Teapot, 2 cup
136	Teapot, 4 cup
137	Teapot, 6 cup
140	Teapot, stacking
145	Tennis set
150	Toast rack, 4 slice
151	Toast rack, 2 slice
155	Trivet
160	Vase, bud
163	Vase, spill, 8"
162	Vase, trumpet 6"
165	Vase, 9"
169	Sugar shaker
170	Biscuit barrel
180	Lamp base

BARKER BROTHERS LTD.

In the Meir Works at Longton, the Barker Brothers factory became noted for its ability "to copy the best new ideas on the market quickly and efficiently." Although originally the company produced both china and earthenware, in 1925 they decided to concentrate on semi-porcelain, which is a high-quality earthenware. John Guildford created patterns for Barker Brothers that were remarkably like those of Clarice Cliff. Their hand-painted pieces looked very like those of Poole Pottery. Like Myott Son & Co. and Wade, they produced several chintz patterns in the 1930s, along with all the other product lines they created. To date none of the chintz patterns have been found with pattern names. They were still producing chintz patterns in the 1950s and they still advertised chintzware in Canadian publications as late as 1957. The trade name "Tudor Ware" or "Royal Tudor Ware" was incorporated into several versions of the Barker Brothers backstamp from about 1937.

The company was acquired by Alfred Clough in 1961 and in turn they were bought up by Coloroll Housewares Group in 1987.

UNKNOWN 1

This is one of the more common Barker Brothers "Royal Tudor Ware" patterns.

Cat. No.	Shape	U.S. $	Can. $	U.K. £
BaB1-42	Cake plate, with server	175.00	125.00	120.00

Cat. No.	Shape	U.S. $	Can. $	U.K. £
BaB1-70	Cream and sugar	100.00	75.00	65.00

UNKNOWN 2

This is one of the earlier Barker Brothers "Royal Tudor Ware" patterns.

Cat. No.	Shape	U.S. $	Can. $	U.K. £
BaB2-42	Cake plate, with server	150.00	115.00	100.00
BaB2-70	Cream and sugar	80.00	65.00	55.00

UNKNOWN 3

This Barker Brothers pattern appears more often in England than North America.

Cat. No.	Shape	U.S. $	Can. $	U.K. £
BaB3-42	Cake plate, with server	165.00	115.00	110.00

Cat. No.	Shape	U.S. $	Can. $	U.K. £
BaB3-70	Cream and sugar	100.00	70.00	60.00

UNKNOWN 4

This is one of the more common Barker Brothers patterns in North America.

Cat. No.	Shape	U.S. $	Can. $	U.K. £
BaB4-42	Cake plate, with server	150.00	115.00	100.00

Cat. No.	Shape	U.S. $	Can. $	U.K. £
BaB4-70	Cream and sugar	100.00	65.00	60.00

GRIMWADES LTD ROYAL WINTON POTTERIES · STOKE-ON-TRENT

BREXTON

UNKNOWN 1

Cat. No.	Shape	U.S. $	Can. $	U.K. £
Bx1-130	Teacup and saucer	50.00	50.00	30.00

Cat. No.	Shape	U.S. $	Can. $	U.K. £
Bx1-180	Lamp base	300.00	250.00	95.00

UNKNOWN 2

Brexton made a number of different lamp shapes using this chintz pattern but many collectors do not like the lime green trim which always appears to a greater or less extent.

Cat. No.	Shape	U.S. $	Can. $	U.K. £
Bx2-130	Teacup and saucer	50.00	50.00	30.00

Cat. No.	Shape	U.S. $	Can. $	U.K. £
Bx2-180	Lamp base	300.00	250.00	95.00

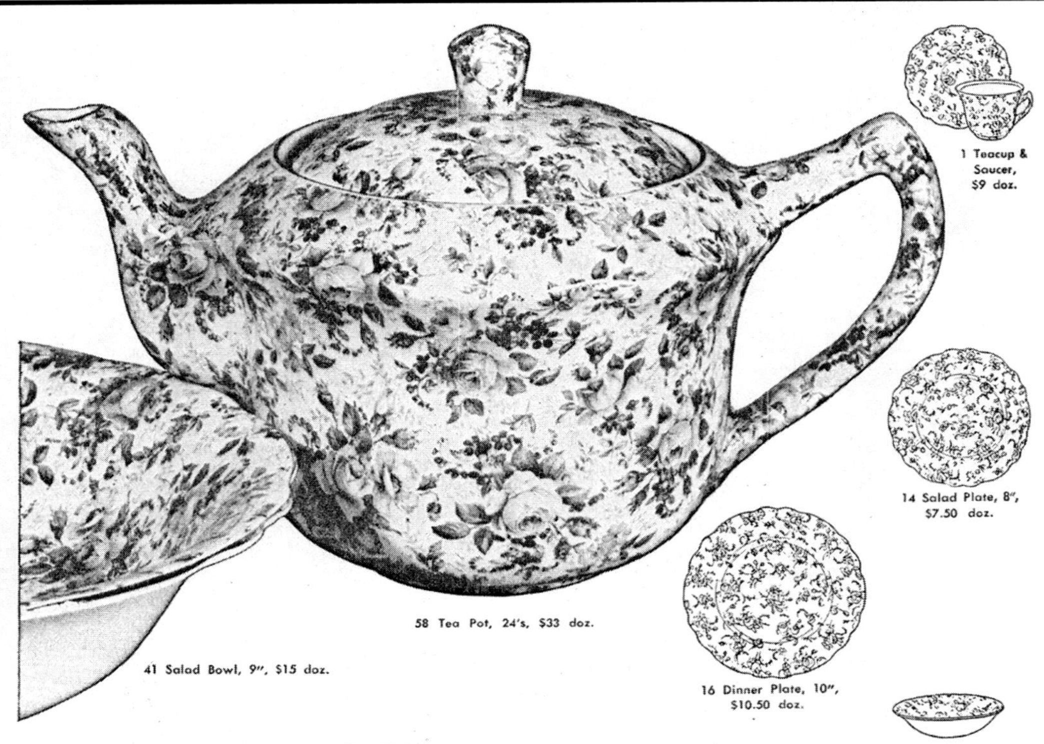

58 Tea Pot, 24's, $33 doz.

41 Salad Bowl, 9", $15 doz.

1 Teacup & Saucer, $9 doz.

14 Salad Plate, 8", $7.50 doz.

16 Dinner Plate, 10", $10.50 doz.

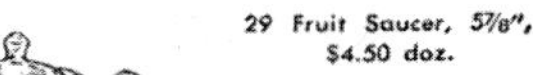

29 Fruit Saucer, 5⅞", $4.50 doz.

50 Coffee Pot, 36's, $22.50 doz.

78 Cov. Sugar & Cream $30 doz.

ENCORE

A war and the sulking British pound delayed the return of ROSALYNDE CHINTZ. Now it's here at devaluation prices. Chintzware aglow with red and yellow roses, blue-bells and bits of green—trimmed in gold. Its James Kent, Ltd. backstamp is your assurance that ROSALYNDE is a sound investment.

Suggestion: The ROSALYNDE replacement market is vast. A postcard advising ROSALYNDE purchasers that you have a fresh stock should prove a profitable mailing.

NOTE

To match the dinnerware, 25 giftware items in ROSALYNDE, such as nut dishes, bonbons, sugar and cream sets, comports, pitchers and sandwich trays are offered at attractive prices. These range from $4 per dozen for a small square nut dish or ashtray to $24 per dozen for a square cake plate (11"). As separate items, open stock or an assorted case, $115.25 value for $107.50 — case and packing, $2. Fancy goods list on request.

Immediate shipment from Philadelphia of all ROSALYNDE items.

NOT ILLUSTRATED

12 Bread & Butter Plate, 6½"	$ 5.00 doz.
15 Luncheon Plate, 9"	9.00 doz.
32 Cereal Bowl, 6⅜"	6.00 doz.
51 Coffee Pot, 24's	33.00 doz.
56 Tea Pot, 36's	24.00 doz.
57 Tea Pot, 30's	28.50 doz.

A special assortment of this dinnerware is available. Value $137.75 for $130 — case and packing, $2.

EBELING & REUSS CO.
Established 1886
707 CHESTNUT STREET, PHILADELPHIA 6, PA.

225 Fifth Avenue NEW YORK 10 — 1557 Merchandise Mart CHICAGO 54 — 527 W. 7th Street LOS ANGELES 14

ELIJAH COTTON LTD.
(LORD NELSON)

The firm advertised themselves as being established since 1758, but it was not until 1889 that they were known as Nelson Pottery in Hanley. To date little has been written about Elijah Cotton. They were better than many of the lower echelon firms at self-promotion. They created a ceramic model of the Nelson Monument in Trafalgar Square — probably copied from the Clarice Cliff Bizooka — using sandwich trays, tea plates and egg cups from their product lines. As was widely reported in the press at the time, they made these models available to any retailer who bought the required amount of product.

Elijah Cotton certainly never had a light hand when it came to either the product or the decoration. During the 1930s the designs were heavily applied to chunky-shaped earthenware by paintresses working by eye and not by printed or sketched outlines. This was a utilitarian pottery and little or no time was spent on the production of bric-a-brac. The *Pottery Gazette* reported in 1931 that they produced a range in domestic ware from plain white glaze upwards. They were big producers of kitchen and hospital plain white and their advertisements from the 1950s feature plain white jugs in a wide variety of shapes. Their chintzes were never applied to handles or spouts, since these required special skill. Often the work is sloppy enough that it is unlikely that another factory would have allowed it to pass.

Although **Marina** was reported a best-seller for Elijah Cotton in 1939, there is certainly never a mention of any member of the royal family taking home a teaset in Nelson chintz. Parsons Steiner were the exclusive distributors for Elijah Cotton in Canada and their advertisements in January 1955 offered a wide range of exclusive chintz designs "Old as the hills - as fresh as a daisy." Interestingly, it is Cotton who, in 1955, came out with **Kaleidoscope**, an all-over, multi-colour snow crystal design more in keeping with the '50s style.

ANEMONE

The pattern number is 2446 . This chintz pattern was not a controlled pattern and was used by other companies such as John Shaw & Sons "Burlington Ware" and Winterton Ltd.

Backstamp not available at press time

Cat. No.	Shape	U.S. $	Can. $	U.K. £
AC-04	Bonbon dish	40.00	40.00	25.00
AC-28	Butter dish	125.00	95.00	75.00
AC-35	Cake plate, open handles	125.00	120.00	75.00
AC-36	Cake plate, tab handles	100.00	110.00	60.00
AC-41	Cake stand, 3 tier	135.00	125.00	85.00
AC-50	Cheese keep	200.00	150.00	115.00
AC-55	Coffee pot, 6 cup	525.00	350.00	255.00
AC-65	Condiment set on tray	150.00	130.00	100.00
AC-70	Cream and sugar	80.00	75.00	50.00
AC-71	Cream and sugar on tray	135.00	125.00	85.00
AC-85	Jam pot with liner	100.00	95.00	65.00
AC-92	Jug, 5" round	200.00	125.00	100.00
AC-96	Jug, 7" straight-sided	250.00	150.00	100.00

Cat. No.	Shape	U.S. $	Can. $	U.K. £
AC-301	Plate, 4" triangular	30.00	25.00	20.00
AC-104	Plate, 7"	50.00	45.00	25.00
AC-105	Plate, 8"	75.00	50.00	45.00
AC-112	Relish dish	150.00	145.00	85.00
AC-117	Salt and pepper	75.00	65.00	45.00
AC-118	Salt and pepper on tray	135.00	125.00	85.00
AC-122	Sandwich tray, 13" x 6"	85.00	85.00	50.00
AC-125	Sauce boat and liner	100.00	110.00	65.00
AC-130	Teacup and saucer	50.00	50.00	35.00
AC-137	Teapot, 6 cup	475.00	325.00	275.00
AC-140	Teapot, stacking	550.00	450.00	275.00
AC-145	Tennis set	85.00	75.00	50.00
AC-160	Vase, bud	100.00	95.00	45.00

BLACK BEAUTY

This is the only Nelson pattern with a black background and is considered the most desirable by many collectors. Advertised in the Canadian *Gift Buyer* in November 1955, it was still being "stocked by wholesalers across Canada."

Cat. No.	Shape	U.S. $	Can. $	U.K. £
BB-04	Bonbon dish	75.00	75.00	45.00
BB-28	Butter dish	225.00	195.00	135.00
BB-35	Cake plate, open handles	200.00	195.00	125.00
BB-36	Cake plate, tab handles	175.00	175.00	105.00
BB-41	Cake stand, 3 tier	225.00	175.00	140.00
BB-50	Cheese keep	325.00	250.00	210.00
BB-55	Coffee pot, 6 cup	850.00	475.00	475.00
BB-65	Condiment set on tray	250.00	195.00	160.00
BB-70	Cream and sugar	135.00	125.00	85.00
BB-71	Cream and sugar on tray	200.00	195.00	135.00
BB-85	Jam pot with liner	165.00	150.00	110.00
BB-92	Jug, 5" round	400.00	225.00	160.00
BB-96	Jug, 7" straight-sided	550.00	250.00	195.00

Cat. No.	Shape	U.S. $	Can. $	U.K. £
BB-301	Plate, 4" triangular	50.00	45.00	30.00
BB-104	Plate, 7"	85.00	60.00	50.00
BB-105	Plate, 8"	125.00	75.00	75.00
BB-112	Relish dish	250.00	195.00	160.00
BB-117	Salt and pepper	100.00	95.00	75.00
BB-118	Salt and pepper on tray	200.00	175.00	125.00
BB-122	Sandwich tray, 13" x 6"	150.00	145.00	95.00
BB-125	Sauce boat and liner	165.00	150.00	110.00
BB-130	Teacup and saucer	100.00	85.00	65.00
BB-137	Teapot, 6 cup	750.00	450.00	475.00
BB-140	Teapot, stacking	900.00	650.00	525.00
BB-145	Tennis set	135.00	95.00	85.00
BB-160	Vase, bud	150.00	150.00	85.00

BRIAR ROSE

This pattern has not proven particularly popular with American collectors.

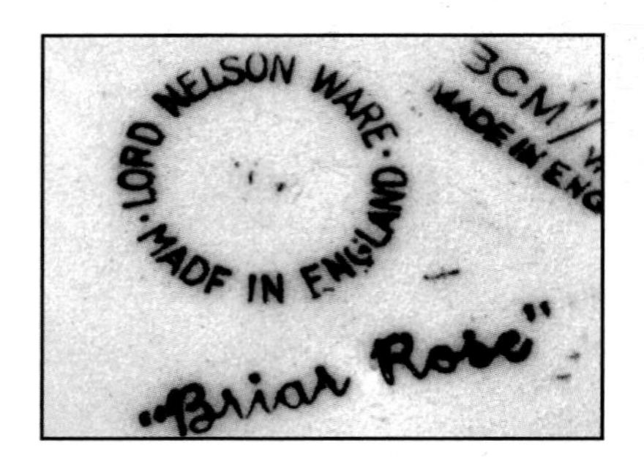

Cat. No.	Shape	U.S. $	Can. $	U.K. £
BR-04	Bonbon dish	45.00	50.00	30.00
BR-28	Butter dish	140.00	125.00	85.00
BR-35	Cake plate, open handles	135.00	145.00	85.00
BR-36	Cake plate, tab handles	125.00	130.00	75.00
BR-41	Cake stand, 3 tier	150.00	145.00	90.00
BR-50	Cheese keep	200.00	195.00	125.00
BR-55	Coffee pot, 6 cup	525.00	400.00	300.00
BR-65	Condiment set on tray	165.00	160.00	100.00
BR-70	Cream and sugar	100.00	95.00	65.00
BR-71	Cream and sugar on tray	150.00	145.00	90.00
BR-85	Jam pot with liner	125.00	125.00	75.00
BR-92	Jug, 5″ round	225.00	150.00	100.00
BR-96	Jug, 7″ straight-sided	300.00	175.00	125.00

Cat. No.	Shape	U.S. $	Can. $	U.K. £
BR-301	Plate, 4″ triangular	40.00	35.00	25.00
BR-104	Plate, 7″	60.00	50.00	35.00
BR-105	Plate, 8″	85.00	60.00	50.00
BR-112	Relish dish	190.00	165.00	115.00
BR-117	Salt and pepper	75.00	75.00	45.00
BR-118	Salt and pepper on tray	150.00	145.00	85.00
BR-122	Sandwich tray, 13″ x 6″	100.00	105.00	65.00
BR-125	Sauce boat and liner	125.00	125.00	75.00
BR-130	Teacup and saucer	65.00	60.00	40.00
BR-137	Teapot, 6 cup	475.00	350.00	325.00
BR-140	Teapot, stacking	650.00	550.00	325.00
BR-145	Tennis set	100.00	85.00	65.00
BR-160	Vase, bud	100.00	120.00	50.00

COUNTRY LANE

This pattern is more common in Australia and New Zealand than it is in North America.

Backstamp not available
at
press time

Cat. No.	Shape	U.S. $	Can. $	U.K. £
CL-04	Bonbon dish	35.00	40.00	25.00
CL-28	Butter dish	105.00	95.00	75.00
CL-35	Cake plate, open handles	90.00	120.00	65.00
CL-36	Cake plate, tab handles	90.00	110.00	65.00
CL-41	Cake stand, 3 tier	115.00	125.00	75.00
CL-50	Cheese keep	150.00	150.00	100.00
CL-55	Coffee pot, 6 cup	400.00	350.00	250.00
CL-65	Condiment set on tray	115.00	130.00	85.00
CL-70	Cream and sugar	65.00	75.00	45.00
CL-71	Cream and sugar on tray	105.00	125.00	75.00
CL-85	Jam pot with liner	75.00	95.00	50.00
CL-92	Jug, 5″ round	150.00	125.00	90.00
CL-96	Jug, 7″ straight-sided	180.00	150.00	100.00

Cat. No.	Shape	U.S. $	Can. $	U.K. £
CL-301	Plate, 4″ triangular	25.00	25.00	20.00
CL-104	Plate, 7″	35.00	45.00	25.00
CL-105	Plate, 8″	45.00	50.00	40.00
CL-112	Relish dish	125.00	145.00	75.00
CL-117	Salt and pepper	65.00	65.00	40.00
CL-118	Salt and pepper on tray	115.00	125.00	75.00
CL-122	Sandwich tray, 13″ x 6″	65.00	85.00	45.00
CL-125	Sauce boat and liner	90.00	110.00	75.00
CL-130	Teacup and saucer	45.00	50.00	30.00
CL-137	Teapot, 6 cup	375.00	325.00	250.00
CL-140	Teapot, stacking	475.00	450.00	275.00
CL-145	Tennis set	65.00	75.00	50.00
CL-160	Vase, bud	80.00	95.00	40.00

GREEN TULIP

This pattern is rare in North America but found more often in New Zealand and Australia. It has recently become as popular as **Black Beauty** in North America.

Cat. No.	Shape	U.S. $	Can. $	U.K. £
GT-04	Bonbon dish	75.00	75.00	45.00
GT-28	Butter dish	225.00	195.00	135.00
GT-35	Cake plate, open handles	200.00	195.00	125.00
GT-36	Cake plate, tab handles	175.00	175.00	100.00
GT-41	Cake stand, 3 tier	225.00	175.00	135.00
GT-50	Cheese keep	325.00	250.00	200.00
GT-55	Coffee pot, 6 cup	900.00	475.00	450.00
GT-65	Condiment set on tray	250.00	195.00	150.00
GT-70	Cream and sugar	135.00	125.00	85.00
GT-71	Cream and sugar on tray	200.00	195.00	125.00
GT-85	Jam pot with liner	165.00	150.00	100.00
GT-92	Jug, 5″ round	400.00	225.00	150.00
GT-96	Jug, 7″ straight-sided	550.00	250.00	165.00

Cat. No.	Shape	U.S. $	Can. $	U.K. £
GT-301	Plate, 4″ triangular	50.00	45.00	30.00
GT-104	Plate, 7″	85.00	60.00	50.00
GT-105	Plate, 8″	125.00	75.00	75.00
GT-112	Relish dish	275.00	195.00	150.00
GT-117	Salt and pepper	100.00	95.00	65.00
GT-118	Salt and pepper on tray	200.00	175.00	125.00
GT-122	Sandwich tray, 13″ x 6″	150.00	145.00	85.00
GT-125	Sauce boat and liner	165.00	150.00	100.00
GT-130	Teacup and saucer	100.00	85.00	65.00
GT-137	Teapot, 6 cup	825.00	450.00	450.00
GT-140	Teapot, stacking	1000.00	650.00	425.00
GT-145	Tennis set	135.00	95.00	85.00
GT-160	Vase, bud	175.00	150.00	75.00

HEATHER

The pattern number is 2750.

Cat. No.	Shape	U.S. $	Can. $	U.K. £
He-04	Bonbon dish	45.00	50.00	30.00
He-28	Butter dish	150.00	125.00	85.00
He-35	Cake plate, open handles	135.00	145.00	80.00
He-36	Cake plate, tab handles	125.00	130.00	75.00
He-41	Cake stand, 3 tier	150.00	145.00	90.00
He-50	Cheese keep	200.00	195.00	125.00
He-55	Coffee pot, 6 cup	650.00	400.00	300.00
He-65	Condiment set on tray	165.00	160.00	100.00
He-70	Cream and sugar	100.00	95.00	65.00
He-71	Cream and sugar on tray	150.00	145.00	90.00
He-85	Jam pot with liner	125.00	120.00	75.00
He-92	Jug, 5" round	225.00	150.00	100.00
He-96	Jug, 7" straight-sided	275.00	175.00	115.00
He-301	Plate, 4" triangular	40.00	35.00	25.00
He-104	Plate, 7"	65.00	50.00	35.00
He-105	Plate, 8"	85.00	60.00	50.00
He-112	Relish dish	200.00	165.00	115.00
He-117	Salt and pepper	75.00	75.00	45.00
He-118	Salt and pepper on tray	150.00	145.00	85.00
He-122	Sandwich tray, 13" x 6"	100.00	105.00	65.00
He-125	Sauce boat and liner	125.00	125.00	75.00
He-130	Teacup and saucer	75.00	60.00	40.00
He-137	Teapot, 6 cup	550.00	350.00	325.00
He-140	Teapot, stacking	650.00	550.00	325.00
He-145	Tennis set	100.00	85.00	60.00
He-160	Vase, bud	125.00	120.00	50.00

MARIGOLD

The pattern number is 2122. This pattern was produced as **Mille Fleurs** by James Kent and pattern number 5007 by A. G. Richardson. The Czechoslovakians also produced this pattern.

Cat. No.	Shape	U.S. $	Can. $	U.K. £
MaG-04	Bonbon dish	45.00	50.00	30.00
MaG-28	Butter dish	130.00	125.00	80.00
MaG-35	Cake plate, open handles	130.00	145.00	75.00
MaG-36	Cake plate, tab handles	105.00	130.00	65.00
MaG-41	Cake stand, 3 tier	160.00	145.00	85.00
MaG-50	Cheese keep	210.00	195.00	125.00
MaG-55	Coffee pot, 6 cup	550.00	400.00	275.00
MaG-65	Condiment set on tray	160.00	160.00	100.00
MaG-70	Cream and sugar	95.00	95.00	50.00
MaG-71	Cream and sugar on tray	145.00	145.00	85.00
MaG-85	Jam pot with liner	110.00	120.00	65.00
MaG-92	Jug, 5″ round	250.00	150.00	125.00
MaG-96	Jug, 7″ straight-sided	300.00	175.00	135.00

Cat. No.	Shape	U.S. $	Can. $	U.K. £
MaG-301	Plate, 4″ triangular	30.00	35.00	20.00
MaG-104	Plate, 7″	50.00	50.00	30.00
MaG-105	Plate, 8″	75.00	60.00	45.00
MaG-112	Relish dish	185.00	165.00	125.00
MaG-117	Salt and pepper	65.00	75.00	40.00
MaG-118	Salt and pepper on tray	135.00	145.00	75.00
MaG-122	Sandwich tray, 13″ x 6″	95.00	105.00	50.00
MaG-125	Sauce boat and liner	135.00	125.00	75.00
MaG-130	Teacup and saucer	75.00	60.00	35.00
MaG-137	Teapot, 6 cup	525.00	350.00	325.00
MaG-140	Teapot, stacking	650.00	550.00	325.00
MaG-145	Tennis set	95.00	85.00	50.00
MaG-160	Vase, bud	125.00	120.00	45.00

MARINA

This chintz pattern was a best seller for Nelson ware in 1939. The pattern itself was registered in 1937, English registration number 821468. This pattern was also produced by Royal Albert in bone china.

Cat. No.	Shape	U.S. $	Can. $	U.K. £
Ma-04	Bonbon dish	45.00	40.00	30.00
Ma-28	Butter dish	150.00	105.00	85.00
Ma-35	Cake plate, open handles	125.00	120.00	75.00
Ma-36	Cake plate, tab handles	125.00	110.00	75.00
Ma-41	Cake stand, 3 tier	150.00	125.00	90.00
Ma-50	Cheese keep	200.00	150.00	125.00
Ma-55	Coffee pot, 6 cup	550.00	350.00	300.00
Ma-65	Condiment set on tray	165.00	130.00	100.00
Ma-70	Cream and sugar	100.00	75.00	65.00
Ma-71	Cream and sugar on tray	150.00	125.00	85.00
Ma-85	Jam pot with liner	115.00	95.00	75.00
Ma-92	Jug, 5″ round	250.00	125.00	100.00
Ma-96	Jug, 7″ straight-sided	300.00	150.00	115.00
Ma-301	Plate, 4″ triangular	40.00	25.00	25.00
Ma-104	Plate, 7″	65.00	45.00	35.00
Ma-105	Plate, 8″	85.00	50.00	50.00
Ma-112	Relish dish	200.00	145.00	125.00
Ma-117	Salt and pepper	75.00	65.00	45.00
Ma-118	Salt and pepper on tray	150.00	125.00	85.00
Ma-122	Sandwich tray, 13″ x 6″	100.00	85.00	65.00
Ma-125	Sauce boat and liner	125.00	110.00	75.00
Ma-130	Teacup and saucer	75.00	50.00	40.00
Ma-137	Teapot, 6 cup	500.00	325.00	325.00
Ma-140	Teapot, stacking	700.00	450.00	325.00
Ma-145	Tennis set	100.00	75.00	65.00
Ma-160	Vase, bud	125.00	95.00	50.00

PANSY

This was not a controlled pattern and was produced by other Staffordshire factories as well as by the Japanese. Both Shelley and Royal Albert produced the pattern in bone china.

Cat. No.	Shape	U.S. $	Can. $	U.K. £
P-04	Bonbon dish	45.00	40.00	30.00
P-28	Butter dish	125.00	105.00	75.00
P-35	Cake plate, open handles	125.00	120.00	75.00
P-36	Cake plate, tab handles	100.00	110.00	65.00
P-41	Cake stand, 3 tier	150.00	125.00	85.00
P-50	Cheese keep	200.00	150.00	125.00
P-55	Coffee pot, 6 cup	550.00	350.00	250.00
P-65	Condiment set on tray	150.00	130.00	100.00
P-70	Cream and sugar	100.00	75.00	65.00
P-71	Cream and sugar on tray	150.00	125.00	85.00
P-85	Jam pot with liner	100.00	95.00	60.00
P-92	Jug, 5″ round	250.00	125.00	125.00
P-96	Jug, 7″ straight-sided	300.00	150.00	150.00
P-301	Plate, 4″ triangular	30.00	25.00	20.00
P-104	Plate, 7″	50.00	45.00	30.00
P-105	Plate, 8″	75.00	50.00	45.00
P-112	Relish dish	175.00	145.00	125.00
P-117	Salt and pepper	65.00	65.00	40.00
P-118	Salt and pepper on tray	135.00	125.00	85.00
P-122	Sandwich tray, 13″ x 6″	90.00	85.00	50.00
P-125	Sauce boat and liner	125.00	110.00	75.00
P-130	Teacup and saucer	75.00	50.00	35.00
P-137	Teapot, 6 cup	525.00	325.00	325.00
P-140	Teapot, stacking	650.00	450.00	325.00
P-145	Tennis set	100.00	75.00	65.00
P-160	Vase, bud	125.00	95.00	45.00

ROSETIME

The English registration number for **Rosetime** was 829287, and the pattern was registered sometime in 1938. This pattern was produced by Royal Albert in bone china.

"Rosetime"
CHINTZ.
REG. No. 829287.

Cat. No.	Shape	U.S. $	Can. $	U.K. £
Ro-04	Bonbon dish	50.00	50.00	35.00
Ro-28	Butter dish	175.00	125.00	100.00
Ro-35	Cake plate, open handles	150.00	145.00	100.00
Ro-36	Cake plate, tab handles	135.00	130.00	85.00
Ro-41	Cake stand, 3 tier	175.00	145.00	100.00
Ro-50	Cheese keep	250.00	195.00	150.00
Ro-55	Coffee pot, 6 cup	650.00	400.00	350.00
Ro-65	Condiment set on tray	200.00	160.00	125.00
Ro-70	Cream and sugar	100.00	95.00	65.00
Ro-71	Cream and sugar on tray	175.00	145.00	100.00
Ro-85	Jam pot with liner	135.00	120.00	85.00
Ro-92	Jug, 5″ round	275.00	150.00	125.00
Ro-96	Jug, 7″ straight-sided	350.00	175.00	135.00
Ro-301	Plate, 4″ triangular	45.00	35.00	30.00
Ro-104	Plate, 7″	65.00	50.00	40.00
Ro-105	Plate, 8″	95.00	60.00	50.00
Ro-112	Relish dish	225.00	165.00	135.00
Ro-117	Salt and pepper	85.00	75.00	50.00
Ro-118	Salt and pepper on tray	165.00	145.00	100.00
Ro-122	Sandwich tray, 13″ x 6″	100.00	105.00	65.00
Ro-125	Sauce boat and liner	135.00	125.00	85.00
Ro-130	Teacup and saucer	75.00	60.00	45.00
Ro-137	Teapot, 6 cup	600.00	350.00	400.00
Ro-140	Teapot, stacking	800.00	550.00	400.00
Ro-145	Tennis set	125.00	85.00	75.00
Ro-160	Vase, bud	150.00	125.00	65.00

ROYAL BROCADE

This pattern was also produced by Royal Albert in bone china.

Cat. No.	Shape	U.S. $	Can. $	U.K. £
RB-04	Bonbon dish	35.00	40.00	25.00
RB-28	Butter dish	110.00	105.00	75.00
RB-35	Cake plate, open handles	90.00	110.00	65.00
RB-36	Cake plate, tab handles	90.00	100.00	65.00
RB-41	Cake stand, 3 tier	110.00	115.00	75.00
RB-50	Cheese keep	150.00	140.00	100.00
RB-55	Coffee pot, 6 cup	400.00	350.00	250.00
RB-65	Condiment set on tray	125.00	120.00	85.00
RB-70	Cream and sugar	65.00	65.00	45.00
RB-71	Cream and sugar on tray	105.00	115.00	75.00
RB-85	Jam pot with liner	75.00	85.00	50.00
RB-92	Jug, 5″ round	150.00	125.00	90.00
RB-96	Jug, 7″ straight-sided	180.00	150.00	100.00
RB-301	Plate, 4″ triangular	25.00	25.00	20.00
RB-104	Plate, 7″	35.00	45.00	25.00
RB-105	Plate, 8″	45.00	50.00	40.00
RB-112	Relish dish	115.00	135.00	75.00
RB-117	Salt and pepper	65.00	55.00	40.00
RB-118	Salt and pepper on tray	115.00	115.00	75.00
RB-122	Sandwich tray, 13″ x 6″	65.00	75.00	45.00
RB-125	Sauce boat and liner	90.00	105.00	75.00
RB-130	Teacup and saucer	45.00	45.00	30.00
RB-137	Teapot, 6 cup	375.00	300.00	250.00
RB-140	Teapot, stacking	550.00	425.00	275.00
RB-145	Tennis set	65.00	65.00	50.00
RB-160	Vase, bud	80.00	80.00	40.00

SKYLARK

This pattern is not common in North America. But, unlike other rare patterns, **Skylark** is not popular with American collectors.

Cat. No.	Shape	U.S. $	Can. $	U.K. £
Sk-04	Bonbon dish	40.00	40.00	25.00
Sk-28	Butter dish	125.00	105.00	70.00
Sk-35	Cake plate, open handles	100.00	115.00	60.00
Sk-36	Cake plate, tab handles	100.00	105.00	60.00
Sk-41	Cake stand, 3 tier	125.00	115.00	70.00
Sk-50	Cheese keep	175.00	150.00	95.00
Sk-55	Coffee pot, 6 cup	425.00	350.00	240.00
Sk-65	Condiment set on tray	135.00	125.00	80.00
Sk-70	Cream and sugar	75.00	75.00	45.00
Sk-71	Cream and sugar on tray	125.00	125.00	70.00
Sk-85	Jam pot with liner	85.00	95.00	50.00
Sk-92	Jug, 5″ round	200.00	125.00	85.00
Sk-96	Jug, 7″ straight-sided	250.00	150.00	100.00

Cat. No.	Shape	U.S. $	Can. $	U.K. £
Sk-301	Plate, 4″ triangular	30.00	25.00	20.00
Sk-104	Plate, 7″	40.00	45.00	25.00
Sk-105	Plate, 8″	65.00	50.00	40.00
Sk-112	Relish dish	125.00	145.00	70.00
Sk-117	Salt and pepper	65.00	65.00	35.00
Sk-118	Salt and pepper on tray	125.00	125.00	70.00
Sk-122	Sandwich tray, 13″ x 6″	75.00	85.00	45.00
Sk-125	Sauce boat and liner	100.00	110.00	60.00
Sk-130	Teacup and saucer	65.00	50.00	30.00
Sk-137	Teapot, 6 cup	400.00	325.00	240.00
Sk-140	Teapot, stacking	600.00	450.00	275.00
Sk-145	Tennis set	75.00	75.00	50.00
Sk-160	Vase, bud	85.00	95.00	40.00

GRIMWADES LTD., WINTON POTTERY, STOKE-ON-TRENT.

EMPIRE PORCELAIN COMPANY LTD.

This company was established at the Empire Works in Stoke around 1896 and continued in business until 1967. Although they called themselves the Empire Porcelain Company they produced mainly fine earthenware, including a number of chintzes. One of their 1930s chintz patterns **Lilac Time** was very popular and was produced in more than one colourway. They were big exporters of china in the 1950s and they had overseas agents in Argentina, Southern Rhodesia, Sweden and Trinidad. The trade name "Empire Ware" or "Shelton Ivory" is often found within the backstamp. Backstamps from the late 1940s and 1950s usually incorporate numbers for the month and year of manufacture.

BLACK MARGUERITE

This pattern was widely produced by a number of Staffordshire companies. The Empire version dates to the 1950s and usually has wide gold banding around the foot, spout and black handle.

Backstamp not available
at
press time

Cat. No.	Shape	U.S. $	Can. $	U.K. £
BM-55	Coffee pot, 6 cup	400.00	250.00	150.00
BM-70	Cream and sugar	65.00	65.00	40.00
BM-75	Demi-tasse	50.00	445.00	25.00
BM-104	Plate, 7"	30.00	30.00	20.00
BM-130	Teacup and saucer	60.00	50.00	30.00
BM-137	Teapot, 6 cup	350.00	200.00	125.00

LILAC TIME

This pattern was produced in two colourways, green and ivory, the green being the most common and the more highly desired.

Cat. No.	Shape	U.S. $	Can. $	U.K. £
LT-55	Coffee pot, 6 cup	550.00	400.00	250.00
LT-70	Cream and sugar	80.00	85.00	50.00
LT-75	Demi-tasse	70.00	45.00	30.00

Cat. No.	Shape	U.S. $	Can. $	U.K. £
LT-104	Plate, 7"	40.00	35.00	25.00
LT-130	Teacup and saucer	75.00	55.00	35.00
LT-137	Teapot, 6 cup	500.00	350.00	275.00

WATER LILY

This pattern seems to appear more often in England than North America.

Cat. No.	Shape	U.S. $	Can. $	U.K. £
WL-55	Coffee pot, 6 cup	350.00	225.00	150.00
WL-70	Cream and sugar	55.00	50.00	30.00
WL-75	Demi-tasse	40.00	40.00	20.00
WL-104	Plate, 7"	25.00	25.00	15.00
WL-130	Teacup and saucer	50.00	45.00	25.00
WL-137	Teapot, 6 cup	300.00	175.00	125.00

FORD & SONS

From 1893 until 1938 this company was known as Ford & Sons and the backstamp was minimal: "F & S" or "F & SONS LTD," or "F & SONS BURSLEM." They produced several of the exotic bird and flower chintzes during the 1920s and perhaps earlier. They do not appear to have produced the all-over floral chintzes in the 1930s style. Although the company name did not change to Ford & Sons (Crownford) Ltd. until 1938, the most common backstamp through the 1930s incorporated the trade name "Crownford Ware."

UNKNOWN

This was not a controlled pattern. It is sometimes found with a Bridgwood & Sons backstamp and it is sometimes unmarked.

Cat. No.	Shape	U.S. $	Can. $	U.K. £
FS-36	Cake plate, tab handles	150.00	95.00	85.00
FS-95	Jug, 7″ straight-sided	350.00	150.00	150.00

Cat. No.	Shape	U.S. $	Can. $	U.K. £
FS-130	Teacup and saucer	85.00	50.00	45.00

GRIMWADES LTD. (ROYAL WINTON)

In 1885 Leonard Lumsden Grimwade founded a pottery with his brother at the Winton Pottery, Stoke-on-Trent. Although the brothers started with a shed, they grew very quickly and by 1900, after the takeover of the Stoke Pottery, Grimwade Brothers had become Grimwades Limited. Atlas China was acquired in 1906, which enabled the Grimwades to produce quality teasets. Tolie Coales, daughter of the Grimwades representative in Canada, still has beautiful teaware which was hand-painted by the art director at Atlas and sent to her mother as a gift.

Export became a very important part of the Grimwades business. Around the turn of the century G.O. Coales came out to Canada. He became a china buyer for Carsley, a Montreal department store and he became the first retailer in Canada to buy from Grimwades. In 1903 Leonard Grimwade persuaded George to become the Grimwades representative for Canada. "Thanks to his undeviating efforts, Royal Winton became known from coast to coast . . . In days when Canada was still a pioneer country, he probed into sparsely settled areas, using the crude transportation methods of the time." His first trips were to Toronto, Quebec and St. John's Newfoundland and it was not until 1910 that he ventured into Western Canada. After that, every January he would leave central Canada and head to the Maritime Provinces. In February he would head west. During the summer he would repeat the journey. In an interview in 1953, Mr. Coales talked of his early plans for Grimwades. His aim was to make the name Grimwades so well known in the retail trade that the salesmen of wholesale houses would be asked for the ware and would start to keep it in stock. "The plan was to give distributors control of the patterns they carried, hoping they would work harder on lines that were exclusive to them." The pattern **Rose du Barry** was advertised by Henry Morgans of Montreal in 1938 and has been found with no name, with the name **Chelsea Rose** and with **Rose du Barry**. The backstamp on **Rose du Barry** always has Henry Morgan & Co. Ltd.; perhaps the name **Rose du Barry** was exclusively given to Morgans by Mr. Coales as part of this plan. The advertisements in the 1950s *Gift Buyer* make it clear that his plan was successful by this point. **English Rose** and **Kew** were exclusive to Dingle, Davidson, **May Festival** and **June Festival** belonged to Michaelson's, **Morning Glory** to Enterprise Sales, **Balmoral** to Nerlich & Company, **Nantwich** and **Orient** to Cassidy's — all in Toronto; **Spring Glory, Pekin** and **Marion** to Anglo-Canadian Mercantile Co. in Montreal. By the time George Coales retired he had crossed the Atlantic more than sixty times and Grimwades was known throughout Canada.

Much less is known about the export of Grimwades to the United States. Clearly there was no George Coales crisscrossing the country with trunk loads of chintz. However, from an article and an advertisement found in the American trade magazine *Crockery & Glass Journal* (May 1933), it is apparent that the firm of Wright, Tyndale & van Roden, Inc., a luxury store in Philadelphia, were given exclusive rights to at least three patterns in 1933 — **Summertime, Somerset** and **Floral Feast**— and these patterns were backstamped "COPYRIGHT Wright, Tyndale & van Roden, Inc. ENGLAND. In 1930 the *Crockery & Glass* published an editorial entitled "Unauthorized Borrowing" discussing the issue of commercial piracy of patterns and shapes. A. G. Richardson took out an advertisement around the same time warning their customers of the pirating of some of their patterns and shapes. The Wright Tyndale backstamp was an attempt to discourage American copyists. Their ad which was aimed at retailers says "each Copyrighted for your protection — all patterns exclusive with us." This relationship must have continued for a number of years. Other Royal Winton patterns with the Wright Tyndale backstamp include **Queen Anne, Hazel, Cranstone, Old Cottage Chintz,** and the 1950s pattern **Fireglow**. It is interesting to discover these marked pieces in New Zealand, Australia, England, and South Africa. Whether pieces were shipped out with the wrong backstamp or they have gradually moved around the world through collectors and antique dealers is open to question. The article in the *Journal* after the introduction of the first patterns is worth quoting: "Assured of a warm welcome are Wright Tyndale & van Roden's three new designs in their English Chintz ware . . . all these, needless to say, are excellently executed on the lovely clean-bodied Royal Winton Ivory . . . I liked particularly well a quaintly square open sugar and creamer on a tray that will retail around $1.50 . . . the fat and inviting tea pot . . . and a large buffet or sandwich plate — 11 ½ inches in diameter — to retail for about $1.95 . . . Good compositions are, to my mind, a tea set for four that you may retail around $10.00 . . . and an individual tray set that will retail around $8.50. I think I should also mention that these three new patterns are copyrighted."

Grimwades Ltd. produced any number of chintzes earlier in the century, but it was not until 1928 with the production of the first "modern" chintz pattern, **Marguerite**, that Grimwades found the line which would become their particular specialty. **Marguerite** chintz was described in the November *Gazette* as "a treatment employing a very pleasing ground tint in natural colours and a theme expressive of the charm of the countryside, the shapes being new and unquestionably appealing." It is said to have come from a design worked by Leonard Grimwade's wife on a cushion. Over the next few years several chintz designs were introduced but in 1932 **Summertime** chintz brought even greater popularity for the firm. The *Gazette* waxed lyrical: "It is a sort of fantasia compounded of roses, daisies, violets, harebells and similar summertime flowers." Although we have been told that **Summertime** is not common in Australia, it was shipped in huge quantities to North America and even today dinner services for 12 turn up with some regularity. The pattern was applied to everything including, clocks, sick feeders for hospitals and even a souvenir plate with Niagara Falls lithographed in the center.

Throughout the 1930s vast quantities of chintzware were produced and a number of new patterns were introduced at the British Industries Fair every year. Ivy Mayer, secretary to the export director Fred Seabridge for thirty years, remembers seeing big red pattern books with each pattern recorded by number. The books have long since disappeared, and dating the patterns has become an exercise in piecing together various bits of information. Every year when new ceramic lines were introduced at the B.I.F., trade publications including *Pottery Gazette* and *Glass Trade Review* might mention particularly popular patterns or patterns which were bought by members of the Royal family, who were staunch supporters of British industry.

It is important to remember that **all** patterns were recorded in order in the pattern books and not simply chintz patterns. There are, therefore, large gaps between the various chintz pattern numbers since many numbers were allocated to the non-chintz patterns produced by Grimwades. We know that the first modern all-over-floral was **Marguerite** and that the pattern was introduced in 1928 with the number 9432 (The *Gazette* refers to pattern number 9467 which is **Marguerite** with blue trim). **Old Cottage Chintz** 9632 and **Delphinium Chintz** 9889 have a slightly old-fashioned appearance and are often featured on the older shapes. Similarly **Springtime** usually appears on older shapes and has been found with the pattern number 10017. Suddenly the number drops to 775 with **Summertime,** which we know from the *Gazette* appeared in 1932. It is logical to assume that Grimwades, like so many other factories, decided the pattern numbers were getting too long to record and started again in the low hundreds with their pattern numbering. **Floral Feast** (1394) and **Somerset** (1420) were exported to America along with **Summertime** in the spring of 1933. **Clevedon** and **Kinver** were mentioned in January 1934 as new patterns intended for the spring of 1934 and the pattern numbers we have found for them are 1844 (**Clevedon**) and 2254 (**Kinver**).

With the pattern numbers that collectors from around the world contributed, we have been able to compile a list of patterns in the order in which they appeared in the pattern book. We have added pattern numbers for patterns with different trim — **June Roses** with gold trim has the pattern number 1924, with silver trim 1945, and with green trim 2036. It is not surprising that so many pattern numbers were used each year when you realize that each trim had a different number. There are several anomalies with the patterns in the late 1930s. Unfortunately, in 1939 the last recorded pattern is **Sweet Nancy** at 5828 and the next is **Julia** at 109. Originally we assumed that this might have been pre- and post war, but **Crocus** is mentioned in the 1939 *Gazette* as a new pattern, and the number recorded for white **Crocus** is 111. A piece of what we thought was **Black Crocus** has been found with the backstamp **Triumph** so we have renamed the pattern. The Canadian trade magazine *Gift Buyer* has been of great help in figuring out when patterns were introduced. The navy background pattern we thought was **June Festival** is, in fact, **May Festival** (135) and was advertised in Canada in May, 1952, then **June Festival** (137), the same pattern with a burgundy background. **May Festival** (139) with the black background came out about the same time. If we assume that something odd happened to the numbering and the patterns around the second World War, we can still figure out roughly which patterns came out from 1950 onwards. **Kew, Dorset** and **Joyce-Lynn** were all advertised in Canada in 1950. In a May 1953 interview with George Coales, he is said to be have been delighted that Grimwades issued **fifteen new patterns in the last year.** The new patterns probably start with **Nantwich** and continue to **Victorian Rose** or **Chelsea**. With copies of chintz patterns from Japan becoming a serious problem, copyright became a worldwide issue in the late 1940s, and many of the new patterns were registered in Canada, the United States, New Zealand and Australia. Both **Cheadle** and **Mayfair** were registered in 1951 and **Stratford** and **Florence** were registered in 1953.

Clearly there were two golden ages of chintz for the Royal Winton factory — the early 1930s and the early 1950s. The Grimwades chintzes caught the public attention in 1932 with **Summertime** and this continued for some years. The second world war meant that most of the factories were reduced to making white ware and orders continued to pile up until 1945. A report in May of 1949 in The *Gift Buyer* laments that "there is still no sign of new patterns from this pottery...none will be issued until present orders are filled . . . new lines already planned by the art department will be speedily brought out." Presumably these are patterns like **Kew** and **Joyce-Lynn** which had been designed but were awaiting release. After the furious designing of fifteen chintz patterns within the year 1952-1953, it would appear that demand gradually fell and no more chintz patterns came out of the design shop.

By the time Howard Potteries took over Grimwades Ltd. in 1964, chintzware was not important to the factory. Norfolk Street had little room for chintz production, according to Ivy Mayer, but special orders were still produced for long-standing customers such as John Bradshaw of Stratford, Canada. Grimwades' history from 1964 to the present is typical of so many of the factories which had competed successfully in a different time but found the second half of the twentieth century crippling. Although the company passed through several hands, Royal Winton continued. From the collapse of the Coloroll Group in 1990, the company has gone from crisis to crisis. Five owners in five years all but finished the firm. Bullers (Staffordshire) Ltd. bought the firm from the liquidators in mid-1995 but subsequently sold it to Taylor Tunnicliffe who moved production from Shelton to Chadwick Street, Longton. Ironically, the company is hoping to re-create some of its old chintz designs in an attempt to move up market into a small specialty chintz niche quite different from the mass production of chintz ware for which they were justly famous for almost thirty years.

DATING AND BACKSTAMPS FOR ROYAL WINTON: TASK FOR A DETECTIVE

There are a number of different routes one could use to try and determine when a particular piece was made but truthfully it will still be —in large part— speculation. *The Pottery Gazette and Glass Trade Review* published an annual Directory and Diary which listed the backstamps used by the various firms in that given year. After going through more than fifty years of these directories we were surprised to find that the backstamp we thought of as "deco" was still listed in the 1970 review. There are at least a couple of pointers, however. The "Grimwades Royal Winton Ivory England" backstamp is listed in 1936 but

then appears to die out as does the backstamp with the globe and a ribbon Grimwades across it. In 1943 the directory lists the A.B.C. Pottery firms and according to this list Grimwades

was a Group III factory and required to mark their wares under glaze with the letter "A." You can be sure, therefore, if your piece has a backstamp with the letter "A" incorporated

into it, it will have been produced after 1943. The 1970 directory still lists a script backstamp incorporating the letter "A" which makes it difficult to narrow it down much further.

You now have a list of the pattern numbers and a rough idea of when these patterns were introduced which will also serve to narrow down the date. We can be reasonably confident that **English Rose**, for example, was a 1950s pattern judging by the pattern number, the registration date and the advertisements in the Canadian publications. The style of the pattern can also be an indicator since it is difficult to imagine **Morning Glory** or **Orient** dating to anything but the 1950s.

Another way of estimating whether your piece is pre-or post-war is to look at where the pattern has been applied. The factory was forced to economize after the war and salt and peppers no longer had pattern around the outside of the underplate. Baskets had pattern only outside, no more borders along the inside edge. Rosebud jam pots with ceramic lids were probably produced only briefly. We know that the Rosebud shape was introduced in 1940 and we have been told that after the war silver plated lids were found to be more economic.

Shapes can be quite a useful way of narrowing down the dates. Shapes like the Duval jug, the Elite teapot, and the Crown bowl, date to the 1920s and they usually appear with early patterns like **Old Cottage Chintz, Beeston** and **Somerset.** Athena and Ascot were shapes which came out in the mid 1930s. Wedgwood plates are mentioned in 1933 and are found with 1930s patterns. The 1950s version of this plate had solid coloured borders instead of embossing. When Athena is missing the little piece off the handle, it is post-war Athena — yet another attempt to cut production costs in tough times. The first mention of Albans, however, is a picture of a Queen Anne teapot in the March 1945 *Pottery Gazette.* If your pot is in the Albans shape you can be reasonably confident that it is also post-war.

Unless you are putting together a dinner service in **Summertime** or **Old Cottage Chintz**, you may not be very concerned about when your piece was made. It is interesting from a mystery or a research point of view but for the most part it is irrelevant in determining value — except for the very late pieces done at Howard Pottery which do not have the same 'Ivory' body and lack the warmth of the earlier chintzes.

Although we have prepared this preliminary list of the Royal Winton patterns in the order in which they appeared, many of the numbers were difficult to decipher and we are still missing pattern numbers for the following patterns: **Morning Glory**, **Peony**, **Rose du Barry** and **Winifred**. We hope readers will be able to help us with these in time for the next edition.

LETTER CODE	PATTERN NAME	PATTERN NUMBER
Pa	Paisley	8152
Fer	Fernese (1925)	8786
Mag	Marguerite (1928)	9432
Mag	Marguerite (blue trim)	9467
OC	Old Cottage	9632
De	Delphinium Chintz	9889
Spt	Springtime	10017
Su	Summertime	775
Cr	Cranstone (gold trim)	1154
FF	Floral Feast	1394
So	Somerset (gold trim)	1420
Ru	Rutland	1470
So	Somerset (blue trim)	1611
Be	Bedale	1703
Cl	Clevedon	1844
Cr	Cranstone (burgundy trim)	1877
JR	June Roses (gold trim)	1924
JR	June Roses (silver trim)	1945
JR	June Roses (green trim)	2036
Crom	Cromer	2078
Pel	Pelham	2201
Bee	Beeston	2203
W	Welbeck	2204
H	Hazel	2208
Ki	Kinver	2254
FF	Floral Feast (blue trim)	2255
Cr	Cranstone (green trim)	2256
Sp	Spring	2506
FiW	Fireglow (original)	2510
Chz	Chintz	2836
QA	Queen Anne	2995
SP	Sweet Pea	3030
Ro	Royalty	3079
WF	Wild Flowers	3149
V	Victorian	3164
Maj	Majestic	3311
Sun	Sunshine	4030
Ri	Richmond	4249
T	Tartans	4514
Q	Quilt	4515
FG	Floral Garden	4547
Be	Bedale (green trim)	4969
A	Anemone	4801
Cly	Clyde (green)	5315
	Clyde (brown)	5637
SN	Sweet Nancy	5828
J	Julia	109
Cro	Crocus	111
Tr	Triumph	112
MF	May Festival (navy)	135
JF	June Festival	137
MF	May Festival (black)	139
Ke	Kew	240
Do	Dorset	274
JL	Joyce-Lynn	275
N	Nantwich	291
Do	Dorset	294
Chd	Cheadle	311
Pe	Pekin (1950s version)	320
Mar	Marion	324
Ba	Balmoral	374
El	Eleanor	375
ER	English Rose	381
May	Mayfair	392
SG	Spring Glory	402
Ev	Evesham	404
Co	Cotswold	408
Sh	Shrewsbury	418
Esl	Estelle	423
VR	Victorian Rose	440
Chl	Chelsea	455
O	Orient	471
Fl	Florence	472
Est	Esther	473
St	Stratford	493
FiB	Fireglow (black)	533

ANEMONE

The pattern number is 4801 and it was available with a light blue, navy blue and black background. Some of the large flowers are hand-painted on top of the transfer.

Cat. No.	Shape	U.S. $	Can. $	U.K. £
A-04	Bonbon dish	40.00	25.00	30.00
A-09	Bowl, 5″	25.00	20.00	20.00
A-14	Bowl, 8″ soup	40.00	40.00	30.00
A-23	Breakfast set	550.00	450.00	375.00
A-28	Butter dish	125.00	95.00	75.00
A-30	Butter pat	35.00	20.00	25.00
A-35	Cake plate, open handles	125.00	85.00	75.00
A-36	Cake plate, tab handles	100.00	75.00	65.00
A-37	Cake plate, 8″ sq. pedestal	125.00	95.00	85.00
A-40	Cake stand, 2 tier	125.00	90.00	85.00
A-45	Canoe-shaped dish	165.00	125.00	115.00
A-50	Cheese keep	150.00	110.00	100.00
A-52	Coaster	30.00	25.00	25.00
A-55	Coffee pot	450.00	300.00	325.00
A-60	Compote, footed	100.00	75.00	75.00
A-65	Condiment set on tray	135.00	95.00	85.00
A-70	Cream and sugar	75.00	55.00	50.00
A-71	Cream and sugar on tray	135.00	95.00	85.00
A-75	Demi-tasse	50.00	35.00	35.00
A-77	Egg cup, footed	45.00	30.00	30.00
A-80	Hot water jug	200.00	145.00	125.00
A-85	Jam pot with liner	100.00	85.00	65.00
A-90	Jug, 4″	165.00	140.00	115.00
A-91	Jug, 4 1/2″	175.00	155.00	135.00
A-92	Jug, 5″	200.00	165.00	150.00

Cat. No.	Shape	U.S. $	Can. $	U.K. £
A-97	Nut dish	35.00	20.00	25.00
A-201	Plate, 4″ sq.	25.00	20.00	20.00
A-202	Plate, 5″ sq.	30.00	20.00	25.00
A-203	Plate, 6″ sq.	35.00	25.00	25.00
A-204	Plate, 7″ sq.	40.00	25.00	30.00
A-205	Plate, 8″ sq.	50.00	40.00	35.00
A-206	Plate, 9″ sq.	65.00	60.00	45.00
A-207	Plate, 10″ sq .	75.00	75.00	50.00
A-112	Relish dish, small	100.00	85.00	65.00
A-115	Salad bowl, chrome rim	100.00	70.00	65.00
A-117	Salt and pepper	50.00	40.00	40.00
A-118	Salt and pepper on tray	125.00	95.00	75.00
A-120	Sandwich tray, 10″ x 6″	75.00	55.00	50.00
A-121	Sandwich tray, 12″ x 7″	100.00	65.00	65.00
A-125	Sauce boat and liner	100.00	75.00	65.00
A-130	Teacup and saucer	65.00	40.00	35.00
A-135	Teapot, 2 cup	275.00	175.00	175.00
A-136	Teapot, 4 cup	325.00	200.00	225.00
A-137	Teapot, 6 cup	425.00	250.00	300.00
A-140	Teapot, stacking	650.00	450.00	325.00
A-145	Tennis set	75.00	45.00	50.00
A-150	Toast rack, 4 slice	165.00	110.00	125.00
A-151	Toast rack, 2 slice	135.00	95.00	85.00
A-155	Trivet	75.00	45.00	50.00
A-160	Vase, bud	85.00	55.00	50.00

BALMORAL

The pattern number is 374, and it was controlled in Canada in 1951 by Nerlich & Company. The wholesale price for the Ascot cream and sugar was $1.90 and the undertrays sold for $17.22 a dozen.

Cat. No.	Shape	U.S. $	Can. $	U.K. £
Ba-04	Bonbon dish	60.00	60.00	55.00
Ba-09	Bowl, 5″	45.00	45.00	45.00
Ba-14	Bowl, 8″ soup	75.00	65.00	60.00
Ba-23	Breakfast set	1,200.00	800.00	650.00
Ba-28	Butter dish	175.00	150.00	150.00
Ba-30	Butter pat	50.00	40.00	45.00
Ba-35	Cake plate, open handles	175.00	165.00	150.00
Ba-36	Cake plate, tab handles	150.00	145.00	135.00
Ba-37	Cake plate, 8″ sq. pedestal	175.00	165.00	150.00
Ba-40	Cake stand, 2 tier	175.00	150.00	150.00
Ba-45	Canoe-shaped dish	250.00	225.00	225.00
Ba-50	Cheese keep	225.00	195.00	175.00
Ba-52	Coaster	45.00	35.00	45.00
Ba-55	Coffee pot	975.00	600.00	575.00
Ba-60	Compote, footed	150.00	135.00	125.00
Ba-65	Condiment set on tray	200.00	165.00	150.00
Ba-70	Cream and sugar	100.00	100.00	85.00
Ba-71	Cream and sugar on tray	200.00	180.00	175.00
Ba-75	Demi-tasse	75.00	60.00	60.00
Ba-77	Egg cup, footed	95.00	65.00	65.00
Ba-80	Hot water jug	450.00	275.00	250.00
Ba-85	Jam pot with liner	150.00	125.00	125.00
Ba-90	Jug, 4″	400.00	225.00	175.00
Ba-91	Jug, 4 1/2″	450.00	250.00	200.00
Ba-92	Jug, 5″	500.00	275.00	225.00

Cat. No.	Shape	U.S. $	Can. $	U.K. £
Ba-97	Nut dish	50.00	40.00	40.00
Ba-201	Plate, 4″ sq.	45.00	40.00	35.00
Ba-202	Plate, 5″ sq.	50.00	40.00	40.00
Ba-203	Plate, 6″ sq.	60.00	50.00	45.00
Ba-204	Plate, 7″ sq.	75.00	50.00	55.00
Ba-205	Plate, 8″ sq.	115.00	75.00	75.00
Ba-206	Plate, 9″ sq.	135.00	90.00	95.00
Ba-207	Plate, 10″ sq.	150.00	110.00	120.00
Ba-112	Relish dish, small	150.00	150.00	125.00
Ba-115	Salad bowl, chrome rim	150.00	110.00	125.00
Ba-117	Salt and pepper	80.00	75.00	60.00
Ba-118	Salt and pepper on tray	150.00	135.00	120.00
Ba-120	Sandwich tray, 10″ x 6″	100.00	95.00	75.00
Ba-121	Sandwich tray, 12″ x 7″	125.00	115.00	125.00
Ba-125	Sauce boat and liner	150.00	130.00	125.00
Ba-130	Teacup and saucer	95.00	70.00	60.00
Ba-135	Teapot, 2 cup	425.00	325.00	275.00
Ba-136	Teapot, 4 cup	650.00	400.00	400.00
Ba-137	Teapot, 6 cup	850.00	450.00	475.00
Ba-140	Teapot, stacking	950.00	625.00	550.00
Ba-145	Tennis set	100.00	85.00	75.00
Ba-150	Toast rack, 4 slice	200.00	195.00	175.00
Ba-151	Toast rack, 2 slice	150.00	135.00	125.00
Ba-155	Trivet	100.00	85.00	75.00
Ba-160	Vase, bud	135.00	110.00	75.00

BEDALE

The pattern number is 1703, and it is an alternate colourway to **Summertime** 775. When it has a green trim, the pattern number is 4969. This is one of the patterns copied by the Japanese.

Cat. No.	Shape	U.S. $	Can. $	U.K. £
Be-04	Bonbon dish	50.00	50.00	40.00
Be-09	Bowl, 5"	40.00	35.00	35.00
Be-14	Bowl, 8" soup	65.00	60.00	50.00
Be-23	Breakfast set	1,000.00	700.00	625.00
Be-28	Butter dish	140.00	125.00	125.00
Be-30	Butter pat	40.00	35.00	35.00
Be-35	Cake plate, open handles	175.00	145.00	150.00
Be-36	Cake plate, tab handles	150.00	125.00	125.00
Be-37	Cake plate, 8" sq. pedestal	175.00	145.00	150.00
Be-40	Cake stand, 2 tier	150.00	145.00	125.00
Be-45	Canoe-shaped dish	200.00	195.00	175.00
Be-50	Cheese keep	175.00	175.00	150.00
Be-52	Coaster	35.00	35.00	30.00
Be-55	Coffee pot	675.00	500.00	550.00
Be-60	Compote, footed	125.00	125.00	85.00
Be-65	Condiment set on tray	165.00	150.00	120.00
Be-70	Cream and sugar	100.00	95.00	75.00
Be-71	Cream and sugar on tray	175.00	145.00	135.00
Be-75	Demi-tasse	65.00	55.00	50.00
Be-77	Egg cup, footed	75.00	60.00	50.00
Be-80	Hot water jug	400.00	275.00	225.00
Be-85	Jam pot with liner	125.00	110.00	125.00
Be-90	Jug, 4 1/2"	325.00	200.00	175.00
Be-91	Jug, 5"	375.00	225.00	200.00
Be-92	Jug, 5 1/2"	400.00	250.00	225.00
Be-97	Nut dish	40.00	35.00	35.00
Be-201	Plate, 4" sq.	45.00	35.00	35.00
Be-202	Plate, 5" sq.	50.00	35.00	40.00
Be-203	Plate, 6" sq.	55.00	45.00	45.00
Be-204	Plate, 7" sq.	65.00	45.00	50.00
Be-205	Plate, 8" sq.	85.00	65.00	60.00
Be-206	Plate, 9" sq.	105.00	75.00	65.00
Be-207	Plate, 10" sq.	125.00	95.00	85.00
Be-112	Relish dish, small	125.00	135.00	125.00
Be-115	Salad bowl, chrome rim	100.00	95.00	85.00
Be-117	Salt and pepper	75.00	65.00	55.00
Be-118	Salt and pepper on tray	135.00	115.00	95.00
Be-120	Sandwich tray, 10" x 6"	100.00	90.00	85.00
Be-121	Sandwich tray, 12" x 7"	100.00	110.00	95.00
Be-125	Sauce boat and liner	125.00	115.00	90.00
Be-130	Teacup and saucer	75.00	60.00	55.00
Be-135	Teapot, 2 cup	300.00	275.00	250.00
Be-136	Teapot, 4 cup	450.00	350.00	375.00
Be-137	Teapot, 6 cup	550.00	400.00	425.00
Be-140	Teapot, stacking	850.00	575.00	525.00
Be-145	Tennis set	85.00	75.00	70.00
Be-150	Toast rack, 4 slice	200.00	185.00	175.00
Be-151	Toast rack, 2 slice	150.00	135.00	125.00
Be-155	Trivet	85.00	75.00	70.00
Be-160	Vase, bud	135.00	95.00	85.00

BEESTON

The pattern number is 2203. This pattern was copied by the Japanese. Beeston is probably the earliest black background pattern and it has become increasingly sought after in the past year.

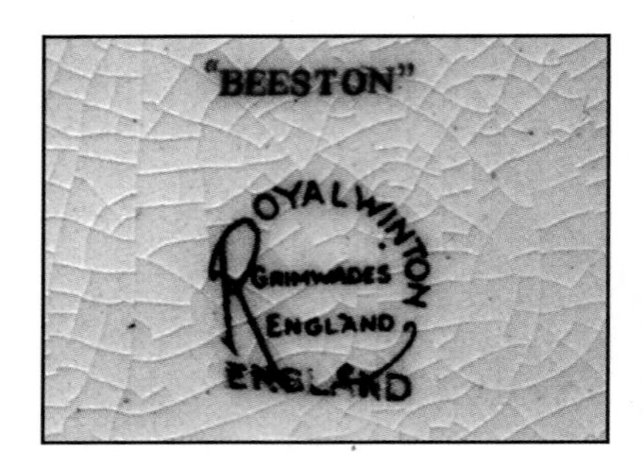

Cat. No.	Shape	U.S. $	Can. $	U.K. £
Bee-04	Bonbon dish	85.00	75.00	60.00
Bee-09	Bowl, 5"	55.00	50.00	45.00
Bee-14	Bowl, 8" soup	95.00	80.00	70.00
Bee-23	Breakfast set	1,300.00	900.00	800.00
Bee-28	Butter dish	245.00	195.00	175.00
Bee-30	Butter pat	75.00	65.00	55.00
Bee-35	Cake plate, open handles	245.00	195.00	175.00
Bee-36	Cake plate, tab handles	220.00	175.00	175.00
Bee-37	Cake plate, 8" sq. pedestal	245.00	195.00	175.00
Bee-40	Cake stand, 2 tier	245.00	195.00	175.00
Bee-45	Canoe-shaped dish	375.00	325.00	265.00
Bee-50	Cheese keep	325.00	225.00	225.00
Bee-52	Coaster	60.00	50.00	45.00
Bee-55	Coffee pot	1,200.00	800.00	700.00
Bee-60	Compote, footed	225.00	175.00	150.00
Bee-65	Condiment set on tray	275.00	225.00	215.00
Bee-70	Cream and sugar	165.00	135.00	125.00
Bee-71	Cream and sugar on tray	325.00	200.00	205.00
Bee-75	Demi-tasse	110.00	95.00	85.00
Bee-77	Egg cup, footed	100.00	90.00	60.00
Bee-80	Hot water jug	575.00	400.00	300.00
Bee-85	Jam pot with liner	220.00	175.00	175.00
Bee-90	Jug, 4"	450.00	325.00	275.00
Bee-91	Jug, 4 1/2"	500.00	350.00	300.00
Bee-92	Jug, 5"	550.00	375.00	325.00

Cat. No.	Shape	U.S. $	Can. $	U.K. £
Bee-97	Nut dish	75.00	65.00	50.00
Bee-201	Plate, 4" sq.	55.00	50.00	45.00
Bee-202	Plate, 5" sq.	65.00	60.00	55.00
Bee-203	Plate, 6" sq.	75.00	70.00	60.00
Bee-204	Plate, 7" sq.	110.00	85.00	75.00
Bee-205	Plate, 8" sq.	145.00	95.00	85.00
Bee-206	Plate, 9" sq.	160.00	110.00	120.00
Bee-207	Plate, 10" sq.	175.00	125.00	135.00
Bee-112	Relish dish, small	220.00	195.00	175.00
Bee-115	Salad bowl, chrome rim	195.00	150.00	150.00
Bee-117	Salt and pepper	110.00	105.00	75.00
Bee-118	Salt and pepper on tray	195.00	150.00	150.00
Bee-120	Sandwich tray, 10" x 6"	165.00	125.00	125.00
Bee-121	Sandwich tray, 12" x 7"	195.00	155.00	145.00
Bee-125	Sauce boat and liner	150.00	175.00	120.00
Bee-130	Teacup and saucer	125.00	110.00	75.00
Bee-135	Teapot, 2 cup	550.00	400.00	360.00
Bee-136	Teapot, 4 cup	800.00	550.00	540.00
Bee-137	Teapot, 6 cup	1000.00	650.00	600.00
Bee-140	Teapot, stacking	1,200.00	850.00	650.00
Bee-145	Tennis set	130.00	115.00	120.00
Bee-150	Toast rack, 4 slice	300.00	225.00	205.00
Bee-151	Toast rack, 2 slice	220.00	175.00	150.00
Bee-155	Trivet	150.00	110.00	100.00
Bee-160	Vase, bud	175.00	135.00	100.00

CARNATION

This pattern is mentioned in March 1933 in *The Pottery, Glass & Brass Salesman*; "reference can be made to a cake plate done in a choice of two all-over chintz decorations for which many doubtless will be able to get $1.25. . . **Carnation** is very well executed and a veritable riot of color." Interestingly, this pattern was sold in Australia with the name backstamp **Ostria**. This pattern does not appear to have been used on many of the Royal Winton shapes.

Cat. No.	Shape	U.S. $	Can. $	U.K. £
Car-35	Cake plate, open handles	100.00	85.00	60.00
Car-115	Salad bowl, chrome rim	100.00	75.00	65.00
Car-130	Teacup and saucer	40.00	45.00	35.00

Cat. No.	Shape	U.S. $	Can. $	U.K. £
Car-203	Plate, 6" sq.	40.00	35.00	30.00
Car-206	Plate, 9" sq.	75.00	65.00	40.00

CHEADLE

The pattern number is 311. This pattern was featured in an American advertisement in early 1950 and has been seen on an invoice as late as 1969. The pattern was registered in Canada in 1951.

Cat. No.	Shape	U.S. $	Can. $	U.K. £
Chd-04	Bonbon dish	60.00	60.00	55.00
Chd-09	Bowl, 5″	45.00	45.00	40.00
Chd-14	Bowl, 8″ soup	70.00	65.00	60.00
Chd-23	Breakfast set	1,100.00	800.00	675.00
Chd-28	Butter dish	175.00	150.00	150.00
Chd-30	Butter pat	50.00	40.00	45.00
Chd-35	Cake plate, open handles	200.00	165.00	175.00
Chd-36	Cake plate, tab handles	175.00	145.00	150.00
Chd-37	Cake plate, 8″ sq. pedestal	200.00	165.00	175.00
Chd-40	Cake stand, 2 tier	175.00	150.00	150.00
Chd-45	Canoe-shaped dish	250.00	225.00	215.00
Chd-50	Cheese keep	225.00	145.00	175.00
Chd-52	Coaster	45.00	35.00	45.00
Chd-55	Coffee pot	900.00	600.00	600.00
Chd-60	Compote, footed	150.00	135.00	125.00
Chd-65	Condiment set on tray	200.00	165.00	150.00
Chd-70	Cream and sugar	100.00	100.00	85.00
Chd-71	Cream and sugar on tray	200.00	180.00	150.00
Chd-75	Demi-tasse	95.00	60.00	60.00
Chd-77	Egg cup, footed	95.00	65.00	55.00
Chd-80	Hot water jug	400.00	275.00	250.00
Chd-85	Jam pot with liner	150.00	125.00	125.00
Chd-90	Jug, 4″	350.00	225.00	200.00
Chd-91	Jug, 4 1/2″	400.00	250.00	225.00
Chd-92	Jug, 5″	450.00	275.00	250.00
Chd-	Lighter	EXTREMELY RARE		

Cat. No.	Shape	U.S. $	Can. $	U.K. £
Chd-97	Nut dish	50.00	40.00	40.00
Chd-201	Plate, 4″ sq.	50.00	40.00	40.00
Chd-202	Plate, 5″ sq.	55.00	40.00	45.00
Chd-203	Plate, 6″ sq.	65.00	50.00	50.00
Chd-204	Plate, 7″ sq.	85.00	50.00	60.00
Chd-205	Plate, 8″ sq.	115.00	75.00	75.00
Chd-206	Plate, 9″ sq.	135.00	90.00	95.00
Chd-207	Plate, 10″ sq.	150.00	110.00	110.00
Chd-112	Relish dish, small	150.00	150.00	125.00
Chd-115	Salad bowl, chrome rim	135.00	110.00	95.00
Chd-117	Salt and pepper	75.00	75.00	60.00
Chd-118	Salt and pepper on tray	150.00	135.00	120.00
Chd-120	Sandwich tray, 10″ x 6″	100.00	95.00	75.00
Chd-121	Sandwich tray, 12″ x 7″	125.00	115.00	85.00
Chd-125	Sauce boat and liner	150.00	135.00	120.00
Chd-130	Teacup and saucer	95.00	70.00	60.00
Chd-135	Teapot, 2 cup	450.00	325.00	300.00
Chd-136	Teapot, 4 cup	650.00	400.00	425.00
Chd-137	Teapot, 6 cup	850.00	450.00	550.00
Chd-140	Teapot, stacking	1,000.00	625.00	625.00
Chd-145	Tennis set	100.00	85.00	75.00
Chd-150	Toast rack, 4 slice	200.00	195.00	150.00
Chd-151	Toast rack, 2 slice	150.00	135.00	120.00
Chd-155	Trivet	100.00	85.00	75.00
Chd-160	Vase, bud	150.00	110.00	85.00

CHELSEA

The pattern number is 455 and the name has been seen on an invoice as late as 1969. The pattern was registered in Canada in 1952. This pattern has become popular with American and English collectors although it is difficult to find.

Cat. No.	Shape	U.S. $	Can. $	U.K. £
Chl-04	Bonbon dish	75.00	75.00	60.00
Chl-09	Bowl, 5"	50.00	50.00	45.00
Chl-14	Bowl, 8" soup	75.00	80.00	65.00
Chl-23	Breakfast set	1,300.00	900.00	750.00
Chl-28	Butter dish	200.00	195.00	165.00
Chl-30	Butter pat	60.00	65.00	55.00
Chl-35	Cake plate, open handles	200.00	195.00	175.00
Chl-36	Cake plate, tab handles	200.00	175.00	175.00
Chl-37	Cake plate, 8" sq. pedestal	225.00	195.00	195.00
Chl-40	Cake stand, 2 tier	225.00	195.00	175.00
Chl-45	Canoe-shaped dish	275.00	325.00	250.00
Chl-50	Cheese keep	275.00	225.00	250.00
Chl-52	Coaster	55.00	50.00	50.00
Chl-55	Coffee pot	1,200.00	800.00	750.00
Chl-60	Compote, footed	175.00	175.00	160.00
Chl-65	Condiment set on tray	250.00	225.00	225.00
Chl-70	Cream and sugar	125.00	135.00	125.00
Chl-71	Cream and sugar on tray	250.00	200.00	205.00
Chl-75	Demi-tasse	100.00	95.00	80.00
Chl-77	Egg cup, footed	95.00	90.00	80.00
Chl-80	Hot water jug	575.00	400.00	315.00
Chl-85	Jam pot with liner	175.00	175.00	160.00
Chl-90	Jug, 4"	450.00	325.00	250.00
Chl-91	Jug, 4 1/2"	500.00	350.00	275.00
Chl-92	Jug, 5"	550.00	375.00	300.00

Cat. No.	Shape	U.S. $	Can. $	U.K. £
Chl-97	Nut dish	50.00	65.00	55.00
Chl-201	Plate, 4" sq.	50.00	50.00	50.00
Chl-202	Plate, 5" sq.	65.00	60.00	55.00
Chl-203	Plate, 6" sq.	75.00	70.00	60.00
Chl-204	Plate, 7" sq.	100.00	85.00	75.00
Chl-205	Plate, 8" sq.	135.00	95.00	85.00
Chl-206	Plate, 9" sq.	150.00	110.00	100.00
Chl-207	Plate, 10" sq.	165.00	125.00	125.00
Chl-112	Relish dish, small	200.00	195.00	150.00
Chl-115	Salad bowl, chrome rim	165.00	150.00	145.00
Chl-117	Salt and pepper	100.00	105.00	80.00
Chl-118	Salt and pepper on tray	175.00	150.00	145.00
Chl-120	Sandwich tray, 10" x 6"	135.00	125.00	100.00
Chl-121	Sandwich tray, 12" x 7"	150.00	155.00	125.00
Chl-125	Sauce boat and liner	150.00	175.00	125.00
Chl-130	Teacup and saucer	115.00	110.00	80.00
Chl-135	Teapot, 2 cup	500.00	400.00	350.00
Chl-136	Teapot, 4 cup	700.00	550.00	525.00
Chl-137	Teapot, 6 cup	850.00	650.00	625.00
Chl-140	Teapot, stacking	1,150.00	850.00	700.00
Chl-145	Tennis set	125.00	115.00	85.00
Chl-150	Toast rack, 4 slice	250.00	225.00	225.00
Chl-151	Toast rack, 2 slice	200.00	175.00	165.00
Chl-155	Trivet	125.00	110.00	85.00
Chl-160	Vase, bud	165.00	135.00	100.00

CHINTZ

The pattern number is 2836 and was probably introduced in the mid 1930s. The pattern has elements of handpainting, including a butterfly.

Cat. No.	Shape	U.S. $	Can. $	U.K. £
Chz-04	Bonbon dish	30.00	15.00	25.00
Chz-09	Bowl, 5″	30.00	15.00	25.00
Chz-14	Bowl, 8″ soup	40.00	20.00	30.00
Chz-23	Breakfast set	650.00	250.00	325.00
Chz-28	Butter dish	100.00	60.00	65.00
Chz-30	Butter pat	25.00	15.00	20.00
Chz-35	Cake plate, open handles	100.00	65.00	65.00
Chz-36	Cake plate, tab handles	85.00	50.00	60.00
Chz-37	Cake plate, 8″ sq. pedestal	100.00	65.00	65.00
Chz-40	Cake stand, 2 tier	100.00	60.00	65.00
Chz-45	Canoe-shaped dish	135.00	75.00	85.00
Chz-50	Cheese keep	125.00	65.00	75.00
Chz-52	Coaster	25.00	15.00	20.00
Chz-55	Coffee pot	375.00	175.00	250.00
Chz-60	Compote, footed	80.00	45.00	50.00
Chz-65	Condiment set on tray	100.00	60.00	65.00
Chz-70	Cream and sugar	50.00	45.00	45.00
Chz-71	Cream and sugar on tray	100.00	65.00	65.00
Chz-75	Demi-tasse	40.00	25.00	30.00
Chz-77	Egg cup, footed	35.00	20.00	25.00
Chz-80	Hot water jug	160.00	200.00	125.00
Chz-85	Jam pot with liner	85.00	50.00	60.00
Chz-90	Jug, 4″	125.00	65.00	65.00
Chz-91	Jug, 4 1/2″	140.00	75.00	85.00
Chz-92	Jug, 5″	150.00	85.00	105.00

Cat. No.	Shape	U.S. $	Can. $	U.K. £
Chz-97	Nut dish	25.00	15.00	20.00
Chz-201	Plate, 4″ sq.	30.00	15.00	20.00
Chz-202	Plate, 5″ sq.	35.00	15.00	25.00
Chz-203	Plate, 6″ sq.	40.00	20.00	30.00
Chz-204	Plate, 7″ sq.	45.00	20.00	35.00
Chz-205	Plate, 8″ sq.	65.00	25.00	45.00
Chz-206	Plate, 9″ sq.	75.00	30.00	50.00
Chz-207	Plate, 10″ sq .	85.00	35.00	55.00
Chz-112	Relish dish, small	85.00	45.00	60.00
Chz-115	Salad bowl, chrome rim	100.00	60.00	65.00
Chz-117	Salt and pepper	50.00	30.00	40.00
Chz-118	Salt and pepper on tray	125.00	60.00	80.00
Chz-120	Sandwich tray, 10″ x 6″	60.00	35.00	45.00
Chz-121	Sandwich tray, 12″ x 7″	75.00	45.00	50.00
Chz-125	Sauce boat and liner	65.00	50.00	45.00
Chz-130	Teacup and saucer	40.00	25.00	30.00
Chz-135	Teapot, 2 cup	175.00	100.00	125.00
Chz-136	Teapot, 4 cup	275.00	125.00	200.00
Chz-137	Teapot, 6 cup	325.00	150.00	225.00
Chz-140	Teapot, stacking	550.00	225.00	275.00
Chz-145	Tennis set	55.00	30.00	40.00
Chz-150	Toast rack, 4 slice	150.00	85.00	100.00
Chz-151	Toast rack, 2 slice	135.00	65.00	85.00
Chz-155	Trivet	55.00	30.00	40.00
Chz-160	Vase, bud	60.00	45.00	45.00

CLEVEDON

The pattern number is 1844 with burgundy trim. This pattern was introduced in 1934 and is an alternate colourway to **Cranstone** pattern 1154.

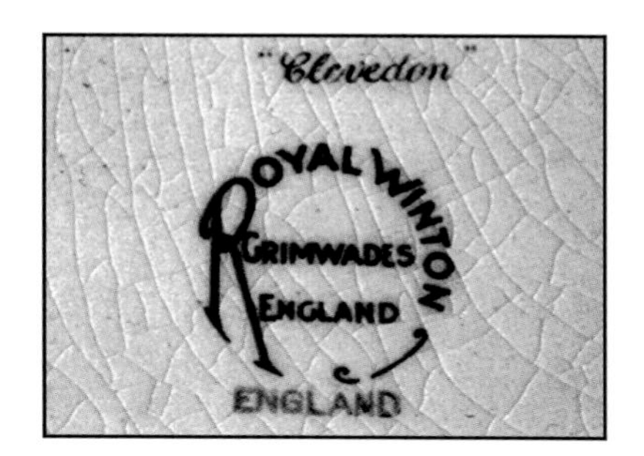

Cat. No.	Shape	U.S. $	Can. $	U.K. £
Cl-04	Bonbon dish	75.00	75.00	60.00
Cl-09	Bowl, 5"	50.00	50.00	40.00
Cl-14	Bowl, 8" soup	85.00	80.00	70.00
Cl-23	Breakfast set	1,200.00	900.00	775.00
Cl-28	Butter dish	225.00	195.00	175.00
Cl-30	Butter pat	65.00	65.00	55.00
Cl-35	Cake plate, open handles	225.00	195.00	175.00
Cl-36	Cake plate, tab handles	200.00	175.00	150.00
Cl-37	Cake plate, 8" sq. pedestal	225.00	195.00	175.00
Cl-40	Cake stand, 2 tier	225.00	195.00	175.00
Cl-45	Canoe-shaped dish	325.00	325.00	250.00
Cl-50	Cheese keep	300.00	225.00	225.00
Cl-52	Coaster	50.00	50.00	45.00
Cl-55	Coffee pot	1000.00	800.00	675.00
Cl-60	Compote, footed	175.00	175.00	150.00
Cl-65	Condiment set on tray	275.00	225.00	225.00
Cl-70	Cream and sugar	150.00	135.00	95.00
Cl-71	Cream and sugar on tray	275.00	200.00	225.00
Cl-75	Demi-tasse	100.00	95.00	75.00
Cl-77	Egg cup, footed	95.00	90.00	70.00
Cl-80	Hot water jug	500.00	400.00	300.00
Cl-85	Jam pot with liner	200.00	175.00	150.00
Cl-90	Jug, 4"	400.00	325.00	225.00
Cl-91	Jug, 4 1/2"	450.00	350.00	250.00
Cl-92	Jug, 5"	500.00	375.00	275.00
Cl-97	Nut dish	65.00	65.00	55.00
Cl-201	Plate, 4" sq.	50.00	50.00	35.00
Cl-202	Plate, 5" sq.	65.00	60.00	45.00
Cl-203	Plate, 6" sq.	75.00	70.00	55.00
Cl-204	Plate, 7" sq.	100.00	85.00	65.00
Cl-205	Plate, 8" sq.	135.00	95.00	85.00
Cl-206	Plate, 9" sq.	150.00	110.00	100.00
Cl-207	Plate, 10" sq.	165.00	125.00	125.00
Cl-112	Relish dish, small	200.00	195.00	150.00
Cl-115	Salad bowl, chrome rim	175.00	150.00	150.00
Cl-117	Salt and pepper	100.00	105.00	75.00
Cl-118	Salt and pepper on tray	175.00	150.00	145.00
Cl-120	Sandwich tray, 10" x 6"	150.00	125.00	120.00
Cl-121	Sandwich tray, 12" x 7"	165.00	155.00	145.00
Cl-125	Sauce boat and liner	165.00	175.00	150.00
Cl-130	Teacup and saucer	100.00	110.00	75.00
Cl-135	Teapot, 2 cup	525.00	400.00	350.00
Cl-136	Teapot, 4 cup	725.00	550.00	500.00
Cl-137	Teapot, 6 cup	825.00	650.00	575.00
Cl-140	Teapot, stacking	1,000.00	850.00	650.00
Cl-145	Tennis set	125.00	115.00	85.00
Cl-150	Toast rack, 4 slice	260.00	225.00	215.00
Cl-151	Toast rack, 2 slice	200.00	175.00	175.00
Cl-155	Trivet	135.00	110.00	90.00
Cl-160	Vase, bud	150.00	135.00	95.00

CLYDE

The pattern number is 5315 for the green-leaf version and 5637 for the brown-leaf version. **Clyde** was probably introduced late in 1939. The three versions of **Clyde** feature green, brown and blue leaves, but the brown and blue versions have not been found with a pattern name backstamp.

Cat. No.	Shape	U.S. $	Can. $	U.K. £
Cly-04	Bonbon dish	25.00	15.00	25.00
Cly-09	Bowl, 5"	25.00	15.00	25.00
Cly-14	Bowl, 8" soup	35.00	20.00	30.00
Cly-23	Breakfast set	450.00	250.00	325.00
Cly-28	Butter dish	90.00	65.00	65.00
Cly-30	Butter pat	25.00	15.00	20.00
Cly-35	Cake plate, open handles	90.00	65.00	75.00
Cly-36	Cake plate, tab handles	75.00	50.00	60.00
Cly-37	Cake plate, 8" sq. pedestal	90.00	65.00	65.00
Cly-40	Cake stand, 2 tier	90.00	65.00	65.00
Cly-45	Canoe-shaped dish	120.00	75.00	85.00
Cly-50	Cheese keep	115.00	75.00	100.00
Cly-52	Coaster	25.00	15.00	20.00
Cly-55	Coffee pot	375.00	175.00	250.00
Cly-60	Compote, footed	65.00	50.00	50.00
Cly-65	Condiment set on tray	90.00	65.00	65.00
Cly-70	Cream and sugar	55.00	45.00	45.00
Cly-71	Cream and sugar on tray	90.00	75.00	65.00
Cly-75	Demi-tasse	35.00	25.00	30.00
Cly-77	Egg cup, footed	35.00	20.00	25.00
Cly-80	Hot water jug	165.00	95.00	125.00
Cly-85	Jam pot with liner	75.00	50.00	60.00
Cly-90	Jug, 4"	135.00	65.00	65.00
Cly-91	Jug, 4 1/2"	150.00	75.00	75.00
Cly-92	Jug, 5"	165.00	85.00	95.00

Cat. No.	Shape	U.S. $	Can. $	U.K. £
Cly-97	Nut dish	25.00	15.00	20.00
Cly-201	Plate, 4" sq.	30.00	15.00	25.00
Cly-202	Plate, 5" sq.	35.00	15.00	25.00
Cly-203	Plate, 6" sq.	40.00	20.00	30.00
Cly-204	Plate, 7" sq.	45.00	20.00	35.00
Cly-205	Plate, 8" sq.	55.00	25.00	45.00
Cly-206	Plate, 9" sq.	65.00	30.00	50.00
Cly-207	Plate, 10" sq.	75.00	35.00	55.00
Cly-112	Relish dish, small	75.00	50.00	60.00
Cly-115	Salad bowl, chrome rim	90.00	65.00	65.00
Cly-117	Salt and pepper	45.00	35.00	40.00
Cly-118	Salt and pepper on tray	100.00	70.00	80.00
Cly-120	Sandwich tray, 10" x 6"	45.00	35.00	45.00
Cly-121	Sandwich tray, 12" x 7"	65.00	45.00	50.00
Cly-125	Sauce boat and liner	65.00	50.00	45.00
Cly-130	Teacup and saucer	35.00	25.00	30.00
Cly-135	Teapot, 2 cup	175.00	100.00	125.00
Cly-136	Teapot, 4 cup	275.00	125.00	175.00
Cly-137	Teapot, 6 cup	325.00	150.00	225.00
Cly-140	Teapot, stacking	400.00	250.00	275.00
Cly-145	Tennis set	45.00	35.00	40.00
Cly-150	Toast rack, 4 slice	150.00	85.00	125.00
Cly-151	Toast rack, 2 slice	90.00	65.00	65.00
Cly-155	Trivet	45.00	25.00	40.00
Cly-160	Vase, bud	50.00	45.00	45.00

COTSWOLD

The pattern number is 408 and the pattern was registered in Canada in 1952.

Cat. No.	Shape	U.S. $	Can. $	U.K. £
Co-03	Basket		RARE	
Co-04	Bonbon dish	50.00	50.00	50.00
Co-09	Bowl, 5″	50.00	35.00	45.00
Co-14	Bowl, 8″ soup	75.00	60.00	60.00
Co-23	Breakfast set	900.00	700.00	650.00
Co-28	Butter dish	165.00	125.00	15.00
Co-30	Butter pat	45.00	35.00	40.00
Co-35	Cake plate, open handles	165.00	145.00	150.00
Co-36	Cake plate, tab handles	150.00	125.00	125.00
Co-37	Cake plate, 8″ sq. pedestal	175.00	145.00	150.00
Co-40	Cake stand, 2 tier	175.00	145.00	150.00
Co-45	Canoe-shaped dish	250.00	195.00	195.00
Co-50	Cheese keep	200.00	175.00	175.00
Co-52	Coaster	40.00	35.00	35.00
Co-55	Coffee pot	750.00	500.00	500.00
Co-60	Compote, footed	135.00	125.00	105.00
Co-65	Condiment set on tray	200.00	150.00	165.00
Co-70	Cream and sugar	100.00	95.00	75.00
Co-71	Cream and sugar on tray	175.00	145.00	150.00
Co-75	Demi-tasse	85.00	60.00	60.00
Co-77	Egg cup, footed	75.00	65.00	55.00
Co-80	Hot water jug	350.00	275.00	225.00
Co-85	Jam pot with liner	150.00	110.00	120.00
Co-90	Jug, 4″	325.00	200.00	150.00
Co-91	Jug, 4 1/2″	375.00	225.00	175.00
Co-92	Jug, 5″	400.00	250.00	200.00

Cat. No.	Shape	U.S. $	Can. $	U.K. £
Co-180	Lamp Base		RARE	
Co-97	Nut dish	45.00	35.00	40.00
Co-201	Plate, 4″ sq.	50.00	35.00	40.00
Co-202	Plate, 5″ sq.	55.00	35.00	50.00
Co-203	Plate, 6″ sq.	60.00	45.00	55.00
Co-204	Plate, 7″ sq.	75.00	45.00	65.00
Co-205	Plate, 8″ sq.	100.00	65.00	75.00
Co-206	Plate, 9″ sq.	120.00	80.00	85.00
Co-207	Plate, 10″ sq.	135.00	95.00	95.00
Co-112	Relish dish, small	150.00	135.00	125.00
Co-115	Salad bowl, chrome rim	125.00	95.00	85.00
Co-117	Salt and pepper	75.00	65.00	60.00
Co-118	Salt and pepper on tray	150.00	115.00	120.00
Co-120	Sandwich tray, 10″ x 6″	100.00	95.00	75.00
Co-121	Sandwich tray, 12″ x 7″	125.00	115.00	95.00
Co-125	Sauce boat and liner	150.00	125.00	120.00
Co-130	Teacup and saucer	95.00	60.00	60.00
Co-135	Teapot, 2 cup	325.00	275.00	225.00
Co-136	Teapot, 4 cup	500.00	350.00	350.00
Co-137	Teapot, 6 cup	600.00	400.00	450.00
Co-140	Teapot, stacking	850.00	575.00	550.00
Co-145	Tennis set	100.00	75.00	75.00
Co-150	Toast rack, 4 slice	200.00	185.00	150.00
Co-151	Toast rack, 2 slice	135.00	125.00	110.00
Co-155	Trivet	100.00	75.00	75.00
Co-160	Vase, bud	125.00	95.00	75.00

CRANSTONE

The pattern number is 1154 with gold trim and an example was purchased by the Queen at the 1935 British Industries Fair. The pattern number for burgundy trim is 1877 and for green trim 2256. The alternate colourway is **Clevedon** 1844. This pattern has become very popular this year.

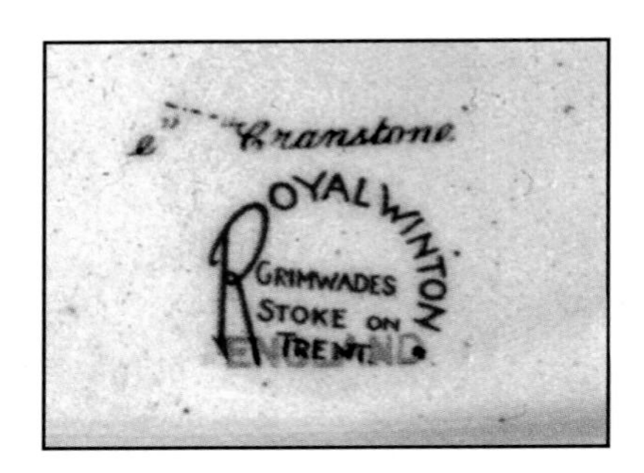

Cat. No.	Shape	U.S. $	Can. $	U.K. £
Cr-04	Bonbon dish	90.00	75.00	65.00
Cr-09	Bowl, 5″	55.00	50.00	50.00
Cr-14	Bowl, 8″ soup	110.00	80.00	75.00
Cr-23	Breakfast set	1,300.00	900.00	800.00
Cr-28	Butter dish	250.00	195.00	175.00
Cr-30	Butter pat	75.00	65.00	50.00
Cr-35	Cake plate, open handles	250.00	195.00	175.00
Cr-36	Cake plate, tab handles	220.00	175.00	150.00
Cr-37	Cake plate, 8″ sq. pedestal	275.00	195.00	200.00
Cr-40	Cake stand, 2 tier	275.00	195.00	200.00
Cr-45	Canoe-shaped dish	375.00	325.00	250.00
Cr-50	Cheese keep	330.00	225.00	225.00
Cr-52	Coaster	70.00	50.00	55.00
Cr-55	Coffee pot	1,200.00	800.00	700.00
Cr-60	Compote, footed	220.00	175.00	150.00
Cr-65	Condiment set on tray	300.00	225.00	215.00
Cr-70	Cream and sugar	165.00	135.00	100.00
Cr-71	Cream and sugar on tray	300.00	200.00	185.00
Cr-75	Demi-tasse	115.00	95.00	75.00
Cr-77	Egg cup, footed	100.00	90.00	70.00
Cr-80	Hot water jug	500.00	400.00	325.00
Cr-85	Jam pot with liner	220.00	175.00	150.00
Cr-90	Jug, 4″	400.00	325.00	250.00
Cr-91	Jug, 4 1/2″	450.00	350.00	275.00
Cr-92	Jug, 5″	500.00	375.00	300.00

Cat. No.	Shape	U.S. $	Can. $	U.K. £
Cr-97	Nut dish	75.00	65.00	50.00
Cr-201	Plate, 4″ sq.	60.00	50.00	45.00
Cr-202	Plate, 5″ sq.	70.00	60.00	50.00
Cr-203	Plate, 6″ sq.	80.00	70.00	55.00
Cr-204	Plate, 7″ sq.	110.00	85.00	65.00
Cr-205	Plate, 8″ sq.	140.00	95.00	80.00
Cr-206	Plate, 9″ sq.	160.00	110.00	95.00
Cr-207	Plate, 10″ sq.	180.00	125.00	115.00
Cr-112	Relish dish, small	220.00	195.00	175.00
Cr-115	Salad bowl, chrome rim	190.00	150.00	150.00
Cr-117	Salt and pepper	110.00	105.00	75.00
Cr-118	Salt and pepper on tray	220.00	150.00	175.00
Cr-120	Sandwich tray, 10″ x 6″	165.00	125.00	125.00
Cr-121	Sandwich tray, 12″ x 7″	195.00	150.00	150.00
Cr-125	Sauce boat and liner	195.00	175.00	150.00
Cr-130	Teacup and saucer	125.00	110.00	75.00
Cr-135	Teapot, 2 cup	550.00	400.00	350.00
Cr-136	Teapot, 4 cup	800.00	550.00	500.00
Cr-137	Teapot, 6 cup	1,000.00	650.00	600.00
Cr-140	Teapot, stacking	1,200.00	850.00	675.00
Cr-145	Tennis set	150.00	115.00	120.00
Cr-150	Toast rack, 4 slice	275.00	225.00	225.00
Cr-151	Toast rack, 2 slice	225.00	175.00	175.00
Cr-155	Trivet	150.00	110.00	120.00
Cr-160	Vase, bud	175.00	135.00	95.00

CROCUS

The pattern number of the white background **Crocus** is 111. The pattern number for the black background is 112 and a piece was found this year with the pattern name **Triumph**. The pattern is mentioned in a 1939 article but it is the one of the few Royal Winton chintz patterns that have never been found with a pattern name backstamp. See **Triumph** (page 102).

Backstamp not available
at
press time

Cat. No.	Shape	U.S. $	Can. $	U.K. £
Cro-04	Bonbon dish	75.00	60.00	50.00
Cro-09	Bowl, 5"	50.00	45.00	35.00
Cro-14	Bowl, 8" soup	80.00	65.00	50.00
Cro-23	Breakfast set	1,000.00	800.00	600.00
Cro-28	Butter dish	200.00	150.00	150.00
Cro-30	Butter pat	60.00	45.00	45.00
Cro-35	Cake plate, open handles	200.00	165.00	150.00
Cro-36	Cake plate, tab handles	175.00	145.00	135.00
Cro-37	Cake plate, 8" sq. pedestal	225.00	165.00	150.00
Cro-40	Cake stand, 2 tier	225.00	150.00	150.00
Cro-45	Canoe-shaped dish	275.00	225.00	200.00
Cro-50	Cheese keep	275.00	195.00	200.00
Cro-52	Coaster	50.00	35.00	40.00
Cro-55	Coffee pot	850.00	600.00	600.00
Cro-60	Compote, footed	175.00	135.00	125.00
Cro-65	Condiment set on tray	250.00	165.00	175.00
Cro-70	Cream and sugar	135.00	100.00	85.00
Cro-71	Cream and sugar on tray	250.00	150.00	175.00
Cro-75	Demi-tasse	100.00	60.00	65.00
Cro-77	Egg cup, footed	85.00	65.00	50.00
Cro-80	Hot water jug	400.00	275.00	250.00
Cro-85	Jam pot with liner	175.00	125.00	135.00
Cro-90	Jug, 4"	350.00	225.00	200.00
Cro-91	Jug, 4 1/2"	400.00	250.00	225.00
Cro-92	Jug, 5"	425.00	275.00	250.00

Cat. No.	Shape	U.S. $	Can. $	U.K. £
Cro-97	Nut dish	50.00	40.00	40.00
Cro-201	Plate, 4" sq.	50.00	40.00	40.00
Cro-202	Plate, 5" sq.	65.00	40.00	45.00
Cro-203	Plate, 6" sq.	75.00	50.00	50.00
Cro-204	Plate, 7" sq.	100.00	55.00	65.00
Cro-205	Plate, 8" sq.	135.00	75.00	75.00
Cro-206	Plate, 9" sq.	150.00	95.00	85.00
Cro-207	Plate, 10" sq .	165.00	111.00	105.00
Cro-112	Relish dish, small	200.00	150.00	125.00
Cro-115	Salad bowl, chrome rim	165.00	110.00	115.00
Cro-117	Salt and pepper	100.00	75.00	65.00
Cro-118	Salt and pepper on tray	175.00	135.00	125.00
Cro-120	Sandwich tray, 10" x 6"	135.00	95.00	95.00
Cro-121	Sandwich tray, 12" x 7"	165.00	115.00	115.00
Cro-125	Sauce boat and liner	165.00	130.00	115.00
Cro-130	Teacup and saucer	110.00	75.00	65.00
Cro-135	Teapot, 2 cup	450.00	325.00	275.00
Cro-136	Teapot, 4 cup	650.00	400.00	425.00
Cro-137	Teapot, 6 cup	750.00	450.00	500.00
Cro-140	Teapot, stacking	950.00	625.00	550.00
Cro-145	Tennis set	125.00	85.00	75.00
Cro-150	Toast rack, 4 slice	250.00	195.00	175.00
Cro-151	Toast rack, 2 slice	200.00	135.00	150.00
Cro-155	Trivet	125.00	85.00	75.00
Cro-160	Vase, bud	135.00	110.00	75.00

CROMER

The pattern number is 2078 and belongs to the "all-over" non-chintz pattern group.

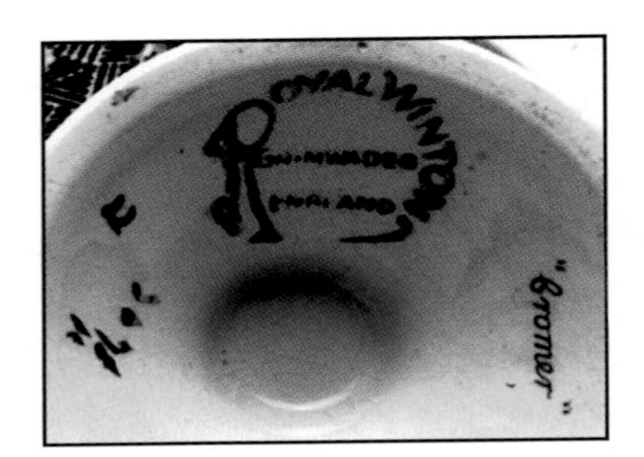

Cat. No.	Shape	U.S. $	Can. $	U.K. £
Crom-04	Bonbon dish	40.00	25.00	30.00
Crom-09	Bowl, 5"	35.00	20.00	25.00
Crom-14	Bowl, 8" soup	50.00	45.00	45.00
Crom-23	Breakfast set	550.00	450.00	400.00
Crom-28	Butter dish	125.00	95.00	80.00
Crom-30	Butter pat	35.00	20.00	25.00
Crom-35	Cake plate, open handles	150.00	85.00	110.00
Crom-36	Cake plate, tab handles	125.00	75.00	80.00
Crom-37	Cake plate, 8" sq. pedestal	150.00	95.00	110.00
Crom-40	Cake stand, 2 tier	150.00	90.00	110.00
Crom-45	Canoe-shaped dish	150.00	125.00	110.00
Crom-50	Cheese keep	150.00	110.00	115.00
Crom-52	Coaster	30.00	25.00	25.00
Crom-55	Coffee pot	450.00	300.00	350.00
Crom-60	Compote, footed	100.00	75.00	70.00
Crom-65	Condiment set on tray	135.00	95.00	95.00
Crom-70	Cream and sugar	75.00	55.00	55.00
Crom-71	Cream and sugar on tray	135.00	95.00	90.00
Crom-75	Demi-tasse	50.00	40.00	35.00
Crom-77	Egg cup, footed	45.00	35.00	40.00
Crom-80	Hot water jug	200.00	145.00	145.00
Crom-85	Jam pot with liner	100.00	85.00	85.00
Crom-90	Jug, 4"	165.00	140.00	110.00
Crom-91	Jug, 4 1/2"	175.00	155.00	125.00
Crom-92	Jug, 5"	200.00	165.00	135.00

Cat. No.	Shape	U.S. $	Can. $	U.K. £
Crom-97	Nut dish	35.00	20.00	25.00
Crom-201	Plate, 4" sq.	35.00	20.00	20.00
Crom-202	Plate, 5" sq.	40.00	20.00	25.00
Crom-203	Plate, 6" sq.	45.00	25.00	30.00
Crom-204	Plate, 7" sq.	50.00	25.00	35.00
Crom-205	Plate, 8" sq.	60.00	40.00	50.00
Crom-206	Plate, 9" sq.	75.00	60.00	60.00
Crom-207	Plate, 10" sq .	95.00	75.00	70.00
Crom-112	Relish dish, small	100.00	85.00	70.00
Crom-115	Salad bowl, chrome rim	100.00	70.00	70.00
Crom-117	Salt and pepper	55.00	45.00	45.00
Crom-118	Salt and pepper on tray	125.00	95.00	80.00
Crom-120	Sandwich tray, 10" x 6"	75.00	55.00	55.00
Crom-121	Sandwich tray, 12" x 7"	85.00	65.00	65.00
Crom-125	Sauce boat and liner	100.00	75.00	70.00
Crom-130	Teacup and saucer	50.00	40.00	35.00
Crom-135	Teapot, 2 cup	200.00	175.00	150.00
Crom-136	Teapot, 4 cup	300.00	200.00	225.00
Crom-137	Teapot, 6 cup	400.00	250.00	300.00
Crom-140	Teapot, stacking	500.00	450.00	375.00
Crom-145	Tennis set	75.00	45.00	55.00
Crom-150	Toast rack, 4 slice	165.00	110.00	125.00
Crom-151	Toast rack, 2 slice	135.00	95.00	95.00
Crom-155	Trivet	75.00	45.00	55.00
Crom-160	Vase, bud	75.00	60.00	65.00

DELPHINIUM CHINTZ

The pattern number is 9889. This pattern was introduced in 1931 in an advertisement in the *Pottery Gazette*. It first appeared a year earlier as a single spray on an ivory ground.

Cat. No.	Shape	U.S. $	Can. $	U.K. £
De-04	Bonbon dish	45.00	25.00	35.00
De-09	Bowl, 5"	40.00	20.00	30.00
De-14	Bowl, 8" soup	75.00	40.00	50.00
De-23	Breakfast set	800.00	450.00	450.00
De-28	Butter dish	135.00	95.00	85.00
De-30	Butter pat	40.00	20.00	30.00
De-35	Cake plate, open handles	135.00	85.00	85.00
De-36	Cake plate, tab handles	125.00	75.00	75.00
De-37	Cake plate, 8" sq. pedestal	150.00	95.00	100.00
De-40	Cake stand, 2 tier	150.00	90.00	100.00
De-45	Canoe-shaped dish	200.00	125.00	125.00
De-50	Cheese keep	175.00	110.00	125.00
De-52	Coaster	35.00	25.00	25.00
De-55	Coffee pot	575.00	300.00	375.00
De-60	Compote, footed	100.00	75.00	65.00
De-65	Condiment set on tray	150.00	95.00	100.00
De-70	Cream and sugar	85.00	55.00	60.00
De-71	Cream and sugar on tray	150.00	95.00	100.00
De-75	Demi-tasse	60.00	40.00	45.00
De-77	Egg cup, footed	65.00	35.00	35.00
De-80	Hot water jug	275.00	150.00	150.00
De-85	Jam pot with liner	125.00	85.00	75.00
De-90	Jug, 4"	250.00	140.00	115.00
De-91	Jug, 4 1/2"	275.00	155.00	135.00
De-92	Jug, 5"	300.00	165.00	150.00

Cat. No.	Shape	U.S. $	Can. $	U.K. £
De-97	Nut dish	40.00	20.00	30.00
De-201	Plate, 4" sq.	35.00	20.00	20.00
De-202	Plate, 5" sq.	40.00	20.00	25.00
De-203	Plate, 6" sq.	45.00	25.00	30.00
De-204	Plate, 7" sq.	50.00	25.00	35.00
De-205	Plate, 8" sq.	60.00	40.00	40.00
De-206	Plate, 9" sq.	75.00	60.00	50.00
De-207	Plate, 10" sq.	95.00	75.00	60.00
De-112	Relish dish, small	125.00	85.00	75.00
De-115	Salad bowl, chrome rim	100.00	75.00	65.00
De-117	Salt and pepper	65.00	50.00	45.00
De-118	Salt and pepper on tray	150.00	105.00	85.00
De-120	Sandwich tray, 10" x 6"	85.00	55.00	60.00
De-121	Sandwich tray, 12" x 7"	100.00	65.00	65.00
De-125	Sauce boat and liner	125.00	85.00	75.00
De-130	Teacup and saucer	60.00	45.00	45.00
De-135	Teapot, 2 cup	275.00	175.00	175.00
De-136	Teapot, 4 cup	375.00	200.00	250.00
De-137	Teapot, 6 cup	475.00	250.00	325.00
De-140	Teapot, stacking	650.00	450.00	425.00
De-145	Tennis set	75.00	50.00	50.00
De-150	Toast rack, 4 slice	175.00	110.00	125.00
De-151	Toast rack, 2 slice	125.00	95.00	75.00
De-155	Trivet	75.00	50.00	50.00
De-160	Vase, bud	100.00	75.00	60.00

DORSET

The pattern number is 274, and this pattern was featured in an advertisement in Toronto, Canada, in 1949. The pattern number of the brown version is 294.

Cat. No.	Shape	U.S. $	Can. $	U.K. £
Do-04	Bonbon dish	35.00	15.00	30.00
Do-09	Bowl, 5″	30.00	20.00	25.00
Do-14	Bowl, 8″ soup	45.00	25.00	40.00
Do-23	Breakfast set	650.00	250.00	375.00
Do-28	Butter dish	115.00	65.00	75.00
Do-30	Butter pat	35.00	20.00	25.00
Do-35	Cake plate, open handles	135.00	65.00	100.00
Do-36	Cake plate, tab handles	115.00	60.00	75.00
Do-37	Cake plate, 8″ sq. pedestal	135.00	65.00	100.00
Do-40	Cake stand, 2 tier	135.00	60.00	100.00
Do-45	Canoe-shaped dish	135.00	75.00	100.00
Do-50	Cheese keep	135.00	75.00	100.00
Do-52	Coaster	30.00	15.00	25.00
Do-55	Coffee pot	375.00	175.00	325.00
Do-60	Compote, footed	90.00	45.00	65.00
Do-65	Condiment set on tray	120.00	65.00	85.00
Do-70	Cream and sugar	65.00	45.00	50.00
Do-71	Cream and sugar on tray	120.00	75.00	85.00
Do-75	Demi-tasse	45.00	30.00	35.00
Do-77	Egg cup, footed	45.00	25.00	35.00
Do-80	Hot water jug	180.00	95.00	150.00
Do-85	Jam pot with liner	90.00	55.00	65.00
Do-90	Jug, 4″	150.00	65.00	100.00
Do-91	Jug, 4 1/2″	175.00	75.00	115.00
Do-92	Jug, 5″	200.00	85.00	125.00

Cat. No.	Shape	U.S. $	Can. $	U.K. £
Do-97	Nut dish	30.00	15.00	25.00
Do-201	Plate, 4″ sq.	30.00	15.00	20.00
Do-202	Plate, 5″ sq.	35.00	15.00	25.00
Do-203	Plate, 6″ sq.	40.00	20.00	30.00
Do-204	Plate, 7″ sq.	45.00	20.00	35.00
Do-205	Plate, 8″ sq.	65.00	25.00	40.00
Do-206	Plate, 9″ sq.	75.00	35.00	45.00
Do-207	Plate, 10″ sq.	85.00	45.00	50.00
Do-112	Relish dish, small	90.00	55.00	65.00
Do-115	Salad bowl, chrome rim	90.00	65.00	65.00
Do-117	Salt and pepper	45.00	35.00	40.00
Do-118	Salt and pepper on tray	110.00	65.00	75.00
Do-120	Sandwich tray, 10″ x 6″	65.00	40.00	50.00
Do-121	Sandwich tray, 12″ x 7″	75.00	50.00	60.00
Do-125	Sauce boat and liner	90.00	45.00	65.00
Do-130	Teacup and saucer	50.00	25.00	35.00
Do-135	Teapot, 2 cup	200.00	100.00	150.00
Do-136	Teapot, 4 cup	300.00	125.00	200.00
Do-137	Teapot, 6 cup	400.00	150.00	275.00
Do-140	Teapot, stacking	500.00	250.00	350.00
Do-145	Tennis set	65.00	35.00	50.00
Do-150	Toast rack, 4 slice	150.00	85.00	115.00
Do-151	Toast rack, 2 slice	120.00	65.00	85.00
Do-155	Trivet	65.00	25.00	50.00
Do-160	Vase, bud	75.00	45.00	50.00

ELEANOR

The pattern number is 375, and was introduced early in the 1950s and remained in production well into the 1960s.

Cat. No.	Shape	U.S. $	Can. $	U.K. £
El-04	Bonbon dish	45.00	50.00	40.00
El-09	Bowl, 5″	40.00	35.00	30.00
El-14	Bowl, 8″ soup	75.00	60.00	55.00
El-23	Breakfast set	750.00	700.00	500.00
El-28	Butter dish	135.00	125.00	95.00
El-30	Butter pat	40.00	35.00	30.00
El-35	Cake plate, open handles	135.00	145.00	95.00
El-36	Cake plate, tab handles	125.00	125.00	85.00
El-37	Cake plate, 8″ sq. pedestal	150.00	145.00	110.00
El-40	Cake stand, 2 tier	150.00	145.00	110.00
El-45	Canoe-shaped dish	200.00	195.00	150.00
El-50	Cheese keep	175.00	175.00	140.00
El-52	Coaster	35.00	35.00	25.00
El-55	Coffee pot	525.00	500.00	375.00
El-60	Compote, footed	100.00	125.00	75.00
El-65	Condiment set on tray	150.00	150.00	110.00
El-70	Cream and sugar	85.00	95.00	65.00
El-71	Cream and sugar on tray	150.00	145.00	120.00
El-75	Demi-tasse	60.00	55.00	50.00
El-77	Egg cup, footed	65.00	60.00	45.00
El-80	Hot water jug	225.00	275.00	175.00
El-85	Jam pot with liner	125.00	110.00	85.00
El-90	Jug, 4″	175.00	200.00	150.00
El-91	Jug, 4 1/2″	200.00	225.00	160.00
El-92	Jug, 5″	225.00	250.00	175.00
El-97	Nut dish	40.00	35.00	30.00
El-201	Plate, 4″ sq.	35.00	35.00	25.00
El-202	Plate, 5″ sq.	40.00	35.00	30.00
El-203	Plate, 6″ sq.	45.00	45.00	35.00
El-204	Plate, 7″ sq.	50.00	45.00	40.00
El-205	Plate, 8″ sq.	75.00	65.00	50.00
El-206	Plate, 9″ sq.	85.00	80.00	55.00
El-207	Plate, 10″ sq.	100.00	95.00	65.00
El-112	Relish dish, small	125.00	135.00	85.00
El-115	Salad bowl, chrome rim	100.00	95.00	75.00
El-117	Salt and pepper	65.00	65.00	50.00
El-118	Salt and pepper on tray	150.00	115.00	110.00
El-120	Sandwich tray, 10″ x 6″	85.00	90.00	65.00
El-121	Sandwich tray, 12″ x 7″	100.00	110.00	70.00
El-125	Sauce boat and liner	125.00	115.00	85.00
El-130	Teacup and saucer	70.00	65.00	55.00
El-135	Teapot, 2 cup	250.00	275.00	195.00
El-136	Teapot, 4 cup	350.00	350.00	275.00
El-137	Teapot, 6 cup	450.00	400.00	350.00
El-140	Teapot, stacking	650.00	575.00	475.00
El-145	Tennis set	75.00	75.00	55.00
El-150	Toast rack, 4 slice	175.00	185.00	135.00
El-151	Toast rack, 2 slice	115.00	135.00	95.00
El-155	Trivet	75.00	75.00	60.00
El-160	Vase, bud	95.00	100.00	70.00

ENGLISH ROSE

The pattern number is 381 and this pattern has become increasingly popular with North American collectors. The pattern was introduced into Canada in 1951 and described in an advertisement as a "warm and colourful pattern depicting the beauty of the English Rose in full bloom." The pattern was exclusive to Dingle, Davidson, Ltd. Toronto. Cups and saucers and 7" plates were available with a black or dark green border.

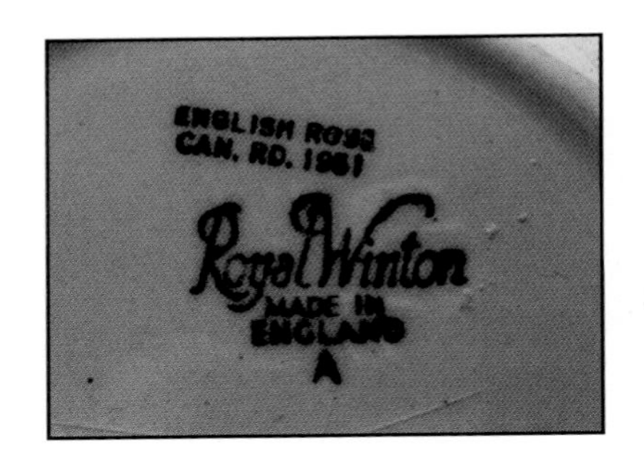

Cat. No.	Shape	U.S. $	Can. $	U.K. £
ER-04	Bonbon dish	85.00	75.00	60.00
ER-09	Bowl, 5"	55.00	50.00	50.00
ER-14	Bowl, 8" soup	110.00	80.00	75.00
ER-23	Breakfast set	1,300.00	900.00	800.00
ER-28	Butter dish	250.00	195.00	175.00
ER-30	Butter pat	75.00	65.00	55.00
ER-35	Cake plate, open handles	250.00	195.00	175.00
ER-36	Cake plate, tab handles	220.00	175.00	170.00
ER-37	Cake plate, 8" sq. pedestal	275.00	195.00	200.00
ER-40	Cake stand, 2 tier	275.00	195.00	200.00
ER-45	Canoe-shaped dish	375.00	325.00	250.00
ER-	Candy Box		RARE	
ER-50	Cheese keep	330.00	225.00	250.00
ER-52	Coaster	65.00	50.00	55.00
ER-55	Coffee pot	1,250.00	800.00	700.00
ER-60	Compote, footed	195.00	175.00	150.00
ER-65	Condiment set on tray	300.00	225.00	200.00
ER-70	Cream and sugar	165.00	135.00	120.00
ER-71	Cream and sugar on tray	300.00	205.00	200.00
ER-75	Demi-tasse	125.00	95.00	75.00
ER-77	Egg cup, footed	110.00	90.00	75.00
ER-80	Hot water jug	500.00	400.00	325.00
ER-85	Jam pot with liner	220.00	175.00	175.00
ER-90	Jug, 4"	400.00	325.00	225.00
ER-91	Jug, 4 1/2"	450.00	350.00	250.00
ER-92	Jug, 5"	500.00	375.00	275.00
ER-97	Nut dish	75.00	65.00	50.00
ER-201	Plate, 4" sq.	65.00	50.00	45.00
ER-202	Plate, 5" sq.	70.00	60.00	50.00
ER-203	Plate, 6" sq.	75.00	70.00	55.00
ER-204	Plate, 7" sq.	110.00	85.00	60.00
ER-205	Plate, 8" sq.	150.00	95.00	85.00
ER-206	Plate, 9" sq.	165.00	110.00	105.00
ER-207	Plate, 10" sq.	195.00	125.00	135.00
ER-112	Relish dish, small	220.00	195.00	150.00
ER-115	Salad bowl, chrome rim	195.00	150.00	150.00
ER-117	Salt and pepper	110.00	105.00	75.00
ER-118	Salt and pepper on tray	220.00	150.00	175.00
ER-120	Sandwich tray, 10" x 6"	165.00	125.00	120.00
ER-121	Sandwich tray, 12" x 7"	195.00	155.00	145.00
ER-125	Sauce boat and liner	195.00	175.00	145.00
ER-130	Teacup and saucer	125.00	110.00	75.00
ER-135	Teapot, 2 cup	550.00	400.00	350.00
ER-136	Teapot, 4 cup	800.00	550.00	500.00
ER-137	Teapot, 6 cup	1000.00	650.00	600.00
ER-140	Teapot, stacking	1,200.00	850.00	700.00
ER-145	Tennis set	165.00	115.00	120.00
ER-150	Toast rack, 4 slice	300.00	225.00	215.00
ER-151	Toast rack, 2 slice	245.00	175.00	175.00
ER-155	Trivet	165.00	110.00	120.00
ER-160	Vase, bud	175.00	135.00	115.00

ESTELLE

The pattern number is 423, and the pattern was introduced early in the 1950s.

Cat. No.	Shape	U.S. $	Can. $	U.K. £
Esl-04	Bonbon dish	50.00	50.00	45.00
Esl-09	Bowl, 5″	50.00	35.00	40.00
Esl-14	Bowl, 8″ soup	75.00	60.00	60.00
Esl-23	Breakfast set	1,100.00	700.00	650.00
Esl-28	Butter dish	150.00	125.00	120.00
Esl-30	Butter pat	45.00	35.00	40.00
Esl-35	Cake plate, open handles	150.00	145.00	125.00
Esl-36	Cake plate, tab handles	150.00	125.00	120.00
Esl-37	Cake plate, 8″ sq. pedestal	175.00	145.00	150.00
Esl-40	Cake stand, 2 tier	175.00	145.00	150.00
Esl-45	Canoe-shaped dish	235.00	195.00	195.00
Esl-50	Cheese keep	200.00	175.00	175.00
Esl-52	Coaster	40.00	35.00	40.00
Esl-55	Coffee pot	900.00	500.00	525.00
Esl-60	Compote, footed	135.00	125.00	95.00
Esl-65	Condiment set on tray	200.00	150.00	175.00
Esl-70	Cream and sugar	100.00	95.00	75.00
Esl-71	Cream and sugar on tray	200.00	145.00	175.00
Esl-75	Demi-tasse	75.00	55.00	60.00
Esl-77	Egg cup, footed	95.00	60.00	55.00
Esl-80	Hot water jug	400.00	275.00	225.00
Esl-85	Jam pot with liner	150.00	110.00	120.00
Esl-90	Jug, 4″	325.00	200.00	150.00
Esl-91	Jug, 4 1/2″	375.00	225.00	175.00
Esl-92	Jug, 5″	400.00	250.00	200.00
Esl-97	Nut dish	45.00	35.00	35.00
Esl-201	Plate, 4″ sq.	50.00	35.00	40.00
Esl-202	Plate, 5″ sq.	55.00	35.00	45.00
Esl-203	Plate, 6″ sq.	60.00	45.00	50.00
Esl-204	Plate, 7″ sq.	75.00	45.00	55.00
Esl-205	Plate, 8″ sq.	95.00	65.00	65.00
Esl-206	Plate, 9″ sq.	115.00	85.00	80.00
Esl-207	Plate, 10″ sq.	135.00	95.00	95.00
Esl-112	Relish dish, small	150.00	135.00	125.00
Esl-115	Salad bowl, chrome rim	125.00	95.00	95.00
Esl-117	Salt and pepper	75.00	65.00	60.00
Esl-118	Salt and pepper on tray	150.00	115.00	120.00
Esl-120	Sandwich tray, 10″ x 6″	100.00	95.00	75.00
Esl-121	Sandwich tray, 12″ x 7″	125.00	115.00	95.00
Esl-125	Sauce boat and liner	150.00	125.00	120.00
Esl-130	Teacup and saucer	95.00	65.00	60.00
Esl-135	Teapot, 2 cup	450.00	275.00	250.00
Esl-136	Teapot, 4 cup	650.00	350.00	375.00
Esl-137	Teapot, 6 cup	850.00	400.00	450.00
Esl-140	Teapot, stacking	950.00	575.00	550.00
Esl-145	Tennis set	100.00	75.00	75.00
Esl-150	Toast rack, 4 slice	200.00	185.00	155.00
Esl-151	Toast rack, 2 slice	135.00	135.00	115.00
Esl-155	Trivet	90.00	75.00	75.00
Esl-160	Vase, bud	125.00	105.00	75.00

ESTHER

The pattern number is 473, and the pattern was registered in Canada in 1952. This pattern has become very popular in the United States and England in the past year.

Cat. No.	Shape	U.S. $	Can. $	U.K. £
Est-04	Bonbon dish	65.00	60.00	55.00
Est-09	Bowl, 5″	50.00	45.00	50.00
Est-14	Bowl, 8″ soup	75.00	60.00	60.00
Est-23	Breakfast set	1,200.00	800.00	800.00
Est-28	Butter dish	175.00	150.00	160.00
Est-30	Butter pat	50.00	40.00	50.00
Est-35	Cake plate, open handles	175.00	165.00	160.00
Est-36	Cake plate, tab handles	75.00	145.00	185.00
Est-37	Cake plate, 8″ sq. pedestal	200.00	165.00	185.00
Est-40	Cake stand, 2 tier	200.00	150.00	185.00
Est-45	Canoe-shaped dish	275.00	225.00	250.00
Est-50	Cheese keep	250.00	195.00	225.00
Est-52	Coaster	50.00	35.00	50.00
Est-55	Coffee pot	950.00	600.00	675.00
Est-60	Compote, footed	175.00	135.00	150.00
Est-65	Condiment set on tray	225.00	165.00	175.00
Est-70	Cream and sugar	125.00	100.00	95.00
Est-71	Cream and sugar on tray	225.00	150.00	195.00
Est-75	Demi-tasse	90.00	60.00	75.00
Est-77	Egg cup, footed	95.00	65.00	65.00
Est-80	Hot water jug	450.00	275.00	295.00
Est-85	Jam pot with liner	175.00	125.00	150.00
Est-90	Jug, 4″	400.00	225.00	250.00
Est-91	Jug, 4 1/2″	450.00	250.00	275.00
Est-92	Jug, 5″	500.00	275.00	300.00
Est-180	Lamp Base	VERY RARE		

Cat. No.	Shape	U.S. $	Can. $	U.K. £
Est-97	Nut dish	50.00	40.00	50.00
Est-201	Plate, 4″ sq.	45.00	40.00	40.00
Est-202	Plate, 5″ sq.	50.00	40.00	45.00
Est-203	Plate, 6″ sq.	55.00	50.00	50.00
Est-204	Plate, 7″ sq.	65.00	50.00	60.00
Est-205	Plate, 8″ sq.	85.00	75.00	75.00
Est-206	Plate, 9″ sq.	135.00	90.00	95.00
Est-207	Plate, 10″ sq.	150.00	110.00	125.00
Est-112	Relish dish, small	175.00	150.00	150.00
Est-115	Salad bowl, chrome rim	150.00	110.00	125.00
Est-117	Salt and pepper	100.00	95.00	80.00
Est-118	Salt and pepper on tray	165.00	150.00	150.00
Est-120	Sandwich tray, 10″ x 6″	125.00	105.00	120.00
Est-121	Sandwich tray, 12″ x 7″	150.00	125.00	140.00
Est-125	Sauce boat and liner	175.00	150.00	150.00
Est-130	Teacup and saucer	95.00	75.00	75.00
Est-135	Teapot, 2 cup	425.00	325.00	375.00
Est-136	Teapot, 4 cup	650.00	400.00	475.00
Est-137	Teapot, 6 cup	850.00	450.00	600.00
Est-140	Teapot, stacking	950.00	675.00	650.00
Est-145	Tennis set	125.00	85.00	85.00
Est-150	Toast rack, 4 slice	275.00	195.00	250.00
Est-151	Toast rack, 2 slice	225.00	145.00	200.00
Est-155	Trivet	125.00	85.00	95.00
Est-160	Vase, bud	150.00	115.00	105.00

EVESHAM

The pattern number is 404, and it was registered in Canada in 1951. The pattern is thought to have been designed by Mabel Till, nee Leigh, a well-known potteries designer. Interestingly this pattern which is not really a chintz has become one of the most sought after patterns around the world.

Cat. No.	Shape	U.S. $	Can. $	U.K. £
Ev-04	Bonbon dish	95.00	85.00	65.00
Ev-09	Bowl, 5"	60.00	65.00	55.00
Ev-14	Bowl, 8" soup	125.00	95.00	85.00
Ev-23	Breakfast set	1,400.00	1,000.00	975.00
Ev-28	Butter dish	275.00	225.00	195.00
Ev-30	Butter pat	90.00	75.00	65.00
Ev-35	Cake plate, open handles	275.00	225.00	195.00
Ev-36	Cake plate, tab handles	250.00	200.00	200.00
Ev-37	Cake plate, 8" sq. pedestal	300.00	225.00	225.00
Ev-40	Cake stand, 2 tier	300.00	225.00	225.00
Ev-45	Canoe-shaped dish	425.00	375.00	300.00
Ev-50	Cheese keep	375.00	300.00	275.00
Ev-52	Coaster	75.00	75.00	55.00
Ev-55	Coffee pot	1,300.00	900.00	825.00
Ev-60	Compote, footed	250.00	220.00	195.00
Ev-65	Condiment set on tray	325.00	275.00	250.00
Ev-70	Cream and sugar	190.00	175.00	125.00
Ev-71	Cream and sugar on tray	325.00	250.00	250.00
Ev-75	Demi-tasse	135.00	115.00	80.00
Ev-77	Egg cup, footed	115.00	110.00	80.00
Ev-80	Hot water jug	550.00	450.00	350.00
Ev-85	Jam pot with liner	275.00	200.00	195.00
Ev-90	Jug, 4"	500.00	350.00	325.00
Ev-91	Jug, 4 1/2"	550.00	375.00	350.00
Ev-92	Jug, 5"	600.00	400.00	375.00
Ev-97	Nut dish	95.00	75.00	60.00
Ev-201	Plate, 4" sq.	80.00	60.00	60.00
Ev-202	Plate, 5" sq.	85.00	65.00	65.00
Ev-203	Plate, 6" sq.	120.00	75.00	75.00
Ev-204	Plate, 7" sq.	165.00	95.00	85.00
Ev-205	Plate, 8" sq.	200.00	115.00	115.00
Ev-206	Plate, 9" sq.	220.00	135.00	135.00
Ev-207	Plate, 10" sq .	250.00	150.00	150.00
Ev-112	Relish dish, small	275.00	225.00	195.00
Ev-115	Salad bowl, chrome rim	325.00	195.00	150.00
Ev-117	Salt and pepper	125.00	125.00	80.00
Ev-118	Salt and pepper on tray	250.00	195.00	195.00
Ev-120	Sandwich tray, 10" x 6"	190.00	150.00	125.00
Ev-121	Sandwich tray, 12" x 7"	220.00	175.00	160.00
Ev-125	Sauce boat and liner	250.00	210.00	195.00
Ev-130	Teacup and saucer	145.00	125.00	80.00
Ev-135	Teapot, 2 cup	600.00	500.00	400.00
Ev-136	Teapot, 4 cup	750.00	650.00	550.00
Ev-137	Teapot, 6 cup	1,000.00	750.00	750.00
Ev-140	Teapot, stacking	1,300.00	950.00	800.00
Ev-145	Tennis set	190.00	135.00	125.00
Ev-150	Toast rack, 4 slice	375.00	275.00	250.00
Ev-151	Toast rack, 2 slice	275.00	225.00	195.00
Ev-155	Trivet	180.00	135.00	125.00
Ev-160	Vase, bud	190.00	150.00	125.00

FERNESE

The pattern number is 8786 and this pattern dates to 1925. This pattern is rare in North America and available on a limited number of shapes.

Backstamp not available at press time

Cat. No.	Shape	U.S. $	Can. $	U.K. £
Fer -35	Cake plate, open handles	110.00	75.00	65.00
Fer-115	Salad bowl, chrome rim	100.00	75.00	60.00
Fer-130	Teacup and saucer	45.00	30.00	40.00

Cat. No.	Shape	U.S. $	Can. $	U.K. £
Fer-203	Plate, 6″ sq.	45.00	25.00	35.00
Fer-206	Plate, 9″ sq.	75.00	40.00	50.00

FIREGLOW BLACK

There are two totally unrelated patterns with the backstamp **Fireglow**. The black background has the pattern number 533, which is the last known chintz pattern number. See **Fireglow White** (page 58) with the much earlier pattern number 2510.

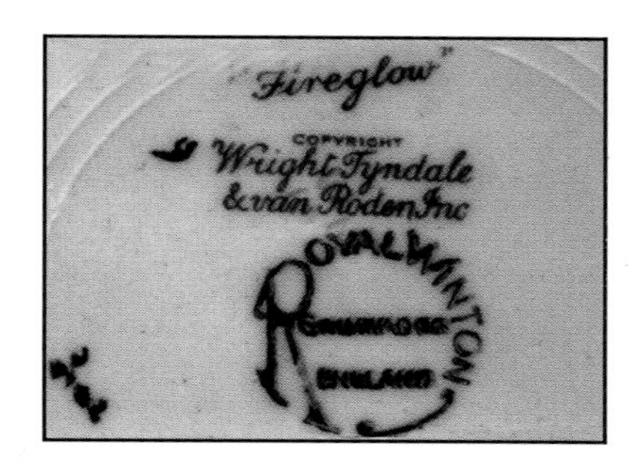

Cat. No.	Shape	U.S. $	Can. $	U.K. £
FiB-04	Bonbon dish	25.00	20.00	25.00
FiB-09	Bowl, 5″	25.00	20.00	25.00
FiB-14	Bowl, 8″ soup	35.00	25.00	30.00
FiB-23	Breakfast set	450.00	300.00	325.00
FiB-28	Butter dish	90.00	75.00	65.00
FiB-30	Butter pat	25.00	20.00	20.00
FiB-35	Cake plate, open handles	90.00	75.00	65.00
FiB-36	Cake plate, tab handles	80.00	65.00	60.00
FiB-37	Cake plate, 8″ sq. pedestal	90.00	75.00	65.00
FiB-40	Cake stand, 2 tier	90.00	75.00	65.00
FiB-45	Canoe-shaped dish	125.00	95.00	85.00
FiB-50	Cheese keep	115.00	75.00	75.00
FiB-52	Coaster	25.00	20.00	20.00
FiB-55	Coffee pot	375.00	200.00	250.00
FiB-60	Compote, footed	70.00	65.00	50.00
FiB-65	Condiment set on tray	90.00	75.00	65.00
FiB-70	Cream and sugar	55.00	50.00	45.00
FiB-71	Cream and sugar on tray	90.00	85.00	65.00
FiB-75	Demi-tasse	35.00	30.00	30.00
FiB-77	Egg cup, footed	35.00	30.00	25.00
FiB-80	Hot water jug	135.00	110.00	125.00
FiB-85	Jam pot with liner	70.00	60.00	50.00
FiB-90	Jug, 4″	135.00	65.00	85.00
FiB-91	Jug, 4 1/2″	150.00	75.00	100.00
FiB-92	Jug, 5″	165.00	85.00	125.00

Cat. No.	Shape	U.S. $	Can. $	U.K. £
FiB-97	Nut dish	25.00	20.00	20.00
FiB-201	Plate, 4″ sq.	25.00	20.00	20.00
FiB-202	Plate, 5″ sq.	30.00	20.00	25.00
FiB-203	Plate, 6″ sq.	35.00	25.00	30.00
FiB-204	Plate, 7″ sq.	40.00	25.00	35.00
FiB-205	Plate, 8″ sq.	50.00	35.00	40.00
FiB-206	Plate, 9″ sq.	65.00	45.00	45.00
FiB-207	Plate, 10″ sq.	75.00	55.00	50.00
FiB-112	Relish dish, small	75.00	65.00	60.00
FiB-115	Salad bowl, chrome rim	90.00	70.00	65.00
FiB-117	Salt and pepper	45.00	35.00	40.00
FiB-118	Salt and pepper on tray	100.00	65.00	75.00
FiB-120	Sandwich tray, 10″ x 6″	55.00	45.00	45.00
FiB-121	Sandwich tray, 12″ x 7″	65.00	55.00	50.00
FiB-125	Sauce boat and liner	60.00	45.00	45.00
FiB-130	Teacup and saucer	40.00	25.00	30.00
FiB-135	Teapot, 2 cup	175.00	125.00	125.00
FiB-136	Teapot, 4 cup	275.00	175.00	200.00
FiB-137	Teapot, 6 cup	325.00	225.00	225.00
FiB-140	Teapot, stacking	400.00	300.00	275.00
FiB-145	Tennis set	50.00	40.00	40.00
FiB-150	Toast rack, 4 slice	135.00	95.00	125.00
FiB-151	Toast rack, 2 slice	100.00	65.00	95.00
FiB-155	Trivet	45.00	35.00	40.00
FiB-160	Vase, bud	60.00	45.00	45.00

FIREGLOW WHITE

The pattern number for the white background **Fireglow** is 2510 which means it was likely introduced in 1935. It is totally unrelated to the black **Fireglow** from the 1950s. See **Fireglow Black** (page 57).

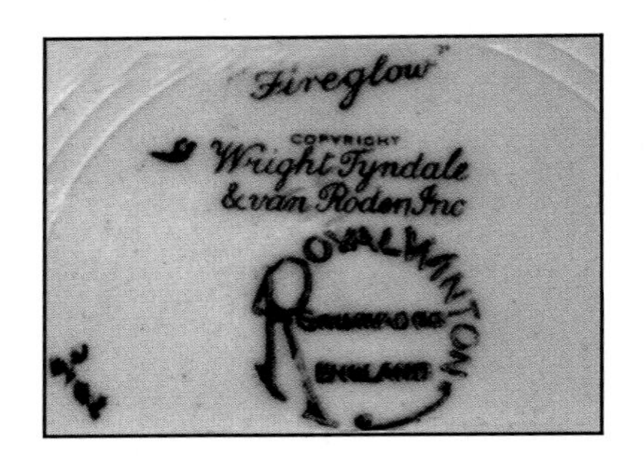

Cat. No.	Shape	U.S. $	Can. $	U.K. £
FiW-04	Bonbon dish	50.00	50.00	35.00
FiW-09	Bowl, 5"	45.00	35.00	35.00
FiW-14	Bowl, 8" soup	75.00	60.00	50.00
FiW-23	Breakfast set	850.00	700.00	475.00
FiW-28	Butter dish	150.00	125.00	100.00
FiW-30	Butter pat	45.00	35.00	85.00
FiW-35	Cake plate, open handles	150.00	145.00	100.00
FiW-36	Cake plate, tab handles	135.00	125.00	95.00
FiW-37	Cake plate, 8" sq. pedestal	150.00	145.00	125.00
FiW-40	Cake stand, 2 tier	150.00	200.00	145.00
FiW-45	Canoe-shaped dish	225.00	195.00	150.00
FiW-50	Cheese keep	200.00	175.00	150.00
FiW-52	Coaster	40.00	35.00	30.00
FiW-55	Coffee pot	575.00	500.00	375.00
FiW-60	Compote, footed	135.00	125.00	85.00
FiW-65	Condiment set on tray	175.00	150.00	125.00
FiW-70	Cream and sugar	100.00	95.00	65.00
FiW-71	Cream and sugar on tray	175.00	145.00	125.00
FiW-75	Demi-tasse	70.00	55.00	50.00
FiW-77	Egg cup, footed	80.00	65.00	45.00
FiW-80	Hot water jug	275.00	275.00	175.00
FiW-85	Jam pot with liner	140.00	110.00	100.00
FiW-90	Jug, 4"	200.00	200.00	125.00
FiW-91	Jug, 4 1/2"	225.00	225.00	150.00
FiW-92	Jug, 5"	250.00	250.00	175.00
FiW-97	Nut dish	45.00	35.00	35.00
FiW-201	Plate, 4" sq.	50.00	35.00	30.00
FiW-202	Plate, 5" sq.	55.00	35.00	35.00
FiW-203	Plate, 6" sq.	60.00	45.00	40.00
FiW-204	Plate, 7" sq.	75.00	45.00	50.00
FiW-205	Plate, 8" sq.	95.00	65.00	65.00
FiW-206	Plate, 9" sq.	115.00	85.00	70.00
FiW-207	Plate, 10" sq .	125.00	100.00	75.00
FiW-112	Relish dish, small	150.00	135.00	100.00
FiW-115	Salad bowl, chrome rim	125.00	95.00	75.00
FiW-117	Salt and pepper	75.00	75.00	50.00
FiW-118	Salt and pepper on tray	150.00	125.00	100.00
FiW-120	Sandwich tray, 10" x 6"	100.00	95.00	65.00
FiW-121	Sandwich tray, 12" x 7"	125.00	115.00	75.00
FiW-125	Sauce boat and liner	135.00	125.00	85.00
FiW-130	Teacup and saucer	85.00	65.00	50.00
FiW-135	Teapot, 2 cup	300.00	275.00	200.00
FiW-136	Teapot, 4 cup	400.00	350.00	250.00
FiW-137	Teapot, 6 cup	500.00	400.00	325.00
FiW-140	Teapot, stacking	675.00	575.00	425.00
FiW-145	Tennis set	100.00	75.00	65.00
FiW-150	Toast rack, 4 slice	200.00	185.00	150.00
FiW-151	Toast rack, 2 slice	150.00	135.00	100.00
FiW-155	Trivet	100.00	75.00	65.00
FiW-160	Vase, bud	100.00	105.00	60.00

FLORAL FEAST

The pattern number is 1394. This was one of the three new patterns — along with **Summertime** and **Somerset** — advertised by Wright, Tyndale & van Roden, Inc. of Philadelphia in the *Crockery and Glass Journal* of May 1933. The patterns were backstamped "COPYRIGHT Wright, Tyndal & van Roden" in an attempt to discourage pattern theft. **Floral Feast** is described "with large sprays and delicate blossoms gracefully intermingled on a deep ivory ground." A 1936 Australian Export Catalogue shows **Floral Feast** with blue trim and the pattern number 2255.

Cat. No.	Shape	U.S. $	Can. $	U.K. £
FF-04	Bonbon dish	50.00	50.00	35.00
FF-09	Bowl, 5"	45.00	35.00	35.00
FF-14	Bowl, 8" soup	75.00	60.00	50.00
FF-23	Breakfast set	859.00	700.00	475.00
FF-28	Butter dish	150.00	125.00	100.00
FF-30	Butter pat	45.00	35.00	35.00
FF-35	Cake plate, open handles	150.00	145.00	100.00
FF-36	Cake plate, tab handles	135.00	125.00	85.00
FF-37	Cake plate, 8" sq. pedestal	150.00	145.00	115.00
FF-40	Cake stand, 2 tier	150.00	145.00	115.00
FF-45	Canoe-shaped dish	225.00	195.00	150.00
FF-50	Cheese keep	200.00	175.00	125.00
FF-52	Coaster	40.00	35.00	30.00
FF-55	Coffee pot	575.00	500.00	375.00
FF-60	Compote, footed	125.00	125.00	75.00
FF-65	Condiment set on tray	175.00	150.00	125.00
FF-70	Cream and sugar	100.00	95.00	65.00
FF-71	Cream and sugar on tray	175.00	145.00	125.00
FF-75	Demi-tasse	75.00	55.00	50.00
FF-77	Egg cup, footed	75.00	69.00	45.00
FF-80	Hot water jug	250.00	275.00	175.00
FF-85	Jam pot with liner	150.00	115.00	100.00
FF-90	Jug, 4"	200.00	200.00	115.00
FF-91	Jug, 4 1/2"	225.00	225.00	135.00
FF-92	Jug, 5"	250.00	250.00	160.00

Cat. No.	Shape	U.S. $	Can. $	U.K. £
FF-97	Nut dish	45.00	35.00	35.00
FF-201	Plate, 4" sq.	50.00	35.00	30.00
FF-202	Plate, 5" sq.	55.00	35.00	35.00
FF-203	Plate, 6" sq.	60.00	45.00	40.00
FF-204	Plate, 7" sq.	75.00	45.00	45.00
FF-205	Plate, 8" sq.	100.00	65.00	60.00
FF-206	Plate, 9" sq.	115.00	85.00	65.00
FF-207	Plate, 10" sq .	125.00	105.00	75.00
FF-112	Relish dish, small	150.00	135.00	100.00
FF-115	Salad bowl, chrome rim	125.00	95.00	75.00
FF-117	Salt and pepper	75.00	65.00	50.00
FF-118	Salt and pepper on tray	150.00	115.00	100.00
FF-120	Sandwich tray, 10" x 6"	100.00	95.00	65.00
FF-121	Sandwich tray, 12" x 7"	125.00	115.00	75.00
FF-125	Sauce boat and liner	125.00	125.00	75.00
FF-130	Teacup and saucer	85.00	65.00	50.00
FF-135	Teapot, 2 cup	300.00	275.00	200.00
FF-136	Teapot, 4 cup	400.00	350.00	250.00
FF-137	Teapot, 6 cup	500.00	400.00	325.00
FF-140	Teapot, stacking	675.00	575.00	425.00
FF-145	Tennis set	100.00	75.00	65.00
FF-150	Toast rack, 4 slice	200.00	185.00	150.00
FF-151	Toast rack, 2 slice	150.00	135.00	100.00
FF-155	Trivet	85.00	75.00	60.00
FF-160	Vase, bud	100.00	95.00	60.00

FLORAL GARDEN

The pattern number is 4547, and there are several colourways. This green colourway has only been found in Australia with a name backstamp and probably dates to 1938.

Backstamp not available
at
press time

Cat. No.	Shape	U.S. $	Can. $	U.K. £
FG-04	Bonbon dish	40.00	25.00	30.00
FG-09	Bowl, 5″	25.00	20.00	20.00
FG-14	Bowl, 8″ soup	40.00	40.00	30.00
FG-23	Breakfast set	550.00	450.00	350.00
FG-28	Butter dish	115.00	95.00	75.00
FG-30	Butter pat	30.00	20.00	25.00
FG-35	Cake plate, open handles	115.00	85.00	75.00
FG-36	Cake plate, tab handles	100.00	75.00	65.00
FG-37	Cake plate, 8″ sq. pedestal	125.00	95.00	75.00
FG-40	Cake stand, 2 tier	125.00	90.00	75.00
FG-45	Canoe-shaped dish	165.00	125.00	115.00
FG-50	Cheese keep	150.00	110.00	100.00
FG-52	Coaster	30.00	25.00	25.00
FG-55	Coffee pot	450.00	300.00	325.00
FG-60	Compote, footed	100.00	75.00	65.00
FG-65	Condiment set on tray	135.00	95.00	85.00
FG-70	Cream and sugar	75.00	60.00	50.00
FG-71	Cream and sugar on tray	135.00	95.00	85.00
FG-75	Demi-tasse	50.00	35.00	35.00
FG-77	Egg cup, footed	65.00	35.00	35.00
FG-80	Hot water jug	225.00	150.00	150.00
FG-85	Jam pot with liner	100.00	85.00	65.00
FG-90	Jug, 4″	165.00	140.00	115.00
FG-91	Jug, 4 1/2″	175.00	155.00	125.00
FG-92	Jug, 5″	200.00	165.00	150.00

Cat. No.	Shape	U.S. $	Can. $	U.K. £
FG-97	Nut dish	35.00	20.00	25.00
FG-201	Plate, 4″ sq.	25.00	20.00	15.00
FG-202	Plate, 5″ sq.	30.00	20.00	20.00
FG-203	Plate, 6″ sq.	35.00	25.00	25.00
FG-204	Plate, 7″ sq.	40.00	25.00	30.00
FG-205	Plate, 8″ sq.	50.00	40.00	35.00
FG-206	Plate, 9″ sq.	65.00	60.00	40.00
FG-207	Plate, 10″ sq.	75.00	75.00	50.00
FG-112	Relish dish, small	100.00	85.00	65.00
FG-115	Salad bowl, chrome rim	85.00	75.00	60.00
FG-117	Salt and pepper	50.00	40.00	40.00
FG-118	Salt and pepper on tray	125.00	85.00	75.00
FG-120	Sandwich tray, 10″ x 6″	75.00	60.00	50.00
FG-121	Sandwich tray, 12″ x 7″	85.00	70.00	60.00
FG-125	Sauce boat and liner	100.00	75.00	75.00
FG-130	Teacup and saucer	65.00	40.00	35.00
FG-135	Teapot, 2 cup	275.00	175.00	200.00
FG-136	Teapot, 4 cup	325.00	200.00	225.00
FG-137	Teapot, 6 cup	425.00	250.00	300.00
FG-140	Teapot, stacking	550.00	350.00	325.00
FG-145	Tennis set	75.00	45.00	50.00
FG-150	Toast rack, 4 slice	165.00	110.00	115.00
FG-151	Toast rack, 2 slice	135.00	95.00	85.00
FG-155	Trivet	75.00	45.00	50.00
FG-160	Vase, bud	80.00	60.00	50.00

FLORENCE

The pattern number is 472, which would indicate that it is one of the last chintz patterns to be produced in the 1950s. The pattern was registered in Canada in 1953. This pattern is quite rare and very sought after by collectors worldwide.

Cat. No.	Shape	U.S. $	Can. $	U.K. £
Fl-04	Bonbon dish	85.00	85.00	80.00
Fl-09	Bowl, 5″	75.00	60.00	60.00
Fl-14	Bowl, 8″ soup	95.00	90.00	80.00
Fl-23	Breakfast set	1,500.00	1,000.00	1000.00
Fl-28	Butter dish	300.00	225.00	225.00
Fl-30	Butter pat	85.00	75.00	65.00
Fl-35	Cake plate, open handles	300.00	225.00	235.00
Fl-36	Cake plate, tab handles	275.00	200.00	225.00
Fl-37	Cake plate, 8″ sq. pedestal	300.00	225.00	250.00
Fl-40	Cake stand, 2 tier	300.00	225.00	250.00
Fl-45	Canoe-shaped dish	425.00	375.00	325.00
Fl-50	Cheese keep	395.00	300.00	325.00
Fl-52	Coaster	80.00	75.00	65.00
Fl-55	Coffee pot	1,300.00	900.00	900.00
Fl-60	Compote, footed	245.00	225.00	195.00
Fl-65	Condiment set on tray	350.00	275.00	275.00
Fl-70	Cream and sugar	200.00	165.00	150.00
Fl-71	Cream and sugar on tray	350.00	250.00	250.00
Fl-75	Demi-tasse	150.00	115.00	90.00
Fl-77	Egg cup, footed	145.00	110.00	85.00
Fl-80	Hot water jug	600.00	450.00	425.00
Fl-85	Jam pot with liner	275.00	200.00	225.00
Fl-90	Jug, 4″	550.00	350.00	325.00
Fl-91	Jug, 4 1/2″	650.00	375.00	385.00
Fl-92	Jug, 5″	750.00	400.00	415.00

Cat. No.	Shape	U.S. $	Can. $	U.K. £
Fl-97	Nut dish	85.00	75.00	60.00
Fl-201	Plate, 4″ sq.	85.00	60.00	60.00
Fl-202	Plate, 5″ sq.	95.00	65.00	70.00
Fl-203	Plate, 6″ sq.	135.00	75.00	80.00
Fl-204	Plate, 7″ sq.	145.00	95.00	90.00
Fl-205	Plate, 8″ sq.	195.00	110.00	130.00
Fl-206	Plate, 9″ sq.	215.00	125.00	145.00
Fl-207	Plate, 10″ sq .	230.00	145.00	165.00
Fl-112	Relish dish, small	275.00	225.00	225.00
Fl-115	Salad bowl, chrome rim	275.00	195.00	225.00
Fl-117	Salt and pepper	140.00	125.00	95.00
Fl-118	Salt and pepper on tray	250.00	195.00	195.00
Fl-120	Sandwich tray, 10″ x 6″	195.00	150.00	150.00
Fl-121	Sandwich tray, 12″ x 7″	220.00	175.00	175.00
Fl-125	Sauce boat and liner	245.00	210.00	145.00
Fl-130	Teacup and saucer	175.00	125.00	90.00
Fl-135	Teapot, 2 cup	700.00	500.00	475.00
Fl-136	Teapot, 4 cup	900.00	650.00	650.00
Fl-137	Teapot, 6 cup	1,200.00	750.00	825.00
Fl-140	Teapot, stacking	1,400.00	950.00	900.00
Fl-145	Tennis set	165.00	135.00	125.00
Fl-150	Toast rack, 4 slice	330.00	275.00	250.00
Fl-151	Toast rack, 2 slice	275.00	225.00	225.00
Fl-155	Trivet	165.00	135.00	125.00
Fl-160	Vase, bud	200.00	150.00	150.00

HAZEL

The pattern number is 2208, and the pattern was mentioned in the *Pottery Gazette* several times in 1934. **Hazel** has a black background with the alternate colourways of a white background, **Spring** 2506, and the yellow **Welbeck** 2204. This pattern was copied by the Japanese including a recent porcelain version by Fitz & Floyd called **Mille Fleurs**.

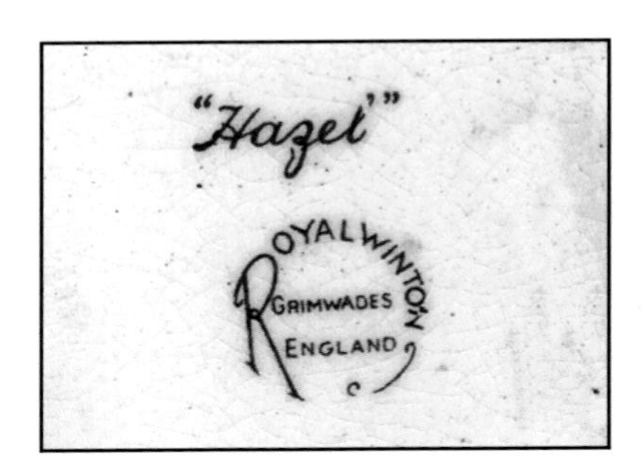

Cat. No.	Shape	U.S. $	Can. $	U.K. £
H-03	Basket		RARE	
H-04	Bonbon dish	75.00	75.00	60.00
H-09	Bowl, 5"	50.00	50.00	45.00
H-14	Bowl, 8" soup	85.00	80.00	70.00
H-23	Breakfast set	1,250.00	900.00	800.00
H-28	Butter dish	225.00	195.00	195.00
H-30	Butter pat	65.00	65.00	55.00
H-35	Cake plate, open handles	225.00	195.00	195.00
H-36	Cake plate, tab handles	200.00	175.00	185.00
H-37	Cake plate, 8" sq. pedestal	225.00	195.00	185.00
H-40	Cake stand, 2 tier	225.00	195.00	175.00
H-	Candlesticks		RARE	
H-45	Canoe-shaped dish	325.00	325.00	250.00
H-50	Cheese keep	275.00	225.00	250.00
H-52	Coaster	50.00	50.00	45.00
H-55	Coffee pot	1,150.00	800.00	725.00
H-60	Compote, footed	185.00	175.00	160.00
H-65	Condiment set on tray	250.00	225.00	225.00
H-70	Cream and sugar	150.00	135.00	125.00
H-71	Cream and sugar on tray	250.00	200.00	215.00
H-75	Demi-tasse	100.00	95.00	80.00
H-77	Egg cup, footed	95.00	90.00	75.00
H-80	Hot water jug	525.00	400.00	300.00
H-85	Jam pot with liner	200.00	175.00	175.00
H-90	Jug, 4"	425.00	325.00	250.00
H-91	Jug, 4 1/2"	475.00	350.00	275.00

Cat. No.	Shape	U.S. $	Can. $	U.K. £
H-92	Jug, 5"	525.00	375.00	300.00
H-97	Nut dish	65.00	65.00	55.00
H-201	Plate, 4" sq.	50.00	50.00	45.00
H-202	Plate, 5" sq.	65.00	60.00	50.00
H-203	Plate, 6" sq.	75.00	70.00	60.00
H-204	Plate, 7" sq.	100.00	85.00	70.00
H-205	Plate, 8" sq.	135.00	95.00	80.00
H-206	Plate, 9" sq.	150.00	115.00	95.00
H-207	Plate, 10" sq.	175.00	125.00	125.00
H-112	Relish dish, small	200.00	195.00	175.00
H-115	Salad bowl, chrome rim	175.00	150.00	150.00
H-117	Salt and pepper	100.00	105.00	80.00
H-118	Salt and pepper on tray	175.00	150.00	150.00
H-120	Sandwich tray, 10" x 6"	150.00	125.00	125.00
H-121	Sandwich tray, 12" x 7"	175.00	145.00	150.00
H-125	Sauce boat and liner	165.00	175.00	150.00
H-130	Teacup and saucer	125.00	105.00	80.00
H-135	Teapot, 2 cup	500.00	400.00	350.00
H-136	Teapot, 4 cup	750.00	550.00	550.00
H-137	Teapot, 6 cup	900.00	650.00	600.00
H-140	Teapot, stacking	1,150.00	850.00	700.00
H-145	Tennis set	125.00	115.00	85.00
H-150	Toast rack, 4 slice	250.00	225.00	225.00
H-151	Toast rack, 2 slice	200.00	175.00	175.00
H-155	Trivet	125.00	110.00	85.00
H-160	Vase, bud	165.00	135.00	125.00

JOYCE-LYNN

The pattern number is 275. This pattern was introduced into Canada in the fall of 1950. Retailers were urged by Enterprise Sales of Toronto, the exclusive Canadian distributor, to carry the pattern because "The brilliance of colour, the red, blue and yellow blossoms with green leaves and highlights of gold coupled with the fine glazing of this beautiful open stock pattern will build sales volume for you."

Cat. No.	Shape	U.S. $	Can. $	U.K. £
JL-04	Bonbon dish	55.00	50.00	35.00
JL-09	Bowl, 5"	45.00	35.00	30.00
JL-14	Bowl, 8" soup	70.00	60.00	45.00
JL-23	Breakfast set	1,100.00	700.00	525.00
JL-28	Butter dish	165.00	125.00	100.00
JL-30	Butter pat	45.00	35.00	30.00
JL-35	Cake plate, open handles	195.00	145.00	125.00
JL-36	Cake plate, tab handles	165.00	125.00	100.00
JL-37	Cake plate, 8" sq. pedestal	225.00	145.00	125.00
JL-40	Cake stand, 2 tier	165.00	145.00	100.00
JL-	Candy Box		RARE	
JL-45	Canoe-shaped dish	220.00	195.00	150.00
JL-50	Cheese keep	195.00	175.00	125.00
JL-52	Coaster	45.00	35.00	25.00
JL-55	Coffee pot	900.00	500.00	425.00
JL-60	Compote, footed	135.00	125.00	75.00
JL-65	Condiment set on tray	180.00	150.00	115.00
JL-70	Cream and sugar	110.00	95.00	65.00
JL-71	Cream and sugar on tray	195.00	145.00	125.00
JL-75	Demi-tasse	90.00	55.00	45.00
JL-77	Egg cup, footed	80.00	60.00	40.00
JL-80	Hot water jug	400.00	275.00	175.00
JL-85	Jam pot with liner	125.00	115.00	75.00
JL-90	Jug, 4"	350.00	200.00	125.00
JL-91	Jug, 4 1/2"	400.00	225.00	150.00
JL-92	Jug, 5"	450.00	250.00	175.00
JL-97	Nut dish	45.00	35.00	30.00
JL-201	Plate, 4" sq.	50.00	35.00	30.00
JL-202	Plate, 5" sq.	55.00	35.00	35.00
JL-203	Plate, 6" sq.	60.00	45.00	40.00
JL-204	Plate, 7" sq.	75.00	45.00	45.00
JL-205	Plate, 8" sq.	100.00	65.00	60.00
JL-206	Plate, 9" sq.	110.00	85.00	65.00
JL-207	Plate, 10" sq.	135.00	95.00	75.00
JL-112	Relish dish, small	145.00	135.00	100.00
JL-115	Salad bowl, chrome rim	110.00	95.00	65.00
JL-117	Salt and pepper	85.00	65.00	50.00
JL-118	Salt and pepper on tray	150.00	115.00	100.00
JL-120	Sandwich tray, 10" x 6"	100.00	95.00	65.00
JL-121	Sandwich tray, 12" x 7"	110.00	115.00	65.00
JL-125	Sauce boat and liner	140.00	125.00	85.00
JL-130	Teacup and saucer	95.00	60.00	45.00
JL-135	Teapot, 2 cup	450.00	275.00	225.00
JL-136	Teapot, 4 cup	650.00	350.00	275.00
JL-137	Teapot, 6 cup	850.00	400.00	350.00
JL-140	Teapot, stacking	1000.00	575.00	425.00
JL-145	Tennis set	95.00	75.00	60.00
JL-150	Toast rack, 4 slice	220.00	185.00	150.00
JL-151	Toast rack, 2 slice	165.00	135.00	100.00
JL-155	Trivet	95.00	75.00	60.00
JL-160	Vase, bud	150.00	95.00	65.00

JULIA

The pattern number is 109 and probably appeared in 1939 and continued well into the 1950s. It is the favourite chintz pattern for collectors around the world and prices for unusual pieces with good colour are very high. Be aware that there are great variations in the depth of color in this pattern, with some examples appearing quite faded.

Cat. No.	Shape	U.S. $	Can. $	U.K. £
J-04	Bonbon dish	125.00	85.00	95.00
J-09	Bowl, 5″	85.00	65.00	65.00
J-14	Bowl, 8″ soup	125.00	95.00	85.00
J-23	Breakfast set	1,600.00	1,100.00	1100.00
J-28	Butter dish	345.00	225.00	250.00
J-30	Butter pat	95.00	75.00	65.00
J-35	Cake plate, open handles	345.00	235.00	275.00
J-36	Cake plate, tab handles	325.00	215.00	250.00
J-37	Cake plate, 8″ sq. pedestal	325.00	245.00	275.00
J-40	Cake stand, 2 tier	325.00	235.00	275.00
J-	Cnadlesticks		RARE	
J-45	Canoe-shaped dish	500.00	395.00	350.00
J-50	Cheese keep	425.00	325.00	350.00
J-52	Coaster	95.00	75.00	65.00
J-55	Coffee pot	1,400.00	950.00	975.00
J-60	Compote, footed	275.00	225.00	200.00
J-65	Condiment set on tray	400.00	285.00	300.00
J-70	Cream and sugar	225.00	175.00	165.00
J-71	Cream and sugar on tray	400.00	275.00	300.00
J-75	Demi-tasse	150.00	125.00	95.00
J-77	Egg cup, footed	165.00	125.00	90.00
J-80	Hot water jug	650.00	475.00	450.00
J-85	Jam pot with liner	315.00	225.00	235.00
J-90	Jug, 4″	650.00	375.00	375.00
J-91	Jug, 4 1/2″	750.00	400.00	425.00
J-92	Jug, 5″	850.00	425.00	475.00
J-97	Nut dish	95.00	75.00	70.00
J-201	Plate, 4″ sq.	90.00	65.00	65.00
J-202	Plate, 5″ sq.	125.00	75.00	80.00
J-203	Plate, 6″ sq.	140.00	80.00	85.00
J-204	Plate, 7″ sq.	160.00	95.00	95.00
J-205	Plate, 8″ sq.	200.00	125.00	125.00
J-206	Plate, 9″ sq.	225.00	145.00	150.00
J-207	Plate, 10″ sq.	250.00	175.00	160.00
J-112	Relish dish, small	310.00	250.00	225.00
J-115	Salad bowl, chrome rim	310.00	225.00	225.00
J-117	Salt and pepper	150.00	135.00	100.00
J-118	Salt and pepper on tray	295.00	225.00	195.00
J-120	Sandwich tray, 10″ x 6″	225.00	175.00	165.00
J-121	Sandwich tray, 12″ x 7″	250.00	195.00	185.00
J-125	Sauce boat and liner	275.00	225.00	185.00
J-130	Teacup and saucer	195.00	135.00	95.00
J-135	Teapot, 2 cup	750.00	525.00	550.00
J-136	Teapot, 4 cup	950.00	675.00	700.00
J-137	Teapot, 6 cup	1,250.00	800.00	800.00
J-140	Teapot, stacking	1500.00	1,000.00	900.00
J-145	Tennis set	175.00	145.00	145.00
J-150	Toast rack, 4 slice	375.00	30.00	275.00
J-151	Toast rack, 2 slice	310.00	250.00	225.00
J-155	Trivet	195.00	150.00	175.00
J-160	Vase, bud	225.00	175.00	165.00

JUNE FESTIVAL

This pattern has a burgundy background and the pattern number is 137. **May Festival** is now known to be the name of the pattern when the background is either black (pattern number 135) or navy (pattern number 139). A Canadian advertisement in January, 1952 suggested that retailers carry "an entirely new pattern in Grimwade's Royal Winton Ware to start 1952 — richly coloured in a deep maroon background with variegated coloured pansies."

Cat. No.	Shape	U.S. $	Can. $	U.K. £
JF-04	Bonbon dish	40.00	30.00	35.00
JF-09	Bowl, 5"	35.00	25.00	30.00
JF-14	Bowl, 8" soup	60.00	45.00	50.00
JF-23	Breakfast set	800.00	500.00	475.00
JF-28	Butter dish	120.00	115.00	85.00
JF-30	Butter pat	35.00	30.00	30.00
JF-35	Cake plate, open handles	125.00	105.00	85.00
JF-36	Cake plate, tab handles	115.00	95.00	75.00
JF-37	Cake plate, 8" sq. pedestal	135.00	125.00	100.00
JF-40	Cake stand, 2 tier	135.00	125.00	100.00
JF-45	Canoe-shaped dish	175.00	150.00	135.00
JF-50	Cheese keep	155.00	125.00	125.00
JF-52	Coaster	35.00	30.00	25.00
JF-55	Coffee pot	525.00	350.00	400.00
JF-60	Compote, footed	90.00	85.00	65.00
JF-65	Condiment set on tray	135.00	115.00	100.00
JF-70	Cream and sugar	75.00	75.00	60.00
JF-71	Cream and sugar on tray	135.00	125.00	100.00
JF-75	Demi-tasse	50.00	40.00	45.00
JF-77	Egg cup, footed	45.00	35.00	35.00
JF-80	Hot water jug	200.00	195.00	170.00
JF-85	Jam pot with liner	115.00	95.00	80.00
JF-90	Jug, 4"	200.00	145.00	130.00
JF-91	Jug, 4 1/2"	225.00	165.00	145.00
JF-92	Jug, 5"	250.00	185.00	160.00
JF-97	Nut dish	35.00	25.00	30.00
JF-201	Plate, 4" sq.	30.00	25.00	20.00
JF-202	Plate, 5" sq.	35.00	25.00	25.00
JF-203	Plate, 6" sq.	40.00	30.00	30.00
JF-204	Plate, 7" sq.	45.00	35.00	35.00
JF-205	Plate, 8" sq.	65.00	45.00	40.00
JF-206	Plate, 9" sq.	85.00	65.00	50.00
JF-207	Plate, 10" sq .	105.00	85.00	60.00
JF-112	Relish dish, small	110.00	95.00	65.00
JF-115	Salad bowl, chrome rim	90.00	75.00	65.00
JF-117	Salt and pepper	60.00	50.00	45.00
JF-118	Salt and pepper on tray	135.00	95.00	100.00
JF-120	Sandwich tray, 10" x 6"	75.00	65.00	60.00
JF-121	Sandwich tray, 12" x 7"	90.00	75.00	65.00
JF-125	Sauce boat and liner	115.00	85.00	75.00
JF-130	Teacup and saucer	90.00	45.00	45.00
JF-135	Teapot, 2 cup	275.00	200.00	185.00
JF-136	Teapot, 4 cup	375.00	275.00	260.00
JF-137	Teapot, 6 cup	475.00	325.00	340.00
JF-140	Teapot, stacking	600.00	475.00	450.00
JF-145	Tennis set	65.00	50.00	50.00
JF-150	Toast rack, 4 slice	150.00	120.00	125.00
JF-151	Toast rack, 2 slice	125.00	95.00	85.00
JF-155	Trivet	65.00	50.00	50.00
JF-160	Vase, bud	95.00	65.00	55.00

JUNE ROSES

The pattern number is 1924 and was probably introduced in 1934. The pattern was also produced with silver trim (pattern number 1945) and with green trim (pattern number 2036). This pattern is often confused with **English Rose** and both patterns have become highly collected in North America.

Cat. No.	Shape	U.S. $	Can. $	U.K. £
JR-04	Bonbon dish	85.00	75.00	60.00
JR-09	Bowl, 5"	55.00	50.00	45.00
JR-14	Bowl, 8" soup	95.00	80.00	70.00
JR-23	Breakfast set	1,300.00	900.00	800.00
JR-28	Butter dish	245.00	195.00	175.00
JR-30	Butter pat	75.00	65.00	55.00
JR-35	Cake plate, open handles	245.00	205.00	175.00
JR-36	Cake plate, tab handles	220.00	195.00	165.00
JR-37	Cake plate, 8" sq. pedestal	245.00	205.00	175.00
JR-40	Cake stand, 2 tier	245.00	215.00	175.00
JR-45	Canoe-shaped dish	395.00	325.00	250.00
JR-50	Cheese keep	325.00	225.00	225.00
JR-52	Coaster	60.00	50.00	45.00
JR-55	Coffee pot	1,200.00	800.00	700.00
JR-60	Compote, footed	195.00	175.00	150.00
JR-65	Condiment set on tray	275.00	225.00	225.00
JR-70	Cream and sugar	165.00	145.00	120.00
JR-71	Cream and sugar on tray	275.00	200.00	225.00
JR-75	Demi-tasse	110.00	95.00	80.00
JR-77	Egg cup, footed	100.00	90.00	75.00
JR-80	Hot water jug	575.00	400.00	300.00
JR-85	Jam pot with liner	220.00	175.00	135.00
JR-90	Jug, 4"	450.00	325.00	250.00
JR-91	Jug, 4 1/2"	500.00	350.00	300.00
JR-92	Jug, 5"	550.00	375.00	325.00
JR-97	Nut dish	75.00	65.00	55.00
JR-201	Plate, 4" sq.	55.00	50.00	50.00
JR-202	Plate, 5" sq.	65.00	60.00	55.00
JR-203	Plate, 6" sq.	75.00	70.00	65.00
JR-204	Plate, 7" sq.	110.00	85.00	75.00
JR-205	Plate, 8" sq.	145.00	95.00	85.00
JR-206	Plate, 9" sq.	165.00	115.00	95.00
JR-207	Plate, 10" sq .	175.00	135.00	125.00
JR-112	Relish dish, small	220.00	195.00	175.00
JR-115	Salad bowl, chrome rim	195.00	150.00	150.00
JR-117	Salt and pepper	110.00	105.00	75.00
JR-118	Salt and pepper on tray	195.00	150.00	145.00
JR-120	Sandwich tray, 10" x 6"	165.00	135.00	120.00
JR-121	Sandwich tray, 12" x 7"	195.00	165.00	145.00
JR-125	Sauce boat and liner	195.00	175.00	145.00
JR-130	Teacup and saucer	125.00	110.00	75.00
JR-135	Teapot, 2 cup	550.00	400.00	350.00
JR-136	Teapot, 4 cup	800.00	550.00	500.00
JR-137	Teapot, 6 cup	1,000.00	650.00	600.00
JR-140	Teapot, stacking	1,200.00	850.00	700.00
JR-145	Tennis set	125.00	115.00	85.00
JR-150	Toast rack, 4 slice	300.00	225.00	225.00
JR-151	Toast rack, 2 slice	220.00	175.00	195.00
JR-155	Trivet	135.00	110.00	95.00
JR-160	Vase, bud	175.00	135.00	95.00

KEW

The pattern number is 240 and was widely produced in the 1950s. The pattern was exclusive to Dingle, Davidson, Toronto and was introduced as a new pattern in June 1949. "The line is made up of giftware and teaware items, in prices ranging from $1.00 retail upwards."

Cat. No.	Shape	U.S. $	Can. $	U.K. £
Ke-04	Bonbon dish	50.00	50.00	40.00
Ke-09	Bowl, 5"	45.00	35.00	40.00
Ke-14	Bowl, 8" soup	75.00	60.00	55.00
Ke-23	Breakfast set	850.00	700.00	525.00
Ke-28	Butter dish	150.00	135.00	110.00
Ke-30	Butter pat	45.00	35.00	40.00
Ke-35	Cake plate, open handles	150.00	145.00	110.00
Ke-36	Cake plate, tab handles	135.00	125.00	100.00
Ke-37	Cake plate, 8" sq. pedestal	165.00	155.00	125.00
Ke-40	Cake stand, 2 tier	165.00	145.00	125.00
Ke-45	Canoe-shaped dish	225.00	195.00	165.00
Ke-50	Cheese keep	200.00	175.00	165.00
Ke-52	Coaster	40.00	35.00	35.00
Ke-55	Coffee pot	575.00	500.00	415.00
Ke-60	Compote, footed	130.00	125.00	95.00
Ke-65	Condiment set on tray	175.00	150.00	140.00
Ke-70	Cream and sugar	100.00	95.00	75.00
Ke-71	Cream and sugar on tray	175.00	145.00	145.00
Ke-75	Demi-tasse	75.00	55.00	55.00
Ke-77	Egg cup, footed	80.00	65.00	55.00
Ke-80	Hot water jug	275.00	275.00	195.00
Ke-85	Jam pot with liner	150.00	115.00	110.00
Ke-90	Jug, 4"	200.00	200.00	135.00
Ke-91	Jug, 4 1/2"	225.00	225.00	165.00
Ke-92	Jug, 5"	250.00	250.00	180.00

Cat. No.	Shape	U.S. $	Can. $	U.K. £
Ke-97	Nut dish	45.00	35.00	35.00
Ke-201	Plate, 4" sq.	45.00	35.00	35.00
Ke-202	Plate, 5" sq.	50.00	35.00	40.00
Ke-203	Plate, 6" sq.	60.00	45.00	45.00
Ke-204	Plate, 7" sq.	75.00	45.00	50.00
Ke-205	Plate, 8" sq.	100.00	65.00	60.00
Ke-206	Plate, 9" sq.	120.00	85.00	75.00
Ke-207	Plate, 10" sq .	135.00	100.00	95.00
Ke-112	Relish dish, small	150.00	135.00	110.00
Ke-115	Salad bowl, chrome rim	125.00	105.00	85.00
Ke-117	Salt and pepper	75.00	65.00	55.00
Ke-118	Salt and pepper on tray	150.00	125.00	100.00
Ke-120	Sandwich tray, 10" x 6"	100.00	95.00	70.00
Ke-121	Sandwich tray, 12" x 7"	115.00	115.00	80.00
Ke-125	Sauce boat and liner	125.00	125.00	85.00
Ke-130	Teacup and saucer	85.00	60.00	55.00
Ke-135	Teapot, 2 cup	300.00	275.00	225.00
Ke-136	Teapot, 4 cup	400.00	350.00	275.00
Ke-137	Teapot, 6 cup	500.00	400.00	325.00
Ke-140	Teapot, stacking	675.00	575.00	500.00
Ke-145	Tennis set	100.00	75.00	75.00
Ke-150	Toast rack, 4 slice	200.00	185.00	165.00
Ke-151	Toast rack, 2 slice	150.00	135.00	120.00
Ke-155	Trivet	100.00	75.00	70.00
Ke-160	Vase, bud	100.00	105.00	65.00

KINVER

The pattern number was 2254, and it was probably introduced in 1934.

Cat. No.	Shape	U.S. $	Can. $	U.K. £
Ki-04	Bonbon dish	80.00	75.00	55.00
Ki-09	Bowl, 5″	50.00	50.00	45.00
Ki-14	Bowl, 8″ soup	100.00	80.00	70.00
Ki-23	Breakfast set	1,300.00	900.00	750.00
Ki-28	Butter dish	225.00	195.00	165.00
Ki-30	Butter pat	65.00	65.00	50.00
Ki-35	Cake plate, open handles	225.00	195.00	180.00
Ki-36	Cake plate, tab handles	200.00	175.00	175.00
Ki-37	Cake plate, 8″ sq. pedestal	250.00	195.00	195.00
Ki-40	Cake stand, 2 tier	250.00	205.00	195.00
Ki-45	Canoe-shaped dish	325.00	325.00	250.00
Ki-50	Cheese keep	300.00	225.00	225.00
Ki-52	Coaster	60.00	50.00	50.00
Ki-55	Coffee pot	1,200.00	800.00	650.00
Ki-60	Compote, footed	200.00	175.00	150.00
Ki-65	Condiment set on tray	275.00	225.00	220.00
Ki-70	Cream and sugar	150.00	135.00	110.00
Ki-71	Cream and sugar on tray	250.00	215.00	220.00
Ki-75	Demi-tasse	100.00	95.00	75.00
Ki-77	Egg cup, footed	100.00	95.00	75.00
Ki-80	Hot water jug	400.00	400.00	300.00
Ki-85	Jam pot with liner	200.00	175.00	165.00
Ki-90	Jug, 4″	450.00	325.00	250.00
Ki-91	Jug, 4 1/2″	500.00	350.00	275.00
Ki-92	Jug, 5″	550.00	375.00	300.00

Cat. No.	Shape	U.S. $	Can. $	U.K. £
Ki-97	Nut dish	75.00	65.00	50.00
Ki-201	Plate, 4″ sq.	60.00	50.00	50.00
Ki-202	Plate, 5″ sq.	65.00	60.00	55.00
Ki-203	Plate, 6″ sq.	75.00	70.00	60.00
Ki-204	Plate, 7″ sq.	115.00	85.00	75.00
Ki-205	Plate, 8″ sq.	150.00	95.00	95.00
Ki-206	Plate, 9″ sq.	175.00	110.00	115.00
Ki-207	Plate, 10″ sq.	185.00	125.00	135.00
Ki-112	Relish dish, small	200.00	195.00	165.00
Ki-115	Salad bowl, chrome rim	175.00	150.00	150.00
Ki-117	Salt and pepper	100.00	105.00	85.00
Ki-118	Salt and pepper on tray	200.00	150.00	150.00
Ki-120	Sandwich tray, 10″ x 6″	150.00	125.00	110.00
Ki-121	Sandwich tray, 12″ x 7″	175.00	150.00	135.00
Ki-125	Sauce boat and liner	175.00	170.00	140.00
Ki-130	Teacup and saucer	125.00	110.00	85.00
Ki-135	Teapot, 2 cup	550.00	400.00	375.00
Ki-136	Teapot, 4 cup	800.00	550.00	475.00
Ki-137	Teapot, 6 cup	1,000.00	650.00	575.00
Ki-140	Teapot, stacking	1,200.00	850.00	675.00
Ki-145	Tennis set	150.00	115.00	110.00
Ki-150	Toast rack, 4 slice	275.00	225.00	220.00
Ki-151	Toast rack, 2 slice	225.00	175.00	175.00
Ki-155	Trivet	150.00	115.00	110.00
Ki-160	Vase, bud	175.00	135.00	95.00

MAJESTIC

The pattern number is 3311, this pattern with a black background was introduced in 1936 after **Royalty** 3079, the alternate colourway in yellow. This pattern has become even more collectible in the last year.

Cat. No.	Shape	U.S. $	Can. $	U.K. £
Maj-04	Bonbon dish	100.00	80.00	85.00
Maj-09	Bowl, 5″	65.00	60.00	60.00
Maj-14	Bowl, 8″ soup	100.00	85.00	85.00
Maj-23	Breakfast set	1300.00	1100.00	1000.00
Maj-28	Butter dish	275.00	215.00	225.00
Maj-30	Butter pat	75.00	70.00	65.00
Maj-35	Cake plate, open handles	275.00	225.00	225.00
Maj-36	Cake plate, tab handles	250.00	250.00	225.00
Maj-37	Cake plate, 8″ sq. pedestal	275.00	225.00	250.00
Maj-40	Cake stand, 2 tier	275.00	225.00	250.00
Maj-45	Canoe-shaped dish	375.00	375.00	325.00
Maj-50	Cheese keep	350.00	300.00	300.00
Maj-52	Coaster	75.00	75.00	60.00
Maj-55	Coffee pot	1,200.00	875.00	875.00
Maj-60	Compote, footed	225.00	215.00	195.00
Maj-65	Condiment set on tray	325.00	265.00	275.00
Maj-70	Cream and sugar	175.00	165.00	165.00
Maj-71	Cream and sugar on tray	325.00	250.00	275.00
Maj-75	Demi-tasse	125.00	115.00	105.00
Maj-77	Egg cup, footed	100.00	110.00	75.00
Maj-80	Hot water jug	575.00	450.00	395.00
Maj-85	Jam pot with liner	250.00	200.00	195.00
Maj-90	Jug, 4″	450.00	350.00	350.00
Maj-91	Jug, 4 1/2″	500.00	375.00	400.00
Maj-92	Jug, 5″	550.00	400.00	425.00

Cat. No.	Shape	U.S. $	Can. $	U.K. £
Maj-97	Nut dish	75.00	75.00	60.00
Maj-201	Plate, 4″ sq.	75.00	60.00	60.00
Maj-202	Plate, 5″ sq.	95.00	65.00	75.00
Maj-203	Plate, 6″ sq.	115.00	75.00	85.00
Maj-204	Plate, 7″ sq.	125.00	95.00	95.00
Maj-205	Plate, 8″ sq.	145.00	115.00	125.00
Maj-206	Plate, 9″ sq.	165.00	125.00	135.00
Maj-207	Plate, 10″ sq.	185.00	150.00	150.00
Maj-112	Relish dish, small	250.00	225.00	225.00
Maj-115	Salad bowl, chrome rim	250.00	195.00	225.00
Maj-117	Salt and pepper	125.00	125.00	95.00
Maj-118	Salt and pepper on tray	225.00	195.00	175.00
Maj-120	Sandwich tray, 10″ x 6″	175.00	150.00	160.00
Maj-121	Sandwich tray, 12″ x 7″	200.00	175.00	175.00
Maj-125	Sauce boat and liner	225.00	210.00	175.00
Maj-130	Teacup and saucer	125.00	125.00	85.00
Maj-135	Teapot, 2 cup	550.00	500.00	450.00
Maj-136	Teapot, 4 cup	800.00	650.00	600.00
Maj-137	Teapot, 6 cup	1,000.00	750.00	750.00
Maj-140	Teapot, stacking	1,200.00	950.00	825.00
Maj-145	Tennis set	165.00	135.00	125.00
Maj-150	Toast rack, 4 slice	300.00	275.00	250.00
Maj-151	Toast rack, 2 slice	225.00	225.00	195.00
Maj-155	Trivet	165.00	135.00	125.00
Maj-160	Vase, bud	175.00	150.00	125.00

MARGUERITE

The Pottery Gazette reported the pattern number as 9467 which is Marguerite with blue trim. Most pieces we see in North America have gold trim and pattern number 9432 is recorded on them. **Marguerite** is considered the first "modern" Winton chintz and was produced in 1928. The design was produced in great quantity for many years with a gold, a blue and a burgundy trim. The blue trim sells for a premium over the burgundy and the gold.

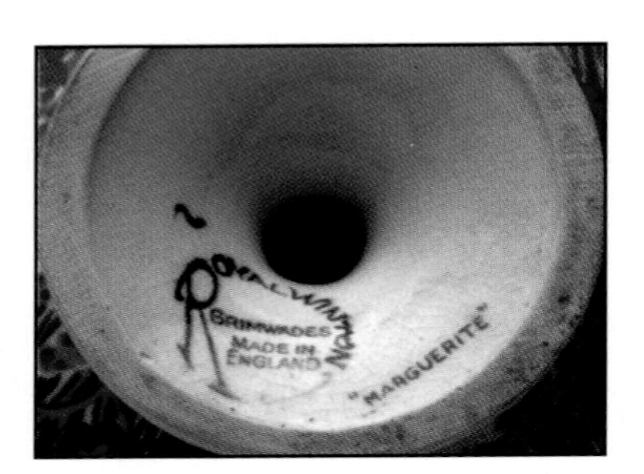

Cat. No.	Shape	U.S. $	Can. $	U.K. £
Mag-04	Bonbon dish	35.00	25.00	30.00
Mag-09	Bowl, 5"	30.00	25.00	25.00
Mag-14	Bowl, 8" soup	45.00	40.00	40.00
Mag-23	Breakfast set	750.00	450.00	375.00
Mag-28	Butter dish	115.00	95.00	75.00
Mag-30	Butter pat	35.00	25.00	25.00
Mag-35	Cake plate, open handles	135.00	85.00	100.00
Mag-36	Cake plate, tab handles	115.00	75.00	75.00
Mag-37	Cake plate, 8" sq. pedestal	135.00	95.00	100.00
Mag-40	Cake stand, 2 tier	135.00	95.00	100.00
Mag-45	Canoe-shaped dish	135.00	125.00	100.00
Mag-50	Cheese keep	135.00	110.00	100.00
Mag-52	Coaster	30.00	25.00	25.00
Mag-55	Coffee pot	400.00	300.00	325.00
Mag-60	Compote, footed	90.00	85.00	65.00
Mag-65	Condiment set on tray	125.00	105.00	85.00
Mag-70	Cream and sugar	65.00	60.00	50.00
Mag-71	Cream and sugar on tray	125.00	105.00	85.00
Mag-75	Demi-tasse	45.00	35.00	35.00
Mag-77	Egg cup, footed	45.00	35.00	35.00
Mag-80	Hot water jug	180.00	175.00	150.00
Mag-85	Jam pot with liner	90.00	85.00	65.00
Mag-90	Jug, 4"	150.00	140.00	115.00
Mag-91	Jug, 4 1/2"	165.00	155.00	125.00
Mag-92	Jug, 5"	185.00	165.00	150.00

Cat. No.	Shape	U.S. $	Can. $	U.K. £
Mag-97	Nut dish	35.00	20.00	25.00
Mag-201	Plate, 4" sq.	30.00	20.00	25.00
Mag-202	Plate, 5" sq.	35.00	25.00	30.00
Mag-203	Plate, 6" sq.	40.00	30.00	35.00
Mag-204	Plate, 7" sq.	45.00	35.00	40.00
Mag-205	Plate, 8" sq.	75.00	40.00	65.00
Mag-206	Plate, 9" sq.	85.00	60.00	65.00
Mag-207	Plate, 10" sq.	105.00	75.00	75.00
Mag-112	Relish dish, small	90.00	85.00	65.00
Mag-115	Salad bowl, chrome rim	90.00	75.00	65.00
Mag-117	Salt and pepper	45.00	45.00	40.00
Mag-118	Salt and pepper on tray	115.00	95.00	75.00
Mag-120	Sandwich tray, 10" x 6"	65.00	65.00	50.00
Mag-121	Sandwich tray, 12" x 7"	75.00	75.00	60.00
Mag-125	Sauce boat and liner	95.00	85.00	65.00
Mag-130	Teacup and saucer	50.00	40.00	35.00
Mag-135	Teapot, 2 cup	175.00	175.00	150.00
Mag-136	Teapot, 4 cup	275.00	200.00	200.00
Mag-137	Teapot, 6 cup	350.00	250.00	275.00
Mag-140	Teapot, stacking	575.00	450.00	350.00
Mag-145	Tennis set	65.00	45.00	50.00
Mag-150	Toast rack, 4 slice	150.00	110.00	115.00
Mag-151	Toast rack, 2 slice	125.00	95.00	85.00
Mag-155	Trivet	65.00	45.00	50.00
Mag-160	Vase, bud	75.00	55.00	50.00

MARION

The pattern number is 324. This post-war pattern was named after the daughter of a major Canadian importer, Rudolf van der Walde of Montreal, and the pattern was controlled to his company Waldonia Ltd.

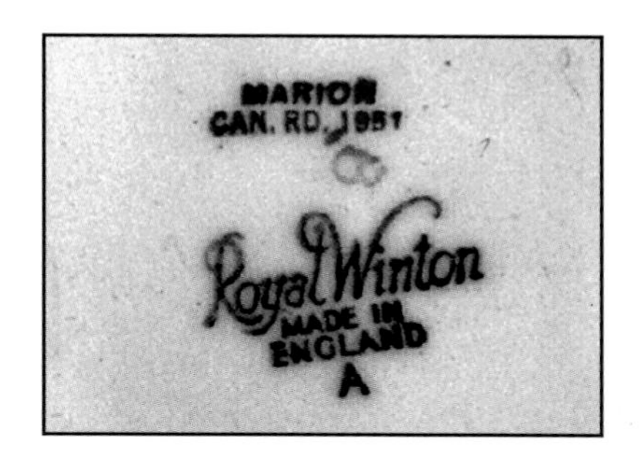

Cat. No.	Shape	U.S. $	Can. $	U.K. £
Mar-03	Basket		RARE	
Mar-04	Bonbon dish	65.00	60.00	60.00
Mar-09	Bowl, 5"	45.00	45.00	45.00
Mar-14	Bowl, 8" soup	80.00	75.00	75.00
Mar-23	Breakfast set	1,100.00	800.00	750.00
Mar-28	Butter dish	200.00	150.00	175.00
Mar-30	Butter pat	65.00	45.00	60.00
Mar-35	Cake plate, open handles	205.00	175.00	175.00
Mar-36	Cake plate, tab handles	180.00	150.00	165.00
Mar-37	Cake plate, 8" sq. pedestal	205.00	175.00	175.00
Mar-40	Cake stand, 2 tier	205.00	165.00	175.00
Mar-	Candy Box		RARE	
Mar-45	Canoe-shaped dish	300.00	225.00	250.00
Mar-50	Cheese keep	250.00	195.00	225.00
Mar-52	Coaster	50.00	45.00	40.00
Mar-55	Coffee pot	900.00	600.00	650.00
Mar-60	Compote, footed	175.00	145.00	135.00
Mar-65	Condiment set on tray	225.00	175.00	200.00
Mar-70	Cream and sugar	135.00	115.00	120.00
Mar-71	Cream and sugar on tray	225.00	175.00	195.00
Mar-75	Demi-tasse	95.00	65.00	85.00
Mar-77	Egg cup, footed	80.00	70.00	70.00
Mar-80	Hot water jug	400.00	275.00	300.00
Mar-85	Jam pot with liner	200.00	135.00	175.00
Mar-90	Jug, 4"	350.00	225.00	250.00
Mar-91	Jug, 4 1/2"	400.00	250.00	275.00
Mar-92	Jug, 5"	450.00	275.00	300.00
Mar-97	Nut dish	65.00	40.00	50.00
Mar-201	Plate, 4" sq.	50.00	40.00	45.00
Mar-202	Plate, 5" sq.	65.00	45.00	50.00
Mar-203	Plate, 6" sq.	75.00	50.00	55.00
Mar-204	Plate, 7" sq.	100.00	60.00	65.00
Mar-205	Plate, 8" sq.	135.00	75.00	85.00
Mar-206	Plate, 9" sq.	150.00	95.00	105.00
Mar-207	Plate, 10" sq.	165.00	115.00	125.00
Mar-112	Relish dish, small	180.00	150.00	175.00
Mar-115	Salad bowl, chrome rim	165.00	120.00	150.00
Mar-117	Salt and pepper	90.00	75.00	75.00
Mar-118	Salt and pepper on tray	175.00	135.00	145.00
Mar-120	Sandwich tray, 10" x 6"	135.00	105.00	120.00
Mar-121	Sandwich tray, 12" x 7"	145.00	125.00	145.00
Mar-125	Sauce boat and liner	165.00	135.00	135.00
Mar-130	Teacup and saucer	100.00	75.00	75.00
Mar-135	Teapot, 2 cup	450.00	325.00	325.00
Mar-136	Teapot, 4 cup	650.00	400.00	525.00
Mar-137	Teapot, 6 cup	850.00	450.00	575.00
Mar-140	Teapot, stacking	1,000.00	650.00	700.00
Mar-145	Tennis set	115.00	85.00	85.00
Mar-150	Toast rack, 4 slice	230.00	195.00	225.00
Mar-151	Toast rack, 2 slice	190.00	135.00	175.00
Mar-155	Trivet	115.00	85.00	85.00
Mar-160	Vase, bud	150.00	115.00	95.00
Mar-	Wall Pocket		VERY RARE	

MAYFAIR

The pattern number is 392, and it was registered in Canada in 1951. This pattern is difficult to find in the United States but it has become sought after in the past year.

Cat. No.	Shape	U.S. $	Can. $	U.K. £
May-04	Bonbon dish	60.00	65.00	55.00
May-09	Bowl, 5″	45.00	50.00	40.00
May-14	Bowl, 8″ soup	70.00	75.00	60.00
May-23	Breakfast set	1,100.00	850.00	675.00
May-28	Butter dish	175.00	160.00	150.00
May-30	Butter pat	50.00	45.00	45.00
May-35	Cake plate, open handles	200.00	175.00	175.00
May-36	Cake plate, tab handles	175.00	150.00	150.00
May-37	Cake plate, 8″ sq. pedestal	200.00	175.00	175.00
May-40	Cake stand, 2 tier	175.00	165.00	150.00
May-45	Canoe-shaped dish	250.00	235.00	215.00
May-50	Cheese keep	225.00	195.00	175.00
May-52	Coaster	45.00	40.00	45.00
May-55	Coffee pot	900.00	650.00	600.00
May-60	Compote, footed	150.00	135.00	125.00
May-65	Condiment set on tray	200.00	175.00	150.00
May-70	Cream and sugar	100.00	115.00	85.00
May-71	Cream and sugar on tray	200.00	175.00	150.00
May-75	Demi-tasse	95.00	70.00	60.00
May-77	Egg cup, footed	95.00	75.00	55.00
May-80	Hot water jug	400.00	325.00	250.00
May-85	Jam pot with liner	150.00	145.00	125.00
May-90	Jug, 4″	350.00	250.00	200.00
May-91	Jug, 4 1/2″	400.00	275.00	225.00
May-92	Jug, 5″	450.00	300.00	250.00

Cat. No.	Shape	U.S. $	Can. $	U.K. £
May-97	Nut dish	50.00	45.00	40.00
May-201	Plate, 4″ sq.	50.00	45.00	40.00
May-202	Plate, 5″ sq.	55.00	50.00	45.00
May-203	Plate, 6″ sq.	65.00	55.00	50.00
May-204	Plate, 7″ sq.	85.00	65.00	60.00
May-205	Plate, 8″ sq.	115.00	85.00	75.00
May-206	Plate, 9″ sq.	135.00	105.00	95.00
May-207	Plate, 10″ sq.	150.00	125.00	110.00
May-112	Relish dish, small	150.00	160.00	125.00
May-115	Salad bowl, chrome rim	135.00	125.00	95.00
May-117	Salt and pepper	75.00	80.00	60.00
May-118	Salt and pepper on tray	150.00	145.00	120.00
May-120	Sandwich tray, 10″ x 6″	100.00	105.00	75.00
May-121	Sandwich tray, 12″ x 7″	125.00	125.00	85.00
May-125	Sauce boat and liner	150.00	135.00	120.00
May-130	Teacup and saucer	95.00	75.00	60.00
May-135	Teapot, 2 cup	450.00	350.00	300.00
May-136	Teapot, 4 cup	650.00	425.00	425.00
May-137	Teapot, 6 cup	850.00	500.00	550.00
May-140	Teapot, stacking	1,000.00	700.00	625.00
May-145	Tennis set	100.00	95.00	75.00
May-150	Toast rack, 4 slice	200.00	220.00	150.00
May-151	Toast rack, 2 slice	150.00	175.00	120.00
May-155	Trivet	100.00	85.00	75.00
May-160	Vase, bud	150.00	115.00	85.00
May-	Wall Pocket		VERY RARE	

MAY FESTIVAL

May Festival has now been found with a pattern name in the backstamp with both the black and the navy background. The pattern number for the black background is 139, and 135 for the navy, and they are the alternate colourways to burgundy **June Festival** (see page 65). Of the three, the black **May Festival** is the most popular and was introduced into Canada in 1952 after the other two colourways. **May Festival** is rarely found with a pattern name backstamp.

Cat. No.	Shape	U.S. $	Can. $	U.K. £
MF-04	Bonbon dish	45.00	30.00	35.00
MF-09	Bowl, 5"	40.00	25.00	30.00
MF-14	Bowl, 8" soup	70.00	45.00	50.00
MF-23	Breakfast set	850.00	475.00	450.00
MF-28	Butter dish	135.00	105.00	100.00
MF-30	Butter pat	45.00	25.00	30.00
MF-35	Cake plate, open handles	135.00	95.00	85.00
MF-36	Cake plate, tab handles	125.00	85.00	75.00
MF-37	Cake plate, 8" sq. pedestal	140.00	115.00	100.00
MF-40	Cake stand, 2 tier	140.00	105.00	100.00
MF-45	Canoe-shaped dish	200.00	135.00	135.00
MF-50	Cheese keep	195.00	115.00	125.00
MF-52	Coaster	40.00	30.00	25.00
MF-55	Coffee pot	550.00	300.00	350.00
MF-60	Compote, footed	100.00	75.00	65.00
MF-65	Condiment set on tray	150.00	105.00	100.00
MF-70	Cream and sugar	85.00	65.00	60.00
MF-71	Cream and sugar on tray	150.00	115.00	100.00
MF-75	Demi-tasse	60.00	35.00	45.00
MF-77	Egg cup, footed	60.00	35.00	35.00
MF-80	Hot water jug	245.00	195.00	150.00
MF-85	Jam pot with liner	135.00	95.00	75.00
MF-90	Jug, 4"	225.00	145.00	135.00
MF-91	Jug, 4 1/2"	250.00	160.00	135.00
MF-92	Jug, 5"	275.00	175.00	150.00
MF-97	Nut dish	45.00	25.00	30.00
MF-201	Plate, 4" sq.	35.00	25.00	25.00
MF-202	Plate, 5" sq.	40.00	30.00	30.00
MF-203	Plate, 6" sq.	45.00	35.00	35.00
MF-204	Plate, 7" sq.	50.00	40.00	35.00
MF-205	Plate, 8" sq.	85.00	50.00	65.00
MF-206	Plate, 9" sq.	100.00	65.00	65.00
MF-207	Plate, 10" sq.	125.00	75.00	75.00
MF-112	Relish dish, small	125.00	95.00	75.00
MF-115	Salad bowl, chrome rim	100.00	75.00	75.00
MF-117	Salt and pepper	75.00	45.00	45.00
MF-118	Salt and pepper on tray	150.00	95.00	100.00
MF-120	Sandwich tray, 10" x 6"	95.00	65.00	60.00
MF-121	Sandwich tray, 12" x 7"	110.00	75.00	65.00
MF-125	Sauce boat and liner	125.00	85.00	75.00
MF-130	Teacup and saucer	70.00	45.00	45.00
MF-135	Teapot, 2 cup	300.00	200.00	175.00
MF-136	Teapot, 4 cup	400.00	275.00	250.00
MF-137	Teapot, 6 cup	500.00	300.00	325.00
MF-140	Teapot, stacking	650.00	450.00	425.00
MF-145	Tennis set	90.00	50.00	50.00
MF-150	Toast rack, 4 slice	175.00	125.00	125.00
MF-151	Toast rack, 2 slice	145.00	95.00	75.00
MF-155	Trivet	80.00	50.00	50.00
MF-160	Vase, bud	100.00	60.00	60.00

MERTON

The pattern is clearly one of the 1920s patterns and it is the Grimwades pattern which most closely remembles the A. G. Richardson chintzes of the same period. It is found in North America on a limited range of shapes.

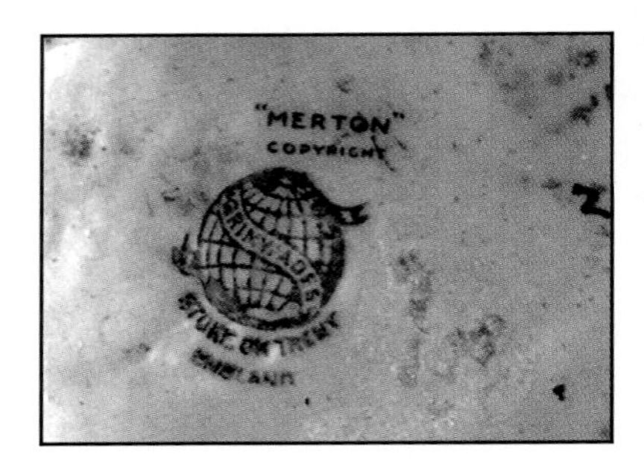

Cat. No.	Shape	U.S. $	Can. $	U.K. £
Mer-35	Cake plate, open handles	175.00	100.00	125.00
Mer-115	Salad bowl, chrome rim	150.00	95.00	100.00
Mer-130	Teacup and saucer	60.00	40.00	40.00

Cat. No.	Shape	U.S. $	Can. $	U.K. £
Mer-203	Plate, 6" sq.	60.00	40.00	40.00
Mer-206	Plate, 9" sq.	100.00	75.00	50.00

MORNING GLORY

The pattern has either a black or a burgundy background. The burgundy background is rarely seen in North America. Introduced into Canada in the spring of 1951 as an Enterprise Sales exclusive it was described in one of their advertisements — "Here is the perfect combination for the Canadian Trade. MORNING GLORY has a jet black background and is high-lighted by delicate pink, yellow and blue morning glories on a pale green vine. This beautiful under glaze pattern is a leader in the 1951 march of profits."

Cat. No.	Shape	U.S. $	Can. $	U.K. £
MG-04	Bonbon dish	45.00	25.00	35.00
MG-09	Bowl, 5"	40.00	25.00	30.00
MG-14	Bowl, 8" soup	75.00	45.00	50.00
MG-23	Breakfast set	850.00	475.00	450.00
MG-28	Butter dish	135.00	105.00	85.00
MG-30	Butter pat	45.00	25.00	30.00
MG-35	Cake plate, open handles	135.00	95.00	85.00
MG-36	Cake plate, tab handles	125.00	85.00	75.00
MG-37	Cake plate,8" sq. pedestal	140.00	115.00	100.00
MG-40	Cake stand, 2 tier	140.00	105.00	100.00
MG-45	Canoe-shaped dish	200.00	135.00	135.00
MG-50	Cheese keep	175.00	115.00	125.00
MG-52	Coaster	40.00	30.00	25.00
MG-55	Coffee pot	550.00	300.00	350.00
MG-60	Compote, footed	100.00	85.00	65.00
MG-65	Condiment set on tray	150.00	105.00	110.00
MG-70	Cream and sugar	85.00	65.00	60.00
MG-71	Cream and sugar on tray	150.00	115.00	110.00
MG-75	Demi-tasse	60.00	35.00	45.00
MG-77	Egg cup, footed	50.00	45.00	35.00
MG-80	Hot water jug	245.00	195.00	160.00
MG-85	Jam pot with liner	125.00	95.00	75.00
MG-90	Jug, 4"	225.00	150.00	125.00
MG-91	Jug, 4 1/2"	250.00	165.00	125.00
MG-92	Jug, 5"	275.00	175.00	150.00

Cat. No.	Shape	U.S. $	Can. $	U.K. £
MG-97	Nut dish	45.00	25.00	30.00
MG-201	Plate, 4" sq.	35.00	25.00	25.00
MG-202	Plate, 5" sq.	40.00	30.00	30.00
MG-203	Plate, 6" sq.	45.00	35.00	35.00
MG-204	Plate, 7" sq.	50.00	40.00	35.00
MG-205	Plate, 8" sq.	85.00	45.00	65.00
MG-206	Plate, 9" sq.	100.00	65.00	65.00
MG-207	Plate, 10" sq.	125.00	75.00	75.00
MG-112	Relish dish, small	125.00	95.00	75.00
MG-115	Salad bowl, chrome rim	100.00	75.00	65.00
MG-117	Salt and pepper	75.00	50.00	45.00
MG-118	Salt and pepper on tray	150.00	105.00	100.00
MG-120	Sandwich tray, 10" x 6"	85.00	65.00	60.00
MG-121	Sandwich tray, 12" x 7"	100.00	75.00	65.00
MG-125	Sauce boat and liner	125.00	85.00	75.00
MG-130	Teacup and saucer	70.00	45.00	45.00
MG-135	Teapot, 2 cup	300.00	200.00	175.00
MG-136	Teapot, 4 cup	400.00	250.00	250.00
MG-137	Teapot, 6 cup	500.00	300.00	325.00
MG-140	Teapot, stacking	650.00	450.00	425.00
MG-145	Tennis set	80.00	50.00	50.00
MG-150	Toast rack, 4 slice	175.00	125.00	125.00
MG-151	Toast rack, 2 slice	125.00	95.00	75.00
MG-155	Trivet	80.00	50.00	50.00
MG-160	Vase, bud	100.00	60.00	60.00

NANTWICH

The pattern number is 291. This pattern was exclusive to Cassidy's and advertised in their 1953 catalogue. This pattern was exported in quantity to North America in the 1950s.

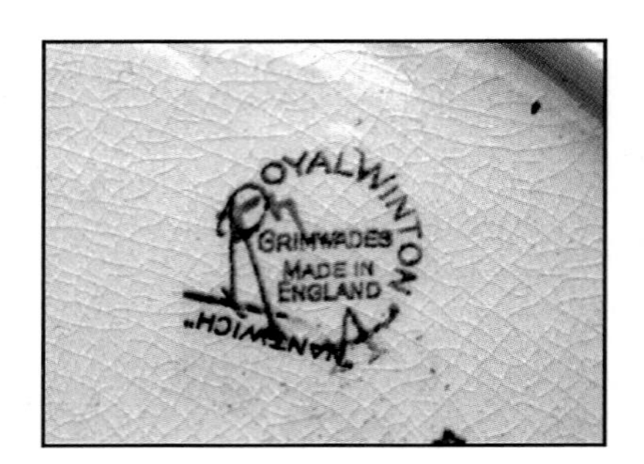

Cat. No.	Shape	U.S. $	Can. $	U.K. £
N-04	Bonbon dish	65.00	60.00	45.00
N-09	Bowl, 5"	50.00	45.00	40.00
N-14	Bowl, 8" soup	75.00	65.00	50.00
N-23	Breakfast set	1,200.00	800.00	650.00
N-28	Butter dish	200.00	150.00	125.00
N-30	Butter pat	50.00	40.00	40.00
N-35	Cake plate, open handles	200.00	175.00	125.00
N-36	Cake plate, tab handles	175.00	160.00	125.00
N-37	Cake plate, 8" sq. pedestal	200.00	185.00	125.00
N-40	Cake stand, 2 tier	200.00	165.00	125.00
N-45	Canoe-shaped dish	275.00	225.00	225.00
N-50	Cheese keep	250.00	195.00	175.00
N-52	Coaster	50.00	45.00	35.00
N-55	Coffee pot	975.00	600.00	575.00
N-60	Compote, footed	150.00	145.00	100.00
N-65	Condiment set on tray	225.00	175.00	150.00
N-70	Cream and sugar	125.00	105.00	75.00
N-71	Cream and sugar on tray	225.00	265.00	150.00
N-75	Demi-tasse	85.00	60.00	60.00
N-77	Egg cup, footed	95.00	70.00	50.00
N-80	Hot water jug	450.00	300.00	225.00
N-85	Jam pot with liner	175.00	135.00	125.00
N-90	Jug, 4"	400.00	225.00	175.00
N-91	Jug, 4 1/2"	450.00	250.00	200.00
N-92	Jug, 5"	500.00	275.00	225.00

Cat. No.	Shape	U.S. $	Can. $	U.K. £
N-97	Nut dish	50.00	40.00	40.00
N-201	Plate, 4" sq.	45.00	40.00	35.00
N-202	Plate, 5" sq.	50.00	45.00	40.00
N-203	Plate, 6" sq.	75.00	50.00	45.00
N-204	Plate, 7" sq.	85.00	60.00	60.00
N-205	Plate, 8" sq.	125.00	75.00	85.00
N-206	Plate, 9" sq.	150.00	95.00	100.00
N-207	Plate, 10" sq.	165.00	115.00	115.00
N-112	Relish dish, small	175.00	150.00	125.00
N-115	Salad bowl, chrome rim	150.00	110.00	100.00
N-117	Salt and pepper	95.00	75.00	60.00
N-118	Salt and pepper on tray	165.00	135.00	115.00
N-120	Sandwich tray, 10" x 6"	125.00	105.00	75.00
N-121	Sandwich tray, 12" x 7"	150.00	125.00	100.00
N-125	Sauce boat and liner	175.00	135.00	125.00
N-130	Teacup and saucer	95.00	70.00	60.00
N-135	Teapot, 2 cup	425.00	325.00	275.00
N-136	Teapot, 4 cup	650.00	400.00	400.00
N-137	Teapot, 6 cup	850.00	500.00	475.00
N-140	Teapot, stacking	950.00	650.00	550.00
N-145	Tennis set	125.00	85.00	75.00
N-150	Toast rack, 4 slice	275.00	195.00	200.00
N-151	Toast rack, 2 slice	225.00	145.00	160.00
N-155	Trivet	125.00	85.00	75.00
N-160	Vase, bud	135.00	115.00	75.00

OFFLEY

A breakfast set in this pattern was advertised in a Toronto newspaper in December 1938 for $9.50. Since **Sandon, Meaford** and **Offley** were introduced six months before and the description of **Offley** in the *Pottery Gazette* matches this pattern we are calling it **Offley** for the moment. This pattern also comes in a brown colourway.

Backstamp not available
at
press time

Cat. No.	Shape	U.S. $	Can. $	U.K. £
Of-04	Bonbon dish	30.00	15.00	25.00
Of-09	Bowl, 5″	30.00	20.00	25.00
Of-14	Bowl, 8″ soup	40.00	25.00	30.00
Of-23	Breakfast set	650.00	275.00	325.00
Of-28	Butter dish	100.00	65.00	65.00
Of-30	Butter pat	25.00	20.00	20.00
Of-35	Cake plate, open handles	100.00	65.00	65.00
Of-36	Cake plate, tab handles	85.00	55.00	60.00
Of-37	Cake plate, 8″ sq. pedestal	100.00	75.00	65.00
Of-40	Cake stand, 2 tier	100.00	70.00	65.00
Of-45	Canoe-shaped dish	135.00	85.00	85.00
Of-50	Cheese keep	125.00	75.00	75.00
Of-52	Coaster	25.00	20.00	20.00
Of-55	Coffee pot	375.00	175.00	250.00
Of-60	Compote, footed	80.00	50.00	50.00
Of-65	Condiment set on tray	100.00	65.00	65.00
Of-70	Cream and sugar	50.00	35.00	45.00
Of-71	Cream and sugar on tray	100.00	65.00	65.00
Of-75	Demi-tasse	40.00	25.00	30.00
Of-77	Egg cup, footed	35.00	30.00	25.00
Of-80	Hot water jug	160.00	95.00	125.00
Of-85	Jam pot with liner	85.00	50.00	60.00
Of-90	Jug, 4″	125.00	65.00	65.00
Of-91	Jug, 4 1/2″	140.00	75.00	85.00
Of-92	Jug, 5″	150.00	85.00	105.00
Of-97	Nut dish	25.00	15.00	20.00
Of-201	Plate, 4″ sq.	30.00	15.00	20.00
Of-202	Plate, 5″ sq.	35.00	20.00	25.00
Of-203	Plate, 6″ sq.	40.00	25.00	30.00
Of-204	Plate, 7″ sq.	45.00	30.00	35.00
Of-205	Plate, 8″ sq.	65.00	35.00	45.00
Of-206	Plate, 9″ sq.	75.00	40.00	50.00
Of-207	Plate, 10″ sq .	85.00	50.00	55.00
Of-112	Relish dish, small	85.00	60.00	60.00
Of-115	Salad bowl, chrome rim	100.00	65.00	65.00
Of-117	Salt and pepper	50.00	35.00	40.00
Of-118	Salt and pepper on tray	125.00	65.00	80.00
Of-120	Sandwich tray, 10″ x 6″	60.00	35.00	45.00
Of-121	Sandwich tray, 12″ x 7″	75.00	45.00	50.00
Of-125	Sauce boat and liner	65.00	50.00	45.00
Of-130	Teacup and saucer	40.00	25.00	30.00
Of-135	Teapot, 2 cup	175.00	100.00	125.00
Of-136	Teapot, 4 cup	275.00	150.00	200.00
Of-137	Teapot, 6 cup	325.00	200.00	225.00
Of-140	Teapot, stacking	550.00	300.00	275.00
Of-145	Tennis set	55.00	35.00	40.00
Of-150	Toast rack, 4 slice	150.00	85.00	100.00
Of-151	Toast rack, 2 slice	135.00	65.00	85.00
Of-155	Trivet	55.00	30.00	40.00
Of-160	Vase, bud	60.00	40.00	45.00

OLD COTTAGE CHINTZ

The pattern number is 9632. The pattern was introduced very early in the 1930s and was produced in great quantities until the 1960s. It has been seen on an invoice as late as 1969. Be aware of the difference in the colour of the pre- and post-war transfer.

Cat. No.	Shape	U.S. $	Can. $	U.K. £
OC-	Ash Box	EXTREMELY RARE		
OC-	Bell	EXTREMELY RARE		
OC-04	Bonbon dish	50.00	50.00	35.00
OC-09	Bowl, 5″	45.00	35.00	35.00
OC-14	Bowl, 8″ soup	75.00	60.00	50.00
OC-23	Breakfast set	850.00	700.00	475.00
OC-28	Butter dish	150.00	125.00	100.00
OC-30	Butter pat	45.00	35.00	35.00
OC-35	Cake plate, open handles	150.00	145.00	100.00
OC-36	Cake plate, tab handles	135.00	125.00	85.00
OC-37	Cake plate,8″ sq. pedestal	150.00	145.00	100.00
OC-40	Cake stand, 2 tier	150.00	135.00	100.00
OC-45	Canoe-shaped dish	225.00	195.00	150.00
OC-50	Cheese keep	200.00	175.00	125.00
OC-52	Coaster	40.00	35.00	30.00
OC-55	Coffee pot	600.00	500.00	375.00
OC-60	Compote, footed	125.00	125.00	75.00
OC-65	Condiment set on tray	175.00	145.00	125.00
OC-70	Cream and sugar	100.00	95.00	65.00
OC-71	Cream and sugar on tray	175.00	145.00	125.00
OC-75	Demi-tasse	75.00	55.00	50.00
OC-77	Egg cup, footed	75.00	60.00	45.00
OC-80	Hot water jug	275.00	275.00	175.00
OC-85	Jam pot with liner	150.00	110.00	100.00
OC-90	Jug, 4″	200.00	200.00	125.00
OC-91	Jug, 4 1/2″	225.00	225.00	150.00
OC-92	Jug, 5″	250.00	250.00	150.00
OC-97	Nut dish	45.00	35.00	35.00
OC-201	Plate, 4″ sq.	50.00	35.00	35.00
OC-202	Plate, 5″ sq.	50.00	40.00	40.00
OC-203	Plate, 6″ sq.	60.00	45.00	45.00
OC-204	Plate, 7″ sq.	75.00	50.00	50.00
OC-205	Plate, 8″ sq.	100.00	65.00	65.00
OC-206	Plate, 9″ sq.	125.00	85.00	75.00
OC-207	Plate, 10″ sq.	125.00	95.00	75.00
OC-112	Relish dish, small	140.00	135.00	100.00
OC-115	Salad bowl, chrome rim	125.00	95.00	75.00
OC-117	Salt and pepper	75.00	65.00	50.00
OC-118	Salt and pepper on tray	150.00	115.00	85.00
OC-120	Sandwich tray, 10″ x 6″	100.00	95.00	65.00
OC-121	Sandwich tray, 12″ x 7″	125.00	115.00	75.00
OC-125	Sauce boat and liner	125.00	125.00	75.00
OC-	Sugar Shaker		VERY RARE	
OC-130	Teacup and saucer	75.00	60.00	50.00
OC-135	Teapot, 2 cup	300.00	275.00	200.00
OC-136	Teapot, 4 cup	400.00	350.00	250.00
OC-137	Teapot, 6 cup	500.00	400.00	325.00
OC-140	Teapot, stacking	750.00	575.00	425.00
OC-145	Tennis set	90.00	75.00	65.00
OC-150	Toast rack, 4 slice	200.00	185.00	150.00
OC-151	Toast rack, 2 slice	150.00	135.00	100.00
OC-155	Trivet	100.00	75.00	65.00
OC-160	Vase, bud	125.00	95.00	65.00

ORIENT

The pattern number is 471, and the pattern was exclusive to Cassidy's of Canada in 1954. Jack Robertson, who was the buyer for Cassidy's, chose this pattern from a sample, but the finished product did not sell well. It is no more popular with chintz colllectors today.

Cat. No.	Shape	U.S. $	Can. $	U.K. £
O-04	Bonbon dish	25.00	20.00	25.00
O-09	Bowl, 5″	25.00	25.00	25.00
O-14	Bowl, 8″ soup	35.00	30.00	30.00
O-23	Breakfast set	450.00	275.00	325.00
O-28	Butter dish	90.00	75.00	65.00
O-30	Butter pat	25.00	20.00	20.00
O-35	Cake plate, open handles	90.00	75.00	75.00
O-36	Cake plate, tab handles	75.00	65.00	60.00
O-37	Cake plate, 8″ sq. pedestal	90.00	75.00	65.00
O-40	Cake stand, 2 tier	90.00	70.00	65.00
O-45	Canoe-shaped dish	120.00	85.00	85.00
O-50	Cheese keep	115.00	75.00	100.00
O-52	Coaster	25.00	20.00	20.00
O-55	Coffee pot	395.00	175.00	275.00
O-60	Compote, footed	65.00	50.00	50.00
O-65	Condiment set on tray	90.00	65.00	65.00
O-70	Cream and sugar	55.00	40.00	45.00
O-71	Cream and sugar on tray	90.00	65.00	65.00
O-75	Demi-tasse	35.00	25.00	30.00
O-77	Egg cup, footed	35.00	30.00	25.00
O-80	Hot water jug	165.00	95.00	125.00
O-85	Jam pot with liner	75.00	60.00	60.00
O-90	Jug, 4″	135.00	65.00	75.00
O-91	Jug, 4 1/2″	150.00	75.00	95.00
O-92	Jug, 5″	165.00	85.00	125.00

Cat. No.	Shape	U.S. $	Can. $	U.K. £
O-97	Nut dish	25.00	20.00	20.00
O-201	Plate, 4″ sq.	30.00	20.00	25.00
O-202	Plate, 5″ sq.	35.00	25.00	25.00
O-203	Plate, 6″ sq.	40.00	30.00	30.00
O-204	Plate, 7″ sq.	45.00	35.00	35.00
O-205	Plate, 8″ sq.	55.00	40.00	45.00
O-206	Plate, 9″ sq.	65.00	50.00	50.00
O-207	Plate, 10″ sq.	75.00	55.00	55.00
O-112	Relish dish, small	75.00	50.00	60.00
O-115	Salad bowl, chrome rim	90.00	60.00	65.00
O-117	Salt and pepper	45.00	35.00	40.00
O-118	Salt and pepper on tray	100.00	65.00	80.00
O-120	Sandwich tray, 10″ x 6″	45.00	35.00	45.00
O-121	Sandwich tray, 12″ x 7″	65.00	45.00	50.00
O-125	Sauce boat and liner	65.00	50.00	45.00
O-130	Teacup and saucer	35.00	25.00	30.00
O-135	Teapot, 2 cup	175.00	100.00	125.00
O-136	Teapot, 4 cup	275.00	150.00	175.00
O-137	Teapot, 6 cup	325.00	175.00	225.00
O-140	Teapot, stacking	425.00	275.00	325.00
O-145	Tennis set	45.00	35.00	40.00
O-150	Toast rack, 4 slice	150.00	85.00	125.00
O-151	Toast rack, 2 slice	90.00	65.00	65.00
O-155	Trivet	45.00	30.00	40.00
O-160	Vase, bud	50.00	40.00	45.00

PAISLEY

This pattern was used by a number of companies including Wade throughout the 1920s and later. The Grimwades version appeared in 1923 in both a rust and a green colorway (pattern number 8152). This pattern has never been popular with chintz collectors but fits into the category of all over transfers including **Tartans** and **Quilt**.

Backstamp not available at press time

Cat. No.	Shape	U.S. $	Can. $	U.K. £
Pa-04	Bonbon dish	25.00	20.00	25.00
Pa-09	Bowl, 5"	25.00	20.00	25.00
Pa-14	Bowl, 8" soup	35.00	30.00	30.00
Pa-23	Breakfast set	475.00	300.00	350.00
Pa-28	Butter dish	90.00	65.00	65.00
Pa-30	Butter pat	25.00	20.00	20.00
Pa-35	Cake plate, open handles	90.00	75.00	75.00
Pa-36	Cake plate, tab handles	75.00	65.00	60.00
Pa-37	Cake plate, 8" sq. pedestal	90.00	85.00	65.00
Pa-40	Cake stand, 2 tier	90.00	80.00	65.00
Pa-45	Canoe-shaped dish	120.00	95.00	85.00
Pa-50	Cheese keep	115.00	85.00	100.00
Pa-52	Coaster	25.00	20.00	20.00
Pa-55	Coffee pot	395.00	175.00	275.00
Pa-60	Compote, footed	65.00	50.00	50.00
Pa-65	Condiment set on tray	90.00	65.00	65.00
Pa-70	Cream and sugar	55.00	45.00	45.00
Pa-71	Cream and sugar on tray	90.00	75.00	65.00
Pa-75	Demi-tasse	35.00	30.00	30.00
Pa-77	Egg cup, footed	35.00	30.00	25.00
Pa-80	Hot water jug	165.00	95.00	125.00
Pa-85	Jam pot with liner	75.00	60.00	60.00
Pa-90	Jug, 4"	135.00	65.00	75.00
Pa-91	Jug, 4 1/2"	150.00	75.00	95.00
Pa-92	Jug, 5"	165.00	85.00	125.00

Cat. No.	Shape	U.S. $	Can. $	U.K. £
Pa-97	Nut dish	25.00	20.00	20.00
Pa-201	Plate, 4" sq.	30.00	20.00	25.00
Pa-202	Plate, 5" sq.	35.00	25.00	25.00
Pa-203	Plate, 6" sq.	40.00	30.00	30.00
Pa-204	Plate, 7" sq.	45.00	35.00	35.00
Pa-205	Plate, 8" sq.	55.00	40.00	45.00
Pa-206	Plate, 9" sq.	65.00	50.00	50.00
Pa-207	Plate, 10" sq.	75.00	60.00	55.00
Pa-112	Relish dish, small	75.00	50.00	60.00
Pa-115	Salad bowl, chrome rim	90.00	65.00	65.00
Pa-117	Salt and pepper	45.00	35.00	40.00
Pa-118	Salt and pepper on tray	100.00	65.00	80.00
Pa-120	Sandwich tray, 10" x 6"	45.00	35.00	45.00
Pa-121	Sandwich tray, 12" x 7"	65.00	45.00	50.00
Pa-125	Sauce boat and liner	65.00	50.00	45.00
Pa-130	Teacup and saucer	35.00	25.00	30.00
Pa-135	Teapot, 2 cup	175.00	100.00	125.00
Pa-136	Teapot, 4 cup	275.00	150.00	175.00
Pa-137	Teapot, 6 cup	325.00	175.00	225.00
Pa-140	Teapot, stacking	425.00	275.00	325.00
Pa-145	Tennis set	45.00	35.00	40.00
Pa-150	Toast rack, 4 slice	150.00	85.00	125.00
Pa-151	Toast rack, 2 slice	90.00	65.00	65.00
Pa-155	Trivet	45.00	25.00	40.00
Pa-160	Vase, bud	50.00	35.00	45.00

PEKIN

The pattern number for the 1950s version is 320, and it was produced with black, burgundy and dark green backgrounds. The pattern was introduced into Canada by Waldonia Ltd. in 1951 as 'Black Pekin' and it was a huge success. The 'Ivory Pekin' followed in 1953. Some of the earlier versions of this pattern are handpainted.

Cat. No.	Shape	U.S. $	Can. $	U.K. £
Pe-04	Bonbon dish	30.00	20.00	30.00
Pe-09	Bowl, 5"	30.00	20.00	25.00
Pe-14	Bowl, 8" soup	40.00	35.00	40.00
Pe-23	Breakfast set	550.00	300.00	375.00
Pe-28	Butter dish	100.00	65.00	75.00
Pe-30	Butter pat	25.00	20.00	25.00
Pe-35	Cake plate, open handles	100.00	75.00	100.00
Pe-36	Cake plate, tab handles	85.00	65.00	75.00
Pe-37	Cake plate, 8" sq. pedestal	100.00	85.00	100.00
Pe-40	Cake stand, 2 tier	100.00	75.00	100.00
Pe-45	Canoe-shaped dish	100.00	85.00	100.00
Pe-50	Cheese keep	125.00	75.00	100.00
Pe-52	Coaster	25.00	25.00	25.00
Pe-55	Coffee pot	375.00	175.00	325.00
Pe-60	Compote, footed	75.00	45.00	65.00
Pe-65	Condiment set on tray	100.00	65.00	85.00
Pe-70	Cream and sugar	60.00	45.00	50.00
Pe-71	Cream and sugar on tray	100.00	75.00	85.00
Pe-75	Demi-tasse	40.00	25.00	35.00
Pe-77	Egg cup, footed	40.00	30.00	35.00
Pe-80	Hot water jug	165.00	95.00	150.00
Pe-85	Jam pot with liner	85.00	65.00	65.00
Pe-90	Jug, 4"	135.00	65.00	100.00
Pe-91	Jug, 4 1/2"	150.00	75.00	125.00
Pe-92	Jug, 5"	165.00	85.00	150.00
Pe-180	Lamp Base		RARE	

Cat. No.	Shape	U.S. $	Can. $	U.K. £
Pe-97	Nut dish	25.00	20.00	25.00
Pe-201	Plate, 4" sq.	30.00	20.00	25.00
Pe-202	Plate, 5" sq.	35.00	25.00	30.00
Pe-203	Plate, 6" sq.	40.00	30.00	35.00
Pe-204	Plate, 7" sq.	45.00	35.00	40.00
Pe-205	Plate, 8" sq.	65.00	40.00	65.00
Pe-206	Plate, 9" sq.	75.00	50.00	65.00
Pe-207	Plate, 10" sq.	85.00	60.00	75.00
Pe-112	Relish dish, small	85.00	50.00	65.00
Pe-115	Salad bowl, chrome rim	90.00	65.00	65.00
Pe-117	Salt and pepper	50.00	35.00	40.00
Pe-118	Salt and pepper on tray	115.00	65.00	75.00
Pe-120	Sandwich tray, 10" x 6"	50.00	40.00	50.00
Pe-121	Sandwich tray, 12" x 7"	75.00	50.00	60.00
Pe-125	Sauce boat and liner	65.00	60.00	65.00
Pe-130	Teacup and saucer	45.00	25.00	35.00
Pe-135	Teapot, 2 cup	175.00	125.00	150.00
Pe-136	Teapot, 4 cup	275.00	175.00	200.00
Pe-137	Teapot, 6 cup	325.00	200.00	275.00
Pe-140	Teapot, stacking	450.00	275.00	350.00
Pe-145	Tennis set	50.00	35.00	50.00
Pe-150	Toast rack, 4 slice	150.00	85.00	115.00
Pe-151	Toast rack, 2 slice	100.00	65.00	85.00
Pe-155	Trivet	50.00	30.00	50.00
Pe-160	Vase, bud	50.00	40.00	50.00

PELHAM

The pattern number is 2201, and the pattern was purchased by Queen Mary at the 1935 British Industries Fair. It came with a teal trim. This pattern is also known as **Sampler**.

Cat. No.	Shape	U.S. $	Can. $	U.K. £
Pel-04	Bonbon dish	45.00	30.00	35.00
Pel-09	Bowl, 5"	40.00	35.00	30.00
Pel-14	Bowl, 8" soup	50.00	50.00	40.00
Pel-23	Breakfast set	750.00	450.00	400.00
Pel-28	Butter dish	125.00	95.00	75.00
Pel-30	Butter pat	35.00	25.00	25.00
Pel-35	Cake plate, open handles	150.00	85.00	100.00
Pel-36	Cake plate, tab handles	135.00	75.00	85.00
Pel-37	Cake plate, 8" sq. pedestal	150.00	95.00	100.00
Pel-40	Cake stand, 2 tier	150.00	85.00	100.00
Pel-45	Canoe-shaped dish	150.00	125.00	100.00
Pel-50	Cheese keep	150.00	115.00	100.00
Pel-52	Coaster	30.00	25.00	25.00
Pel-55	Coffee pot	475.00	300.00	325.00
Pel-60	Compote, footed	100.00	75.00	65.00
Pel-65	Condiment set on tray	150.00	95.00	85.00
Pel-70	Cream and sugar	75.00	55.00	50.00
Pel-71	Cream and sugar on tray	135.00	95.00	85.00
Pel-75	Demi-tasse	50.00	35.00	40.00
Pel-77	Egg cup, footed	65.00	40.00	35.00
Pel-80	Hot water jug	225.00	195.00	150.00
Pel-85	Jam pot with liner	100.00	85.00	65.00
Pel-90	Jug, 4"	175.00	150.00	125.00
Pel-91	Jug, 4 1/2"	200.00	165.00	150.00
Pel-92	Jug, 5"	225.00	175.00	150.00
Pel-97	Nut dish	35.00	20.00	25.00
Pel-201	Plate, 4" sq.	35.00	20.00	25.00
Pel-202	Plate, 5" sq.	40.00	25.00	30.00
Pel-203	Plate, 6" sq.	45.00	30.00	35.00
Pel-204	Plate, 7" sq.	50.00	35.00	40.00
Pel-205	Plate, 8" sq.	75.00	40.00	50.00
Pel-206	Plate, 9" sq.	95.00	60.00	60.00
Pel-207	Plate, 10" sq.	125.00	75.00	65.00
Pel-112	Relish dish, small	125.00	95.00	75.00
Pel-115	Salad bowl, chrome rim	100.00	75.00	65.00
Pel-117	Salt and pepper	65.00	45.00	45.00
Pel-118	Salt and pepper on tray	135.00	95.00	85.00
Pel-120	Sandwich tray, 10" x 6"	75.00	60.00	50.00
Pel-121	Sandwich tray, 12" x 7"	100.00	70.00	65.00
Pel-125	Sauce boat and liner	125.00	80.00	75.00
Pel-130	Teacup and saucer	65.00	40.00	40.00
Pel-135	Teapot, 2 cup	325.00	175.00	200.00
Pel-136	Teapot, 4 cup	375.00	225.00	250.00
Pel-137	Teapot, 6 cup	450.00	300.00	300.00
Pel-140	Teapot, stacking	600.00	450.00	300.00
Pel-145	Tennis set	75.00	45.00	50.00
Pel-150	Toast rack, 4 slice	175.00	125.00	125.00
Pel-151	Toast rack, 2 slice	150.00	100.00	100.00
Pel-155	Trivet	75.00	45.00	50.00
Pel-160	Vase, bud	95.00	85.00	50.00

PEONY

This large flower chintz pattern is very much a 1950s chintz and was exported to North America in great quantities.

Cat. No.	Shape	U.S. $	Can. $	U.K. £
Peo-04	Bonbon dish	40.00	25.00	35.00
Peo-09	Bowl, 5″	40.00	25.00	30.00
Peo-14	Bowl, 8″ soup	50.00	45.00	40.00
Peo-23	Breakfast set	800.00	500.00	400.00
Peo-28	Butter dish	125.00	95.00	75.00
Peo-30	Butter pat	35.00	25.00	25.00
Peo-35	Cake plate, open handles	135.00	85.00	100.00
Peo-36	Cake plate, tab handles	125.00	75.00	85.00
Peo-37	Cake plate, 8″ sq. pedestal	135.00	95.00	100.00
Peo-40	Cake stand, 2 tier	150.00	85.00	100.00
Peo-45	Canoe-shaped dish	150.00	125.00	100.00
Peo-50	Cheese keep	150.00	115.00	100.00
Peo-52	Coaster	35.00	30.00	25.00
Peo-55	Coffee pot	525.00	300.00	325.00
Peo-60	Compote, footed	100.00	75.00	65.00
Peo-65	Condiment set on tray	150.00	95.00	100.00
Peo-70	Cream and sugar	80.00	60.00	50.00
Peo-71	Cream and sugar on tray	135.00	105.00	85.00
Peo-75	Demi-tasse	50.00	35.00	40.00
Peo-77	Egg cup, footed	45.00	30.00	35.00
Peo-80	Hot water jug	200.00	175.00	150.00
Peo-85	Jam pot with liner	110.00	85.00	75.00
Peo-90	Jug, 4″	200.00	140.00	125.00
Peo-91	Jug, 4 1/2″	225.00	155.00	150.00
Peo-92	Jug, 5″	250.00	165.00	150.00
Peo-97	Nut dish	40.00	25.00	25.00
Peo-201	Plate, 4″ sq.	35.00	25.00	25.00
Peo-202	Plate, 5″ sq.	40.00	30.00	30.00
Peo-203	Plate, 6″ sq.	45.00	35.00	35.00
Peo-204	Plate, 7″ sq.	50.00	40.00	40.00
Peo-205	Plate, 8″ sq.	75.00	45.00	50.00
Peo-206	Plate, 9″ sq.	90.00	60.00	60.00
Peo-207	Plate, 10″ sq.	115.00	75.00	70.00
Peo-112	Relish dish, small	125.00	85.00	75.00
Peo-115	Salad bowl, chrome rim	100.00	75.00	65.00
Peo-117	Salt and pepper	65.00	45.00	45.00
Peo-118	Salt and pepper on tray	135.00	95.00	85.00
Peo-120	Sandwich tray, 10″ x 6″	75.00	60.00	50.00
Peo-121	Sandwich tray, 12″ x 7″	100.00	70.00	65.00
Peo-125	Sauce boat and liner	125.00	75.00	75.00
Peo-130	Teacup and saucer	70.00	40.00	40.00
Peo-135	Teapot, 2 cup	275.00	175.00	205.00
Peo-136	Teapot, 4 cup	375.00	225.00	250.00
Peo-137	Teapot, 6 cup	475.00	300.00	300.00
Peo-140	Teapot, stacking	600.00	450.00	300.00
Peo-145	Tennis set	75.00	50.00	50.00
Peo-150	Toast rack, 4 slice	175.00	125.00	125.00
Peo-151	Toast rack, 2 slice	150.00	100.00	100.00
Peo-155	Trivet	75.00	50.00	50.00
Peo-160	Vase, bud	95.00	60.00	50.00

QUEEN ANNE

The pattern number is 2995 and it was introduced at the 1936 British Industries Fair. The alternate colourway is **Victorian** 3164 with a black background. Neither have proved to be popular with chintz collectors.

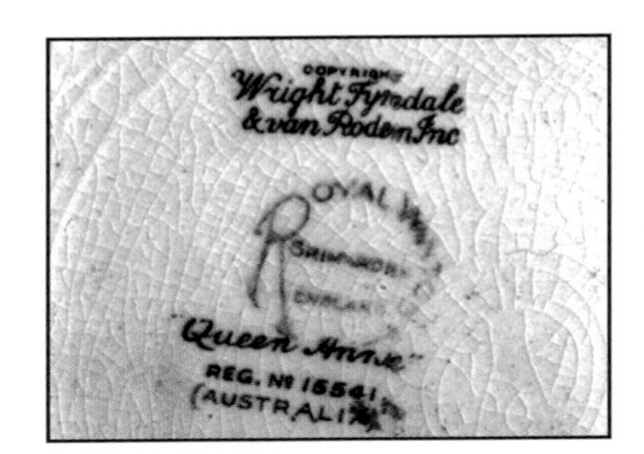

Cat. No.	Shape	U.S. $	Can. $	U.K. £
QA-04	Bonbon dish	35.00	20.00	30.00
QA-09	Bowl, 5″	30.00	20.00	25.00
QA-14	Bowl, 8″ soup	45.00	35.00	40.00
QA-23	Breakfast set	500.00	275.00	375.00
QA-28	Butter dish	115.00	60.00	75.00
QA-30	Butter pat	35.00	20.00	25.00
QA-35	Cake plate, open handles	135.00	75.00	100.00
QA-36	Cake plate, tab handles	112.00	65.00	90.00
QA-37	Cake plate, 8″ sq. pedestal	135.00	85.00	100.00
QA-40	Cake stand, 2 tier	135.00	80.00	100.00
QA-45	Canoe-shaped dish	135.00	95.00	100.00
QA-50	Cheese keep	135.00	80.00	100.00
QA-52	Coaster	30.00	20.00	25.00
QA-55	Coffee pot	400.00	175.00	325.00
QA-60	Compote, footed	90.00	50.00	65.00
QA-65	Condiment set on tray	120.00	65.00	85.00
QA-70	Cream and sugar	70.00	45.00	50.00
QA-71	Cream and sugar on tray	120.00	95.00	85.00
QA-75	Demi-tasse	45.00	35.00	35.00
QA-77	Egg cup, footed	45.00	40.00	35.00
QA-80	Hot water jug	180.00	95.00	150.00
QA-85	Jam pot with liner	90.00	60.00	65.00
QA-90	Jug, 4″	150.00	65.00	100.00
QA-91	Jug, 4 1/2″	160.00	75.00	125.00
QA-92	Jug, 5″	180.00	85.00	150.00

Cat. No.	Shape	U.S. $	Can. $	U.K. £
QA-97	Nut dish	35.00	20.00	25.00
QA-201	Plate, 4″ sq.	30.00	20.00	25.00
QA-202	Plate, 5″ sq.	35.00	25.00	30.00
QA-203	Plate, 6″ sq.	40.00	30.00	35.00
QA-204	Plate, 7″ sq.	45.00	35.00	40.00
QA-205	Plate, 8″ sq.	65.00	40.00	65.00
QA-206	Plate, 9″ sq.	75.00	45.00	65.00
QA-207	Plate, 10″ sq.	95.00	65.00	75.00
QA-112	Relish dish, small	90.00	65.00	65.00
QA-115	Salad bowl, chrome rim	80.00	60.00	65.00
QA-117	Salt and pepper	45.00	35.00	40.00
QA-118	Salt and pepper on tray	105.00	75.00	90.00
QA-120	Sandwich tray, 10″ x 6″	70.00	40.00	50.00
QA-121	Sandwich tray, 12″ x 7″	80.00	50.00	60.00
QA-125	Sauce boat and liner	90.00	65.00	75.00
QA-130	Teacup and saucer	50.00	30.00	35.00
QA-135	Teapot, 2 cup	180.00	125.00	150.00
QA-136	Teapot, 4 cup	270.00	175.00	200.00
QA-137	Teapot, 6 cup	360.00	225.00	275.00
QA-140	Teapot, stacking	450.00	275.00	350.00
QA-145	Tennis set	50.00	35.00	50.00
QA-150	Toast rack, 4 slice	150.00	95.00	125.00
QA-151	Toast rack, 2 slice	115.00	75.00	85.00
QA-155	Trivet	65.00	30.00	50.00
QA-160	Vase, bud	65.00	40.00	50.00

QUILT

The pattern number is 4515. This all-over pattern was clearly intended to be a companion pattern to **Tartans** 4514 . Both were intended to appeal to the non-chintz customer and were produced late in the 1930s when chintz was so longer new and buyers were looking for something fresh.

Cat. No.	Shape	U.S. $	Can. $	U.K. £
Q-04	Bonbon dish	40.00	30.00	35.00
Q-09	Bowl, 5"	35.00	30.00	30.00
Q-14	Bowl, 8" soup	45.00	45.00	40.00
Q-23	Breakfast set	575.00	450.00	420.00
Q-28	Butter dish	115.00	95.00	80.00
Q-30	Butter pat	35.00	20.00	25.00
Q-35	Cake plate, open handles	135.00	95.00	115.00
Q-36	Cake plate, tab handles	115.00	85.00	95.00
Q-37	Cake plate, 8" sq. pedestal	135.00	105.00	105.00
Q-40	Cake stand, 2 tier	135.00	95.00	105.00
Q-45	Canoe-shaped dish	135.00	125.00	105.00
Q-50	Cheese keep	135.00	115.00	105.00
Q-52	Coaster	30.00	25.00	25.00
Q-55	Coffee pot	425.00	300.00	340.00
Q-60	Compote, footed	90.00	75.00	65.00
Q-65	Condiment set on tray	135.00	105.00	105.00
Q-70	Cream and sugar	70.00	60.00	50.00
Q-71	Cream and sugar on tray	120.00	115.00	90.00
Q-75	Demi-tasse	50.00	35.00	40.00
Q-77	Egg cup, footed	45.00	40.00	35.00
Q-80	Hot water jug	180.00	195.00	160.00
Q-85	Jam pot with liner	100.00	85.00	70.00
Q-90	Jug, 4"	160.00	150.00	130.00
Q-91	Jug, 4 1/2"	180.00	165.00	145.00
Q-92	Jug, 5"	200.00	175.00	160.00
Q-97	Nut dish	35.00	20.00	25.00
Q-201	Plate, 4" sq.	30.00	20.00	20.00
Q-202	Plate, 5" sq.	35.00	25.00	25.00
Q-203	Plate, 6" sq.	40.00	30.00	30.00
Q-204	Plate, 7" sq.	45.00	35.00	35.00
Q-205	Plate, 8" sq.	60.00	40.00	45.00
Q-206	Plate, 9" sq.	75.00	60.00	55.00
Q-207	Plate, 10" sq.	105.00	75.00	60.00
Q-112	Relish dish, small	115.00	95.00	75.00
Q-115	Salad bowl, chrome rim	90.00	80.00	75.00
Q-117	Salt and pepper	60.00	45.00	45.00
Q-118	Salt and pepper on tray	115.00	95.00	85.00
Q-120	Sandwich tray, 10" x 6"	70.00	60.00	50.00
Q-121	Sandwich tray, 12" x 7"	90.00	70.00	65.00
Q-125	Sauce boat and liner	115.00	75.00	75.00
Q-130	Teacup and saucer	50.00	45.00	40.00
Q-135	Teapot, 2 cup	275.00	200.00	200.00
Q-136	Teapot, 4 cup	300.00	250.00	250.00
Q-137	Teapot, 6 cup	400.00	300.00	300.00
Q-140	Teapot, stacking	450.00	450.00	300.00
Q-145	Tennis set	65.00	50.00	50.00
Q-150	Toast rack, 4 slice	150.00	125.00	125.00
Q-151	Toast rack, 2 slice	115.00	105.00	100.00
Q-155	Trivet	65.00	45.00	50.00
Q-160	Vase, bud	75.00	60.00	50.00

RICHMOND

The pattern number is 4249, and the pattern was registered in Canada in 1938.

Cat. No.	Shape	U.S. $	Can. $	U.K. £
Ri-04	Bonbon dish	50.00	50.00	35.00
Ri-09	Bowl, 5″	40.00	35.00	30.00
Ri-14	Bowl, 8″ soup	65.00	60.00	50.00
Ri-23	Breakfast set	850.00	700.00	525.00
Ri-28	Butter dish	150.00	125.00	95.00
Ri-30	Butter pat	40.00	35.00	30.00
Ri-35	Cake plate, open handles	175.00	150.00	135.00
Ri-36	Cake plate, tab handles	150.00	140.00	110.00
Ri-37	Cake plate, 8″ sq. pedestal	185.00	160.00	135.00
Ri-40	Cake stand, 2 tier	150.00	145.00	110.00
Ri-45	Canoe-shaped dish	200.00	195.00	165.00
Ri-50	Cheese keep	185.00	175.00	135.00
Ri-52	Coaster	35.00	35.00	25.00
Ri-55	Coffee pot	625.00	500.00	500.00
Ri-60	Compote, footed	125.00	135.00	80.00
Ri-65	Condiment set on tray	165.00	150.00	105.00
Ri-70	Cream and sugar	100.00	95.00	70.00
Ri-71	Cream and sugar on tray	175.00	155.00	135.00
Ri-75	Demi-tasse	65.00	55.00	50.00
Ri-77	Egg cup, footed	55.00	60.00	50.00
Ri-80	Hot water jug	275.00	275.00	195.00
Ri-85	Jam pot with liner	125.00	110.00	80.00
Ri-90	Jug, 4″	200.00	200.00	145.00
Ri-91	Jug, 4 1/2″	225.00	225.00	165.00
Ri-92	Jug, 5″	250.00	250.00	175.00
Ri-97	Nut dish	40.00	35.00	30.00
Ri-201	Plate, 4″ sq.	50.00	35.00	30.00
Ri-202	Plate, 5″ sq.	55.00	40.00	35.00
Ri-203	Plate, 6″ sq.	60.00	45.00	40.00
Ri-204	Plate, 7″ sq.	75.00	50.00	45.00
Ri-205	Plate, 8″ sq.	95.00	65.00	55.00
Ri-206	Plate, 9″ sq.	105.00	75.00	65.00
Ri-207	Plate, 10″ sq.	125.00	95.00	75.00
Ri-112	Relish dish, small	125.00	135.00	80.00
Ri-115	Salad bowl, chrome rim	100.00	95.00	75.00
Ri-117	Salt and pepper	75.00	65.00	55.00
Ri-118	Salt and pepper on tray	135.00	115.00	95.00
Ri-120	Sandwich tray, 10″ x 6″	100.00	95.00	70.00
Ri-121	Sandwich tray, 12″ x 7″	100.00	115.00	80.00
Ri-125	Sauce boat and liner	125.00	125.00	80.00
Ri-130	Teacup and saucer	65.00	60.00	50.00
Ri-135	Teapot, 2 cup	275.00	275.00	250.00
Ri-136	Teapot, 4 cup	375.00	350.00	300.00
Ri-137	Teapot, 6 cup	475.00	400.00	375.00
Ri-140	Teapot, stacking	625.00	575.00	475.00
Ri-145	Tennis set	85.00	75.00	65.00
Ri-150	Toast rack, 4 slice	200.00	185.00	165.00
Ri-151	Toast rack, 2 slice	150.00	135.00	125.00
Ri-155	Trivet	85.00	75.00	65.00
Ri-160	Vase, bud	85.00	95.00	75.00

ROSE DU BARRY

This pattern has a **Rose Du Barry** backstamp in North America, but in Australia the backstamp is **Chelsea Rose**. Shelley called this pattern **Briar Rose** and James Kent also used the same litho and the backstamp is James Kent **Chelsea Rose**. Most of the Winton pieces found in North America have "Henry Morgan & Co. Ltd." as well as the pattern name in the backstamp. This may have been an exclusive name for Morgan's. In 1938 a **Rose Du Barry** breakfast set was advertised in a Montreal newspaper by Morgan's for sale at $2.50.

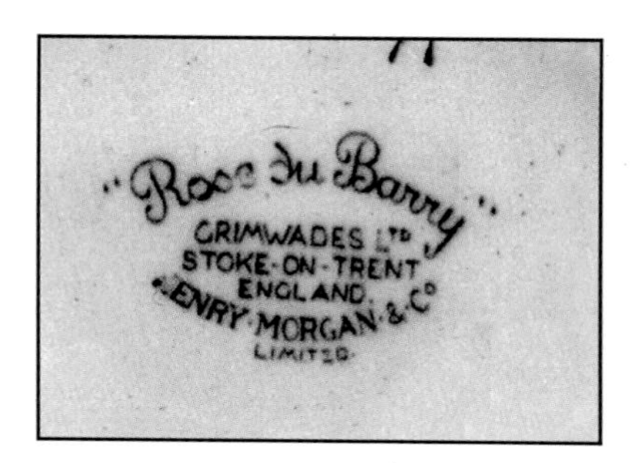

Cat. No.	Shape	U.S. $	Can. $	U.K. £
RD-04	Bonbon dish	45.00	25.00	35.00
RD-09	Bowl, 5"	40.00	25.00	30.00
RD-14	Bowl, 8" soup	75.00	40.00	50.00
RD-23	Breakfast set	750.00	500.00	450.00
RD-28	Butter dish	135.00	95.00	85.00
RD-30	Butter pat	40.00	25.00	30.00
RD-35	Cake plate, open handles	135.00	95.00	85.00
RD-36	Cake plate, tab handles	125.00	85.00	75.00
RD-37	Cake plate, 8" sq. pedestal	150.00	105.00	100.00
RD-40	Cake stand, 2 tier	150.00	100.00	100.00
RD-45	Canoe-shaped dish	200.00	125.00	125.00
RD-50	Cheese keep	175.00	110.00	125.00
RD-52	Coaster	35.00	25.00	25.00
RD-55	Coffee pot	525.00	325.00	375.00
RD-60	Compote, footed	100.00	75.00	65.00
RD-65	Condiment set on tray	150.00	100.00	100.00
RD-70	Cream and sugar	85.00	60.00	60.00
RD-71	Cream and sugar on tray	150.00	105.00	100.00
RD-75	Demi-tasse	60.00	35.00	45.00
RD-77	Egg cup, footed	75.00	40.00	35.00
RD-80	Hot water jug	225.00	195.00	150.00
RD-85	Jam pot with liner	125.00	85.00	75.00
RD-90	Jug, 4"	175.00	140.00	125.00
RD-91	Jug, 4 1/2"	200.00	155.00	135.00
RD-92	Jug, 5"	225.00	165.00	150.00

Cat. No.	Shape	U.S. $	Can. $	U.K. £
RD-97	Nut dish	40.00	20.00	30.00
RD-201	Plate, 4" sq.	35.00	20.00	25.00
RD-202	Plate, 5" sq.	40.00	25.00	30.00
RD-203	Plate, 6" sq.	45.00	30.00	35.00
RD-204	Plate, 7" sq.	50.00	35.00	35.00
RD-205	Plate, 8" sq.	85.00	45.00	60.00
RD-206	Plate, 9" sq.	100.00	60.00	65.00
RD-207	Plate, 10" sq.	125.00	75.00	75.00
RD-112	Relish dish, small	125.00	95.00	75.00
RD-115	Salad bowl, chrome rim	100.00	85.00	65.00
RD-117	Salt and pepper	65.00	45.00	45.00
RD-118	Salt and pepper on tray	115.00	95.00	100.00
RD-120	Sandwich tray, 10" x 6"	75.00	55.00	60.00
RD-121	Sandwich tray, 12" x 7"	95.00	65.00	65.00
RD-125	Sauce boat and liner	125.00	75.00	75.00
RD-130	Teacup and saucer	60.00	45.00	45.00
RD-135	Teapot, 2 cup	325.00	200.00	175.00
RD-136	Teapot, 4 cup	375.00	250.00	250.00
RD-137	Teapot, 6 cup	450.00	300.00	325.00
RD-140	Teapot, stacking	600.00	450.00	425.00
RD-145	Tennis set	80.00	50.00	50.00
RD-150	Toast rack, 4 slice	175.00	125.00	125.00
RD-151	Toast rack, 2 slice	135.00	95.00	85.00
RD-155	Trivet	75.00	45.00	50.00
RD-160	Vase, bud	95.00	60.00	60.00

ROYALTY

The pattern number is 3079. The pattern was introduced at the 1936 British Industries Fair. The alternate colourway is **Majestic** 3311 with a black background. This pattern is very popular with chintz collectors around the world.

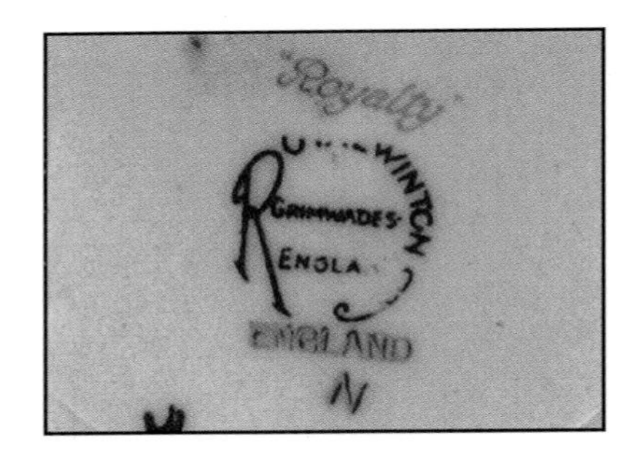

Cat. No.	Shape	U.S. $	Can. $	U.K. £
Roy-04	Bonbon dish	80.00	75.00	65.00
Roy-09	Bowl, 5"	50.00	50.00	55.00
Roy-14	Bowl, 8" soup	100.00	80.00	85.00
Roy-23	Breakfast set	1,300.00	900.00	975.00
Roy-28	Butter dish	225.00	195.00	205.00
Roy-30	Butter pat	75.00	65.00	65.00
Roy-35	Cake plate, open handles	225.00	195.00	205.00
Roy-36	Cake plate, tab handles	200.00	175.00	195.00
Roy-37	Cake plate, 8" sq. pedestal	250.00	205.00	225.00
Roy-40	Cake stand, 2 tier	250.00	200.00	225.00
Roy-45	Canoe-shaped dish	350.00	325.00	300.00
Roy-50	Cheese keep	300.00	225.00	275.00
Roy-52	Coaster	60.00	50.00	55.00
Roy-55	Coffee pot	1,200.00	800.00	800.00
Roy-60	Compote, footed	200.00	175.00	150.00
Roy-65	Condiment set on tray	275.00	225.00	250.00
Roy-70	Cream and sugar	150.00	135.00	125.00
Roy-71	Cream and sugar on tray	275.00	215.00	250.00
Roy-75	Demi-tasse	100.00	95.00	80.00
Roy-77	Egg cup, footed	100.00	90.00	80.00
Roy-80	Hot water jug	550.00	400.00	350.00
Roy-85	Jam pot with liner	225.00	175.00	165.00
Roy-90	Jug, 4"	450.00	325.00	325.00
Roy-91	Jug, 4 1/2"	500.00	350.00	350.00
Roy-92	Jug, 5"	550.00	375.00	375.00

Cat. No.	Shape	U.S. $	Can. $	U.K. £
Roy-97	Nut dish	70.00	65.00	60.00
Roy-201	Plate, 4" sq.	65.00	50.00	55.00
Roy-202	Plate, 5" sq.	75.00	60.00	65.00
Roy-203	Plate, 6" sq.	100.00	70.00	75.00
Roy-204	Plate, 7" sq.	135.00	85.00	95.00
Roy-205	Plate, 8" sq.	175.00	95.00	115.00
Roy-206	Plate, 9" sq.	175.00	115.00	135.00
Roy-207	Plate, 10" sq.	200.00	135.00	150.00
Roy-112	Relish dish, small	225.00	195.00	175.00
Roy-115	Salad bowl, chrome rim	100.00	150.00	85.00
Roy-117	Salt and pepper	100.00	105.00	75.00
Roy-118	Salt and pepper on tray	200.00	160.00	165.00
Roy-120	Sandwich tray, 10" x 6"	150.00	125.00	125.00
Roy-121	Sandwich tray, 12" x 7"	175.00	150.00	145.00
Roy-125	Sauce boat and liner	200.00	175.00	165.00
Roy-130	Teacup and saucer	100.00	110.00	75.00
Roy-135	Teapot, 2 cup	550.00	400.00	375.00
Roy-136	Teapot, 4 cup	800.00	550.00	525.00
Roy-137	Teapot, 6 cup	950.00	650.00	600.00
Roy-140	Teapot, stacking	1,200.00	800.00	800.00
Roy-145	Tennis set	150.00	115.00	125.00
Roy-150	Toast rack, 4 slice	300.00	225.00	245.00
Roy-151	Toast rack, 2 slice	225.00	185.00	195.00
Roy-155	Trivet	150.00	110.00	125.00
Roy-160	Vase, bud	175.00	135.00	125.00

RUTLAND

The pattern number is 1470 with green trim, and the pattern was probably introduced in 1933.

Cat. No.	Shape	U.S. $	Can. $	U.K. £
Ru-04	Bonbon dish	50.00	30.00	40.00
Ru-09	Bowl, 5″	40.00	30.00	35.00
Ru-14	Bowl, 8″ soup	65.00	45.00	50.00
Ru-23	Breakfast set	850.00	500.00	525.00
Ru-28	Butter dish	150.00	95.00	120.00
Ru-30	Butter pat	40.00	25.00	35.00
Ru-35	Cake plate, open handles	175.00	95.00	145.00
Ru-36	Cake plate, tab handles	150.00	85.00	125.00
Ru-37	Cake plate, 8″ sq. pedestal	175.00	115.00	145.00
Ru-40	Cake stand, 2 tier	150.00	105.00	125.00
Ru-45	Canoe-shaped dish	200.00	125.00	175.00
Ru-50	Cheese keep	175.00	115.00	145.00
Ru-52	Coaster	35.00	25.00	30.00
Ru-55	Coffee pot	575.00	350.00	475.00
Ru-60	Compote, footed	120.00	85.00	85.00
Ru-65	Condiment set on tray	165.00	105.00	125.00
Ru-70	Cream and sugar	100.00	65.00	75.00
Ru-71	Cream and sugar on tray	175.00	115.00	145.00
Ru-75	Demi-tasse	65.00	40.00	50.00
Ru-77	Egg cup, footed	75.00	45.00	50.00
Ru-80	Hot water jug	250.00	195.00	200.00
Ru-85	Jam pot with liner	125.00	95.00	80.00
Ru-90	Jug, 4″	200.00	140.00	165.00
Ru-91	Jug, 4 1/2″	225.00	155.00	195.00
Ru-92	Jug, 5″	250.00	165.00	215.00
Ru-97	Nut dish	40.00	25.00	30.00
Ru-201	Plate, 4″ sq.	45.00	25.00	30.00
Ru-202	Plate, 5″ sq.	50.00	30.00	35.00
Ru-203	Plate, 6″ sq.	60.00	35.00	40.00
Ru-204	Plate, 7″ sq.	65.00	40.00	45.00
Ru-205	Plate, 8″ sq.	75.00	45.00	50.00
Ru-206	Plate, 9″ sq.	95.00	65.00	65.00
Ru-207	Plate, 10″ sq.	125.00	75.00	75.00
Ru-112	Relish dish, small	135.00	95.00	120.00
Ru-115	Salad bowl, chrome rim	100.00	85.00	75.00
Ru-117	Salt and pepper	75.00	50.00	60.00
Ru-118	Salt and pepper on tray	135.00	105.00	110.00
Ru-120	Sandwich tray, 10″ x 6″	100.00	65.00	70.00
Ru-121	Sandwich tray, 12″ x 7″	125.00	75.00	85.00
Ru-125	Sauce boat and liner	125.00	85.00	85.00
Ru-130	Teacup and saucer	85.00	45.00	55.00
Ru-135	Teapot, 2 cup	300.00	175.00	250.00
Ru-136	Teapot, 4 cup	400.00	250.00	300.00
Ru-137	Teapot, 6 cup	500.00	300.00	375.00
Ru-140	Teapot, stacking	675.00	450.00	525.00
Ru-145	Tennis set	75.00	50.00	70.00
Ru-150	Toast rack, 4 slice	200.00	120.00	165.00
Ru-151	Toast rack, 2 slice	150.00	95.00	125.00
Ru-155	Trivet	75.00	50.00	70.00
Ru-160	Vase, bud	100.00	65.00	75.00

SHREWSBURY

The pattern number is 418. This post-war pattern was one of the Royal Winton patterns produced by Howard Potteries after the takeover in 1964.

Cat. No.	Shape	U.S.$	Can. $	U.K. £
Sh-04	Bonbon dish	50.00	50.00	40.00
Sh-09	Bowl, 5″	45.00	35.00	40.00
Sh-14	Bowl, 8″ soup	75.00	60.00	60.00
Sh-23	Breakfast set	1,100.00	700.00	650.00
Sh-28	Butter dish	150.00	125.00	120.00
Sh-30	Butter pat	45.00	35.00	45.00
Sh-35	Cake plate, open handles	150.00	145.00	125.00
Sh-36	Cake plate, tab handles	135.00	135.00	110.00
Sh-37	Cake plate, 8″ sq. pedestal	175.00	155.00	125.00
Sh-40	Cake stand, 2 tier	175.00	150.00	125.00
Sh-45	Canoe-shaped dish	235.00	195.00	195.00
Sh-50	Cheese keep	200.00	175.00	195.00
Sh-52	Coaster	40.00	35.00	35.00
Sh-55	Coffee pot	900.00	500.00	550.00
Sh-60	Compote, footed	135.00	125.00	85.00
Sh-65	Condiment set on tray	200.00	150.00	145.00
Sh-70	Cream and sugar	100.00	95.00	75.00
Sh-71	Cream and sugar on tray	200.00	145.00	145.00
Sh-75	Demi-tasse	75.00	55.00	60.00
Sh-77	Egg cup, footed	95.00	60.00	60.00
Sh-80	Hot water jug	400.00	275.00	225.00
Sh-85	Jam pot with liner	150.00	110.00	115.00
Sh-90	Jug, 4″	325.00	200.00	175.00
Sh-91	Jug, 4 1/2″	375.00	225.00	200.00
Sh-92	Jug, 5″	400.00	250.00	225.00

Cat. No.	Shape	U.S. $	Can. $	U.K. £
Sh-97	Nut dish	45.00	35.00	40.00
Sh-201	Plate, 4″ sq.	50.00	35.00	40.00
Sh-202	Plate, 5″ sq.	55.00	40.00	45.00
Sh-203	Plate, 6″ sq.	60.00	45.00	50.00
Sh-204	Plate, 7″ sq.	75.00	50.00	65.00
Sh-205	Plate, 8″ sq.	100.00	65.00	75.00
Sh-206	Plate, 9″ sq.	115.00	85.00	95.00
Sh-207	Plate, 10″ sq.	135.00	105.00	115.00
Sh-112	Relish dish, small	150.00	145.00	125.00
Sh-115	Salad bowl, chrome rim	125.00	115.00	95.00
Sh-117	Salt and pepper	75.00	65.00	60.00
Sh-118	Salt and pepper on tray	150.00	115.00	115.00
Sh-120	Sandwich tray, 10″ x 6″	100.00	95.00	75.00
Sh-121	Sandwich tray, 12″ x 7″	125.00	115.00	85.00
Sh-125	Sauce boat and liner	150.00	125.00	85.00
Sh-130	Teacup and saucer	95.00	60.00	60.00
Sh-135	Teapot, 2 cup	450.00	275.00	250.00
Sh-136	Teapot, 4 cup	650.00	350.00	375.00
Sh-137	Teapot, 6 cup	850.00	400.00	450.00
Sh-140	Teapot, stacking	950.00	575.00	550.00
Sh-145	Tennis set	100.00	75.00	75.00
Sh-150	Toast rack, 4 slice	200.00	195.00	175.00
Sh-151	Toast rack, 2 slice	135.00	145.00	135.00
Sh-155	Trivet	90.00	75.00	75.00
Sh-160	Vase, bud	125.00	100.00	75.00

SOMERSET

Somerset was probably introduced late in 1932. This pattern came with both a gold trim (1420) and a blue trim (1611). This was one of the three new patterns — along with **Summertime** and **Floral Feast** — advertised by Wright, Tyndale & van Roden, Inc. of Philadelphia in the *Crockery and Glass Journal* of May 1933. The patterns were backstamped copyright "Wright, Tyndal & van Roden" in an attempt to discourage American companies from pattern theft. "**Somerset** boasts of varied colored delphiniums — blue, rose and yellow — in a well arranged pattern with the green leaves giving cool relief."

Cat. No.	Shape	U.S. $	Can. $	U.K. £
So-04	Bonbon dish	85.00	75.00	60.00
So-09	Bowl, 5"	55.00	50.00	50.00
So-14	Bowl, 8" soup	95.00	80.00	70.00
So-23	Breakfast set	1,300.00	900.00	800.00
So-28	Butter dish	245.00	195.00	175.00
So-30	Butter pat	75.00	65.00	50.00
So-35	Cake plate, open handles	245.00	195.00	175.00
So-36	Cake plate, tab handles	220.00	175.00	160.00
So-37	Cake plate, 8" sq. pedestal	245.00	205.00	175.00
So-40	Cake stand, 2 tier	245.00	200.00	175.00
So-45	Canoe-shaped dish	395.00	325.00	275.00
So-50	Cheese keep	325.00	225.00	250.00
So-52	Coaster	60.00	50.00	45.00
So-55	Coffee pot	1,200.00	800.00	750.00
So-60	Compote, footed	195.00	175.00	145.00
So-65	Condiment set on tray	275.00	225.00	215.00
So-70	Cream and sugar	165.00	135.00	120.00
So-71	Cream and sugar on tray	275.00	200.00	195.00
So-75	Demi-tasse	110.00	95.00	75.00
So-77	Egg cup, footed	100.00	90.00	70.00
So-80	Hot water jug	575.00	400.00	300.00
So-85	Jam pot with liner	220.00	175.00	125.00
So-90	Jug, 4"	450.00	325.00	275.00
So-91	Jug, 4 1/2"	500.00	350.00	300.00
So-92	Jug, 5"	550.00	375.00	325.00
So-97	Nut dish	75.00	65.00	50.00
So-201	Plate, 4" sq.	55.00	50.00	50.00
So-202	Plate, 5" sq.	65.00	60.00	50.00
So-203	Plate, 6" sq.	75.00	70.00	60.00
So-204	Plate, 7" sq.	110.00	85.00	80.00
So-205	Plate, 8" sq.	145.00	95.00	95.00
So-206	Plate, 9" sq.	165.00	110.00	125.00
So-207	Plate, 10" sq.	175.00	125.00	150.00
So-112	Relish dish, small	220.00	195.00	175.00
So-115	Salad bowl, chrome rim	195.00	150.00	150.00
So-117	Salt and pepper	110.00	105.00	75.00
So-118	Salt and pepper on tray	195.00	150.00	145.00
So-120	Sandwich tray, 10" x 6"	165.00	135.00	125.00
So-121	Sandwich tray, 12" x 7"	195.00	165.00	145.00
So-125	Sauce boat and liner	195.00	175.00	120.00
So-169	Sugar Shaker		VERY RARE	
So-130	Teacup and saucer	125.00	110.00	75.00
So-135	Teapot, 2 cup	550.00	400.00	350.00
So-136	Teapot, 4 cup	800.00	550.00	500.00
So-137	Teapot, 6 cup	1,000.00	650.00	600.00
So-140	Teapot, stacking	1,200.00	850.00	700.00
So-145	Tennis set	125.00	115.00	85.00
So-150	Toast rack, 4 slice	300.00	225.00	215.00
So-151	Toast rack, 2 slice	220.00	175.00	185.00
So-155	Trivet	135.00	110.00	85.00
So-160	Vase, bud	175.00	135.00	105.00

SPRING

The pattern number is 2506, and it was introduced some months after the alternate colourways **Hazel** 2208 and **Welbeck** 2204. This pattern is difficult to find in North America. This pattern was copied by the Japanese.

Cat. No.	Shape	U.S. $	Can. $	U.K. £
Sp-04	Bonbon dish	85.00	75.00	60.00
Sp-09	Bowl, 5"	55.00	50.00	45.00
Sp-14	Bowl, 8" soup	95.00	80.00	70.00
Sp-23	Breakfast set	1,300.00	900.00	800.00
Sp-28	Butter dish	245.00	195.00	175.00
Sp-30	Butter pat	75.00	65.00	55.00
Sp-35	Cake plate, open handles	245.00	195.00	175.00
Sp-36	Cake plate, tab handles	220.00	185.00	165.00
Sp-37	Cake plate, 8" sq. pedestal	245.00	205.00	175.00
Sp-40	Cake stand, 2 tier	245.00	200.00	175.00
Sp-45	Canoe-shaped dish	395.00	325.00	275.00
Sp-50	Cheese keep	325.00	225.00	250.00
Sp-52	Coaster	60.00	50.00	45.00
Sp-55	Coffee pot	1,200.00	800.00	700.00
Sp-60	Compote, footed	195.00	175.00	145.00
Sp-65	Condiment set on tray	275.00	225.00	215.00
Sp-70	Cream and sugar	165.00	145.00	120.00
Sp-71	Cream and sugar on tray	275.00	215.00	225.00
Sp-75	Demi-tasse	110.00	95.00	75.00
Sp-77	Egg cup, footed	100.00	90.00	70.00
Sp-80	Hot water jug	575.00	400.00	300.00
Sp-85	Jam pot with liner	220.00	175.00	135.00
Sp-90	Jug, 4"	450.00	325.00	250.00
Sp-91	Jug, 4 1/2"	500.00	350.00	300.00
Sp-92	Jug, 5"	550.00	375.00	325.00

Cat. No.	Shape	U.S. $	Can. $	U.K. £
Sp-97	Nut dish	75.00	65.00	50.00
Sp-201	Plate, 4" sq.	55.00	50.00	50.00
Sp-202	Plate, 5" sq.	65.00	60.00	55.00
Sp-203	Plate, 6" sq.	75.00	70.00	60.00
Sp-204	Plate, 7" sq.	110.00	85.00	75.00
Sp-205	Plate, 8" sq.	145.00	95.00	85.00
Sp-206	Plate, 9" sq.	165.00	110.00	115.00
Sp-207	Plate, 10" sq.	175.00	125.00	135.00
Sp-112	Relish dish, small	220.00	195.00	175.00
Sp-115	Salad bowl, chrome rim	195.00	165.00	150.00
Sp-117	Salt and pepper	110.00	105.00	75.00
Sp-118	Salt and pepper on tray	195.00	165.00	145.00
Sp-120	Sandwich tray, 10" x 6"	165.00	145.00	120.00
Sp-121	Sandwich tray, 12" x 7"	195.00	165.00	145.00
Sp-125	Sauce boat and liner	195.00	175.00	120.00
Sp-130	Teacup and saucer	125.00	110.00	85.00
Sp-135	Teapot, 2 cup	550.00	400.00	350.00
Sp-136	Teapot, 4 cup	800.00	550.00	500.00
Sp-137	Teapot, 6 cup	1,000.00	650.00	600.00
Sp-140	Teapot, stacking	1,200.00	850.00	700.00
Sp-145	Tennis set	125.00	115.00	85.00
Sp-150	Toast rack, 4 slice	300.00	225.00	215.00
Sp-151	Toast rack, 2 slice	220.00	185.00	185.00
Sp-155	Trivet	135.00	115.00	85.00
Sp-160	Vase, bud	175.00	135.00	85.00

SPRING GLORY

The pattern number is 402, and it is one of the series of 1950s large-flower open chintz patterns. The pattern usually comes with a black background and occasionally burgundy. The black background was advertised in Canada in March 1952 as available on all tableware except dinnerware pieces. These large patterns are not very popular in North America but they are rare in Australia and therefore of interest to collectors there.

Cat. No.	Shape	U.S. $	Can. $	U.K. £
SG-04	Bonbon dish	45.00	25.00	40.00
SG-09	Bowl, 5″	40.00	25.00	35.00
SG-14	Bowl, 8″ soup	75.00	45.00	60.00
SG-23	Breakfast set	850.00	450.00	525.00
SG-28	Butter dish	135.00	95.00	100.00
SG-30	Butter pat	45.00	25.00	40.00
SG-35	Cake plate, open handles	135.00	95.00	100.00
SG-36	Cake plate, tab handles	125.00	85.00	95.00
SG-37	Cake plate, 8″ sq. pedestal	140.00	110.00	120.00
SG-40	Cake stand, 2 tier	140.00	100.00	120.00
SG-45	Canoe-shaped dish	200.00	135.00	145.00
SG-50	Cheese keep	175.00	115.00	145.00
SG-52	Coaster	40.00	30.00	30.00
SG-55	Coffee pot	550.00	325.00	425.00
SG-60	Compote, footed	100.00	75.00	75.00
SG-65	Condiment set on tray	150.00	105.00	120.00
SG-70	Cream and sugar	85.00	60.00	70.00
SG-71	Cream and sugar on tray	150.00	100.00	120.00
SG-75	Demi-tasse	60.00	35.00	55.00
SG-77	Egg cup, footed	50.00	30.00	45.00
SG-80	Hot water jug	245.00	195.00	195.00
SG-85	Jam pot with liner	125.00	95.00	85.00
SG-90	Jug, 4″	225.00	140.00	150.00
SG-91	Jug, 4 1/2″	250.00	155.00	175.00
SG-92	Jug, 5″	275.00	165.00	200.00
SG-97	Nut dish	45.00	25.00	35.00
SG-201	Plate, 4″ sq.	35.00	25.00	30.00
SG-202	Plate, 5″ sq.	40.00	30.00	35.00
SG-203	Plate, 6″ sq.	45.00	35.00	40.00
SG-204	Plate, 7″ sq.	50.00	40.00	45.00
SG-205	Plate, 8″ sq.	85.00	45.00	55.00
SG-206	Plate, 9″ sq.	100.00	65.00	75.00
SG-207	Plate, 10″ sq.	125.00	75.00	85.00
SG-112	Relish dish, small	125.00	95.00	85.00
SG-115	Salad bowl, chrome rim	100.00	85.00	75.00
SG-117	Salt and pepper	75.00	45.00	55.00
SG-118	Salt and pepper on tray	150.00	95.00	110.00
SG-120	Sandwich tray, 10″ x 6″	85.00	65.00	70.00
SG-121	Sandwich tray, 12″ x 7″	100.00	75.00	85.00
SG-125	Sauce boat and liner	125.00	85.00	85.00
SG-130	Teacup and saucer	70.00	45.00	55.00
SG-135	Teapot, 2 cup	300.00	200.00	215.00
SG-136	Teapot, 4 cup	400.00	275.00	300.00
SG-137	Teapot, 6 cup	500.00	300.00	375.00
SG-140	Teapot, stacking	650.00	450.00	500.00
SG-145	Tennis set	80.00	50.00	60.00
SG-150	Toast rack, 4 slice	175.00	125.00	150.00
SG-151	Toast rack, 2 slice	125.00	95.00	115.00
SG-155	Trivet	80.00	45.00	60.00
SG-160	Vase, bud	100.00	60.00	70.00

SPRINGTIME

This pattern, number 10017, was introduced in 1932 and was much in demand at the British Industries Fair that year. This pattern is difficult to find in North America.

Cat. No.	Shape	U.S. $	Can. $	U.K. £
Spt-04	Bonbon dish	50.00	50.00	45.00
Spt-09	Bowl, 5″	45.00	35.00	30.00
Spt-14	Bowl, 8″ soup	75.00	60.00	40.00
Spt-23	Breakfast set	850.00	700.00	575.00
Spt-28	Butter dish	150.00	135.00	120.00
Spt-30	Butter pat	45.00	35.00	40.00
Spt-35	Cake plate, open handles	150.00	145.00	125.00
Spt-36	Cake plate, tab handles	135.00	135.00	115.00
Spt-37	Cake plate, 8″ sq. pedestal	150.00	150.00	125.00
Spt-40	Cake stand, 2 tier	150.00	145.00	125.00
Spt-45	Canoe-shaped dish	225.00	195.00	195.00
Spt-50	Cheese keep	200.00	175.00	200.00
Spt-52	Coaster	40.00	35.00	40.00
Spt-55	Coffee pot	575.00	500.00	475.00
Spt-60	Compote, footed	135.00	125.00	85.00
Spt-65	Condiment set on tray	175.00	150.00	145.00
Spt-70	Cream and sugar	100.00	95.00	75.00
Spt-71	Cream and sugar on tray	175.00	150.00	145.00
Spt-75	Demi-tasse	70.00	55.00	55.00
Spt-77	Egg cup, footed	80.00	60.00	50.00
Spt-80	Hot water jug	275.00	275.00	215.00
Spt-85	Jam pot with liner	140.00	115.00	85.00
Spt-90	Jug, 4″	200.00	200.00	175.00
Spt-91	Jug, 4 1/2″	225.00	225.00	200.00
Spt-92	Jug, 5″	250.00	250.00	225.00

Cat. No.	Shape	U.S. $	Can. $	U.K. £
Spt-97	Nut dish	45.00	35.00	35.00
Spt-201	Plate, 4″ sq.	45.00	35.00	35.00
Spt-202	Plate, 5″ sq.	50.00	40.00	40.00
Spt-203	Plate, 6″ sq.	60.00	45.00	45.00
Spt-204	Plate, 7″ sq.	75.00	50.00	55.00
Spt-205	Plate, 8″ sq.	95.00	65.00	65.00
Spt-206	Plate, 9″ sq.	110.00	85.00	85.00
Spt-207	Plate, 10″ sq.	125.00	95.00	100.00
Spt-112	Relish dish, small	150.00	145.00	85.00
Spt-115	Salad bowl, chrome rim	125.00	115.00	85.00
Spt-117	Salt and pepper	75.00	65.00	55.00
Spt-118	Salt and pepper on tray	150.00	115.00	85.00
Spt-120	Sandwich tray, 10″ x 6″	100.00	95.00	85.00
Spt-121	Sandwich tray, 12″ x 7″	125.00	115.00	95.00
Spt-125	Sauce boat and liner	135.00	125.00	90.00
Spt-130	Teacup and saucer	85.00	60.00	55.00
Spt-135	Teapot, 2 cup	300.00	275.00	300.00
Spt-136	Teapot, 4 cup	400.00	350.00	350.00
Spt-137	Teapot, 6 cup	500.00	400.00	425.00
Spt-140	Teapot, stacking	675.00	575.00	475.00
Spt-145	Tennis set	100.00	75.00	70.00
Spt-150	Toast rack, 4 slice	200.00	185.00	175.00
Spt-151	Toast rack, 2 slice	150.00	135.00	145.00
Spt-155	Trivet	95.00	75.00	70.00
Spt-160	Vase, bud	100.00	95.00	75.00

STRATFORD

The pattern number is 493 and it was registered in Canada in 1953. One of the last of the Royal Winton chintz patterns it is very popular in the United States.

Cat. No.	Shape	U.S. $	Can. $	U.K. £
St-04	Bonbon dish	125.00	85.00	85.00
St-09	Bowl, 5″	85.00	60.00	60.00
St-14	Bowl, 8″ soup	125.00	95.00	85.00
St-23	Breakfast set	1,600.00	1,000.00	1050.00
St-28	Butter dish	345.00	225.00	225.00
St-30	Butter pat	95.00	75.00	65.00
St-35	Cake plate, open handles	345.00	250.00	225.00
St-36	Cake plate, tab handles	325.00	225.00	195.00
St-37	Cake plate, 8″ sq. pedestal	345.00	275.00	225.00
St-40	Cake stand, 2 tier	325.00	245.00	225.00
St-45	Canoe-shaped dish	500.00	375.00	350.00
St-50	Cheese keep	425.00	300.00	325.00
St-52	Coaster	95.00	75.00	65.00
St-55	Coffee pot	1,400.00	900.00	975.00
St-60	Compote, footed	275.00	220.00	195.00
St-65	Condiment set on tray	400.00	275.00	275.00
St-70	Cream and sugar	225.00	165.00	165.00
St-71	Cream and sugar on tray	400.00	250.00	295.00
St-75	Demi-tasse	150.00	115.00	95.00
St-77	Egg cup, footed	165.00	110.00	85.00
St-80	Hot water jug	650.00	450.00	425.00
St-85	Jam pot with liner	315.00	200.00	175.00
St-90	Jug, 4″	650.00	350.00	375.00
St-91	Jug, 4 1/2″	750.00	375.00	400.00
St-92	Jug, 5″	850.00	400.00	425.00

Cat. No.	Shape	U.S. $	Can. $	U.K. £
St-97	Nut dish	95.00	75.00	65.00
St-201	Plate, 4″ sq.	90.00	60.00	65.00
St-202	Plate, 5″ sq.	125.00	65.00	75.00
St-203	Plate, 6″ sq.	140.00	75.00	85.00
St-204	Plate, 7″ sq.	160.00	95.00	105.00
St-205	Plate, 8″ sq.	200.00	115.00	125.00
St-206	Plate, 9″ sq.	225.00	125.00	145.00
St-207	Plate, 10″ sq.	250.00	145.00	165.00
St-112	Relish dish, small	310.00	225.00	225.00
St-115	Salad bowl, chrome rim	310.00	195.00	225.00
St-117	Salt and pepper	150.00	125.00	90.00
St-118	Salt and pepper on tray	295.00	195.00	175.00
St-120	Sandwich tray, 10″ x 6″	225.00	150.00	165.00
St-121	Sandwich tray, 12″ x 7″	250.00	175.00	195.00
St-125	Sauce boat and liner	275.00	210.00	195.00
St-130	Teacup and saucer	195.00	125.00	85.00
St-135	Teapot, 2 cup	750.00	500.00	475.00
St-136	Teapot, 4 cup	950.00	650.00	600.00
St-137	Teapot, 6 cup	1,250.00	750.00	800.00
St-140	Teapot, stacking	1,500.00	950.00	950.00
St-145	Tennis set	175.00	135.00	150.00
St-150	Toast rack, 4 slice	375.00	275.00	265.00
St-151	Toast rack, 2 slice	310.00	225.00	210.00
St-155	Trivet	195.00	135.00	135.00
St-160	Vase, bud	225.00	150.00	145.00

SUMMERTIME

The pattern number is 775 for the gold trim and 1612 for the green trim. This pattern was introduced in 1932. This was one of the three new patterns — along with **Somerset** and **Floral Feast** — advertised by Wright, Tyndale & van Roden, Inc. of Philadelphia in the *Crockery and Glass Journal* of May 1933. The alternate colourway is **Bedale** 1703. **Summertime** was perhaps the most popular and most widely produced Winton pattern until production ceased well into the 1960s. Complete dinner services were sold in this pattern and still turn up regularly in North America. Be aware of the difference in the colour of the pre- and post-war transfer.

Cat. No.	Shape	U.S. $	Can. $	U.K. £
Su-04	Bonbon dish	65.00	55.00	45.00
Su-09	Bowl, 5"	50.00	45.00	40.00
Su-14	Bowl, 8" soup	75.00	65.00	50.00
Su-23	Breakfast set	900.00	800.00	625.00
Su-28	Butter dish	190.00	150.00	135.00
Su-30	Butter pat	55.00	40.00	40.00
Su-35	Cake plate, open handles	190.00	165.00	135.00
Su-36	Cake plate, tab handles	175.00	155.00	125.00
Su-37	Cake plate, 8" sq. pedestal	200.00	175.00	150.00
Su-40	Cake stand, 2 tier	200.00	165.00	150.00
Su-	Candlesticks		RARE	
Su-45	Canoe-shaped dish	275.00	225.00	175.00
Su-50	Cheese keep	250.00	195.00	175.00
Su0	Clock		VERY RARE	
Su-52	Coaster	50.00	35.00	35.00
Su-55	Coffee pot	750.00	600.00	525.00
Su-60	Compote, footed	160.00	135.00	115.00
Su-65	Condiment set on tray	225.00	165.00	150.00
Su-70	Cream and sugar	125.00	100.00	75.00
Su-71	Cream and sugar on tray	225.00	150.00	160.00
Su-75	Demi-tasse	85.00	60.00	60.00
Su-77	Egg cup, footed	75.00	65.00	50.00
Su-80	Hot water jug	325.00	275.00	225.00
Su-85	Jam pot with liner	175.00	135.00	125.00
Su-90	Jug, 4"	275.00	225.00	200.00
Su-91	Jug, 4 1/2"	300.00	250.00	200.00
Su-92	Jug, 5"	325.00	275.00	225.00
Su-180	Lamp Base		RARE	
Su-97	Nut dish	50.00	40.00	40.00
Su-201	Plate, 4" sq.	45.00	40.00	35.00
Su-202	Plate, 5" sq.	50.00	45.00	40.00
Su-203	Plate, 6" sq.	65.00	50.00	45.00
Su-204	Plate, 7" sq.	75.00	60.00	60.00
Su-205	Plate, 8" sq.	110.00	75.00	85.00
Su-206	Plate, 9" sq.	135.00	95.00	100.00
Su-207	Plate, 10" sq.	160.00	110.00	115.00
Su-112	Relish dish, small	175.00	150.00	125.00
Su-115	Salad bowl, chrome rim	150.00	125.00	100.00
Su-117	Salt and pepper	100.00	75.00	65.00
Su-118	Salt and pepper on tray	165.00	135.00	115.00
Su-120	Sandwich tray, 10" x 6"	125.00	95.00	75.00
Su-121	Sandwich tray, 12" x 7"	150.00	125.00	100.00
Su-125	Sauce boat and liner	175.00	135.00	125.00
Su-130	Teacup and saucer	85.00	70.00	60.00
Su-135	Teapot, 2 cup	450.00	325.00	325.00
Su-136	Teapot, 4 cup	550.00	400.00	375.00
Su-137	Teapot, 6 cup	650.00	450.00	450.00
Su-140	Teapot, stacking	950.00	625.00	550.00
Su-145	Tennis set	115.00	80.00	75.00
Su-150	Toast rack, 4 slice	275.00	195.00	200.00
Su-151	Toast rack, 2 slice	225.00	145.00	160.00
Su-155	Trivet	115.00	75.00	75.00
Su-160	Vase, bud	150.00	115.00	75.00

SUNSHINE

The pattern number is 4030, and the pattern was probably introduced in 1937. Be aware that this pattern sometimes has deep pink flowers and sometimes a burnt orange colour. These prices are for the deep pink since most chintz collectors do not like orange.

Cat. No.	Shape	U.S. $	Can. $	U.K. £
Sun-04	Bonbon dish	60.00	60.00	45.00
Sun-09	Bowl, 5"	40.00	45.00	30.00
Sun-14	Bowl, 8" soup	60.00	65.00	45.00
Sun-23	Breakfast set	950.00	800.00	550.00
Sun-28	Butter dish	175.00	150.00	125.00
Sun-30	Butter pat	50.00	45.00	35.00
Sun-35	Cake plate, open handles	175.00	175.00	125.00
Sun-36	Cake plate, tab handles	150.00	165.00	115.00
Sun-37	Cake plate, 8" sq. pedestal	175.00	195.00	125.00
Sun-40	Cake stand, 2 tier	175.00	185.00	125.00
Sun-45	Canoe-shaped dish	250.00	225.00	175.00
Sun-50	Cheese keep	225.00	195.00	160.00
Sun-52	Coaster	45.00	45.00	35.00
Sun-55	Coffee pot	750.00	600.00	475.00
Sun-60	Compote, footed	150.00	135.00	100.00
Sun-65	Condiment set on tray	200.00	165.00	150.00
Sun-70	Cream and sugar	100.00	100.00	65.00
Sun-71	Cream and sugar on tray	200.00	150.00	150.00
Sun-75	Demi-tasse	75.00	60.00	50.00
Sun-77	Egg cup, footed	75.00	65.00	45.00
Sun-80	Hot water jug	325.00	300.00	200.00
Sun-85	Jam pot with liner	150.00	125.00	85.00
Sun-90	Jug, 4"	275.00	225.00	175.00
Sun-91	Jug, 4 1/2"	300.00	250.00	200.00
Sun-92	Jug, 5"	325.00	275.00	200.00

Cat. No.	Shape	U.S. $	Can. $	U.K. £
Sun-97	Nut dish	50.00	45.00	35.00
Sun-201	Plate, 4" sq.	35.00	40.00	25.00
Sun-202	Plate, 5" sq.	40.00	45.00	30.00
Sun-203	Plate, 6" sq.	45.00	50.00	35.00
Sun-204	Plate, 7" sq.	50.00	60.00	40.00
Sun-205	Plate, 8" sq.	75.00	75.00	50.00
Sun-206	Plate, 9" sq.	100.00	95.00	65.00
Sun-207	Plate, 10" sq.	125.00	115.00	75.00
Sun-112	Relish dish, small	150.00	150.00	100.00
Sun-115	Salad bowl, chrome rim	135.00	115.00	85.00
Sun-117	Salt and pepper	80.00	75.00	50.00
Sun-118	Salt and pepper on tray	150.00	135.00	100.00
Sun-120	Sandwich tray, 10" x 6"	125.00	110.00	75.00
Sun-121	Sandwich tray, 12" x 7"	125.00	125.00	75.00
Sun-125	Sauce boat and liner	150.00	135.00	100.00
Sun-130	Teacup and saucer	85.00	70.00	50.00
Sun-135	Teapot, 2 cup	450.00	325.00	275.00
Sun-136	Teapot, 4 cup	550.00	400.00	350.00
Sun-137	Teapot, 6 cup	650.00	450.00	400.00
Sun-140	Teapot, stacking	950.00	650.00	400.00
Sun-145	Tennis set	100.00	85.00	65.00
Sun-150	Toast rack, 4 slice	250.00	195.00	175.00
Sun-151	Toast rack, 2 slice	200.00	145.00	150.00
Sun-155	Trivet	100.00	85.00	65.00
Sun-160	Vase, bud	125.00	115.00	75.00

SWEET NANCY

The pattern number is 5828, and it was probably introduced in 1939.

Cat. No.	Shape	U.S. $	Can. $	U.K. £
SN-04	Bonbon dish	40.00	25.00	40.00
SN-09	Bowl, 5″	35.00	25.00	35.00
SN-14	Bowl, 8″ soup	60.00	45.00	55.00
SN-23	Breakfast set	750.00	450.00	500.00
SN-28	Butter dish	120.00	95.00	95.00
SN-30	Butter pat	35.00	25.00	35.00
SN-35	Cake plate, open handles	120.00	95.00	95.00
SN-36	Cake plate, tab handles	105.00	85.00	85.00
SN-37	Cake plate, 8″ sq. pedestal	135.00	105.00	110.00
SN-40	Cake stand, 2 tier	135.00	100.00	110.00
SN-45	Canoe-shaped dish	170.00	135.00	150.00
SN-50	Cheese keep	150.00	115.00	145.00
SN-52	Coaster	35.00	25.00	30.00
SN-55	Coffee pot	475.00	325.00	400.00
SN-60	Compote, footed	90.00	75.00	75.00
SN-65	Condiment set on tray	135.00	105.00	120.00
SN-70	Cream and sugar	75.00	65.00	65.00
SN-71	Cream and sugar on tray	135.00	115.00	110.00
SN-75	Demi-tasse	50.00	35.00	50.00
SN-77	Egg cup, footed	50.00	30.00	45.00
SN-80	Hot water jug	200.00	195.00	165.00
SN-85	Jam pot with liner	115.00	135.00	80.00
SN-90	Jug, 4″	200.00	140.00	125.00
SN-91	Jug, 4 1/2″	225.00	155.00	150.00
SN-92	Jug, 5″	250.00	165.00	175.00

Cat. No.	Shape	U.S. $	Can. $	U.K. £
SN-97	Nut dish	35.00	25.00	35.00
SN-201	Plate, 4″ sq.	30.00	25.00	30.00
SN-202	Plate, 5″ sq.	35.00	30.00	35.00
SN-203	Plate, 6″ sq.	40.00	35.00	40.00
SN-204	Plate, 7″ sq.	45.00	40.00	45.00
SN-205	Plate, 8″ sq.	65.00	45.00	55.00
SN-206	Plate, 9″ sq.	85.00	65.00	70.00
SN-207	Plate, 10″ sq.	100.00	75.00	85.00
SN-112	Relish dish, small	115.00	95.00	85.00
SN-115	Salad bowl, chrome rim	90.00	75.00	75.00
SN-117	Salt and pepper	60.00	45.00	50.00
SN-118	Salt and pepper on tray	135.00	95.00	100.00
SN-120	Sandwich tray, 10″ x 6″	75.00	65.00	70.00
SN-121	Sandwich tray, 12″ x 7″	80.00	75.00	85.00
SN-125	Sauce boat and liner	115.00	85.00	85.00
SN-130	Teacup and saucer	65.00	40.00	50.00
SN-135	Teapot, 2 cup	250.00	175.00	195.00
SN-136	Teapot, 4 cup	350.00	225.00	275.00
SN-137	Teapot, 6 cup	450.00	275.00	350.00
SN-140	Teapot, stacking	650.00	450.00	475.00
SN-145	Tennis set	65.00	50.00	55.00
SN-150	Toast rack, 4 slice	150.00	125.00	135.00
SN-151	Toast rack, 2 slice	125.00	95.00	95.00
SN-155	Trivet	65.00	45.00	55.00
SN-160	Vase, bud	80.00	60.00	65.00

SWEET PEA

The pattern number is 3030, and the pattern was introduced in 1936 with great success. It can be found with gold and deep blue trim. It is still a favorite with English collectors and may be the most popular with collectors in Australia. There are great variations in the depth of colour in examples of this pattern, with some pieces appearing very faded.

Cat. No.	Shape	U.S. $	Can. $	U.K. £
SP-04	Bonbon dish	85.00	75.00	65.00
SP-09	Bowl, 5″	55.00	50.00	50.00
SP-14	Bowl, 8″ soup	95.00	85.00	75.00
SP-23	Breakfast set	1,300.00	900.00	850.00
SP-28	Butter dish	245.00	195.00	195.00
SP-30	Butter pat	75.00	65.00	55.00
SP-35	Cake plate, open handles	245.00	215.00	195.00
SP-36	Cake plate, tab handles	220.00	195.00	175.00
SP-37	Cake plate, 8″ sq. pedestal	245.00	215.00	195.00
SP-40	Cake stand, 2 tier	245.00	200.00	195.00
SP-45	Canoe-shaped dish	395.00	325.00	275.00
SP-50	Cheese keep	325.00	250.00	250.00
SP-52	Coaster	60.00	55.00	55.00
SP-55	Coffee pot	1,200.00	850.00	800.00
SP-60	Compote, footed	195.00	175.00	150.00
SP-65	Condiment set on tray	275.00	225.00	250.00
SP-70	Cream and sugar	165.00	135.00	125.00
SP-71	Cream and sugar on tray	275.00	215.00	250.00
SP-75	Demi-tasse	110.00	95.00	80.00
SP-77	Egg cup, footed	100.00	90.00	70.00
SP-80	Hot water jug	575.00	400.00	350.00
SP-85	Jam pot with liner	220.00	175.00	160.00
SP-90	Jug, 4″	450.00	325.00	275.00
SP-91	Jug, 4 1/2″	500.00	350.00	300.00
SP-92	Jug, 5″	550.00	375.00	325.00
SP-97	Nut dish	75.00	65.00	55.00
SP-201	Plate, 4″ sq.	55.00	50.00	55.00
SP-202	Plate, 5″ sq.	65.00	60.00	60.00
SP-203	Plate, 6″ sq.	75.00	70.00	65.00
SP-204	Plate, 7″ sq.	110.00	85.00	75.00
SP-205	Plate, 8″ sq.	150.00	95.00	95.00
SP-206	Plate, 9″ sq.	160.00	115.00	135.00
SP-207	Plate, 10″ sq.	175.00	135.00	150.00
SP-112	Relish dish, small	220.00	195.00	195.00
SP-115	Salad bowl, chrome rim	195.00	150.00	150.00
SP-117	Salt and pepper	110.00	105.00	80.00
SP-118	Salt and pepper on tray	195.00	165.00	165.00
SP-120	Sandwich tray, 10″ x 6″	165.00	145.00	135.00
SP-121	Sandwich tray, 12″ x 7″	195.00	165.00	150.00
SP-125	Sauce boat and liner	195.00	175.00	150.00
SP-130	Teacup and saucer	125.00	110.00	75.00
SP-135	Teapot, 2 cup	550.00	400.00	350.00
SP-136	Teapot, 4 cup	800.00	550.00	500.00
SP-137	Teapot, 6 cup	1,000.00	650.00	600.00
SP-140	Teapot, stacking	1,200.00	875.00	800.00
SP-145	Tennis set	125.00	115.00	115.00
SP-150	Toast rack, 4 slice	300.00	225.00	250.00
SP-151	Toast rack, 2 slice	225.00	175.00	215.00
SP-155	Trivet	135.00	110.00	125.00
SP-160	Vase, bud	175.00	135.00	125.00

TARTANS

The pattern number is 4514. The pattern is clearly a companion to **Quilt** 4515, both patterns are intended for a non-chintz customer and were introduced late in the 1930s.

Cat. No.	Shape	U.S. $	Can. $	U.K. £
T-04	Bonbon dish	35.00	20.00	30.00
T-09	Bowl, 5″	30.00	20.00	25.00
T-14	Bowl, 8″ soup	45.00	30.00	40.00
T-23	Breakfast set	500.00	275.00	375.00
T-28	Butter dish	115.00	65.00	75.00
T-30	Butter pat	30.00	20.00	25.00
T-35	Cake plate, open handles	135.00	75.00	100.00
T-36	Cake plate, tab handles	115.00	65.00	75.00
T-37	Cake plate, 8″ sq. pedestal	135.00	85.00	100.00
T-40	Cake stand, 2 tier	135.00	80.00	100.00
T-45	Canoe-shaped dish	135.00	95.00	100.00
T-50	Cheese keep	135.00	75.00	100.00
T-52	Coaster	30.00	25.00	25.00
T-55	Coffee pot	400.00	175.00	300.00
T-60	Compote, footed	85.00	50.00	60.00
T-65	Condiment set on tray	120.00	65.00	85.00
T-70	Cream and sugar	65.00	45.00	50.00
T-71	Cream and sugar on tray	120.00	85.00	85.00
T-75	Demi-tasse	45.00	25.00	35.00
T-77	Egg cup, footed	45.00	30.00	35.00
T-80	Hot water jug	180.00	95.00	150.00
T-85	Jam pot with liner	90.00	60.00	65.00
T-90	Jug, 4″	150.00	65.00	45.00
T-91	Jug, 4 1/2″	165.00	75.00	125.00
T-92	Jug, 5″	180.00	85.00	150.00
T-97	Nut dish	30.00	20.00	25.00
T-201	Plate, 4″ sq.	30.00	20.00	20.00
T-202	Plate, 5″ sq.	35.00	25.00	25.00
T-203	Plate, 6″ sq.	40.00	30.00	30.00
T-204	Plate, 7″ sq.	45.00	35.00	35.00
T-205	Plate, 8″ sq.	50.00	40.00	40.00
T-206	Plate, 9″ sq.	65.00	45.00	45.00
T-207	Plate, 10″ sq.	75.00	50.00	50.00
T-112	Relish dish, small	90.00	75.00	65.00
T-115	Salad bowl, chrome rim	80.00	65.00	60.00
T-117	Salt and pepper	45.00	35.00	40.00
T-118	Salt and pepper on tray	115.00	75.00	75.00
T-120	Sandwich tray, 10″ x 6″	65.00	40.00	50.00
T-121	Sandwich tray, 12″ x 7″	75.00	50.00	60.00
T-125	Sauce boat and liner	90.00	65.00	65.00
T-130	Teacup and saucer	45.00	25.00	35.00
T-135	Teapot, 2 cup	180.00	100.00	150.00
T-136	Teapot, 4 cup	270.00	125.00	200.00
T-137	Teapot, 6 cup	350.00	150.00	275.00
T-140	Teapot, stacking	450.00	250.00	350.00
T-145	Tennis set	65.00	35.00	50.00
T-150	Toast rack, 4 slice	145.00	95.00	115.00
T-151	Toast rack, 2 slice	105.00	75.00	100.00
T-155	Trivet	50.00	30.00	50.00
T-160	Vase, bud	65.00	40.00	50.00

TRIUMPH

The pattern number is 112 and is the black background alternate to **White Crocus**, pattern number 111, (see page 47). This pattern was called **Black Crocus** until a piece was found in England in the summer of 1996 with the backstamp **Triumph.**

Cat. No.	Shape	U.S. $	Can. $	U.K. £
Tr -04	Bonbon dish	60.00	60.00	50.00
Tr -09	Bowl, 5″	45.00	45.00	40.00
Tr -14	Bowl, 8″ soup	75.00	65.00	55.00
Tr -23	Breakfast set	1,200.00	850.00	600.00
Tr -28	Butter dish	175.00	150.00	140.00
Tr -30	Butter pat	50.00	40.00	40.00
Tr -35	Cake plate, open handles	175.00	165.00	140.00
Tr -36	Cake plate, tab handles	150.00	155.00	125.00
Tr -37	Cake plate, 8″ sq. pedestal	175.00	175.00	140.00
Tr -40	Cake stand, 2 tier	175.00	165.00	140.00
Tr -45	Canoe-shaped dish	250.00	225.00	205.00
Tr -50	Cheese keep	225.00	195.00	160.00
Tr -52	Coaster	45.00	35.00	40.00
Tr -55	Coffee pot	975.00	600.00	550.00
Tr -60	Compote, footed	150.00	135.00	115.00
Tr -65	Condiment set on tray	200.00	175.00	140.00
Tr -70	Cream and sugar	100.00	100.00	75.00
Tr -71	Cream and sugar on tray	200.00	165.00	140.00
Tr -75	Demi-tasse	75.00	60.00	55.00
Tr -77	Egg cup, footed	95.00	65.00	60.00
Tr -80	Hot water jug	450.00	300.00	235.00
Tr -85	Jam pot with liner	150.00	135.00	115.00
Tr -90	Jug, 4″	400.00	225.00	175.00
Tr -91	Jug, 4 1/2″	450.00	250.00	200.00
Tr -92	Jug, 5″	500.00	275.00	225.00
Tr -97	Nut dish	50.00	40.00	40.00
Tr -201	Plate, 4″ sq.	45.00	40.00	40.00
Tr -202	Plate, 5″ sq.	50.00	45.00	45.00
Tr -203	Plate, 6″ sq.	50.00	50.00	55.00
Tr -204	Plate, 7″ sq.	75.00	60.00	65.00
Tr -205	Plate, 8″ sq.	115.00	75.00	85.00
Tr -206	Plate, 9″ sq.	135.00	95.00	95.00
Tr -207	Plate, 10″ sq.	150.00	115.00	110.00
Tr -112	Relish dish, small	150.00	145.00	115.00
Tr -115	Salad bowl, chrome rim	150.00	125.00	115.00
Tr -117	Salt and pepper	80.00	75.00	55.00
Tr -118	Salt and pepper on tray	150.00	135.00	110.00
Tr -120	Sandwich tray, 10″ x 6″	100.00	95.00	75.00
Tr -121	Sandwich tray, 12″ x 7″	125.00	115.00	115.00
Tr -125	Sauce boat and liner	150.00	130.00	115.00
Tr -130	Teacup and saucer	95.00	70.00	60.00
Tr -135	Teapot, 2 cup	425.00	325.00	275.00
Tr -136	Teapot, 4 cup	650.00	400.00	400.00
Tr -137	Teapot, 6 cup	850.00	450.00	475.00
Tr -140	Teapot, stacking	950.00	650.00	550.00
Tr -145	Tennis set	100.00	85.00	70.00
Tr-150	Toast rack, 4 slice	200.00	195.00	165.00
Tr -151	Toast rack, 2 slice	150.00	145.00	120.00
Tr -155	Trivet	100.00	85.00	70.00
Tr-160	Vase, bud	135.00	115.00	75.00

VICTORIAN

The pattern number is 3164 and it was introduced in 1936 shortly after the alternate colourway **Queen Anne** 2995. The pattern was very popular at the time and sold in quantity.

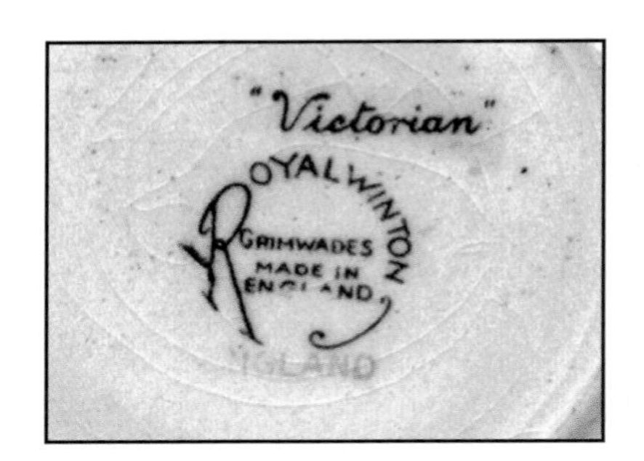

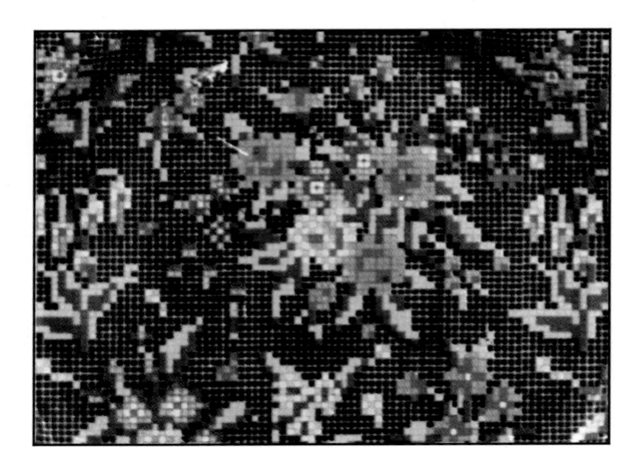

Cat. No.	Shape	U.S. $	Can. $	U.K. £
V-04	Bonbon dish	40.00	20.00	35.00
V-09	Bowl, 5″	35.00	20.00	30.00
V-14	Bowl, 8″ soup	45.00	25.00	40.00
V-23	Breakfast set	525.00	300.00	425.00
V-28	Butter dish	115.00	65.00	75.00
V-30	Butter pat	30.00	20.00	25.00
V-35	Cake plate, open handles	135.00	75.00	100.00
V-36	Cake plate, tab handles	115.00	65.00	85.00
V-37	Cake plate,8″ sq. pedestal	135.00	85.00	100.00
V-40	Cake stand, 2 tier	135.00	80.00	100.00
V-45	Canoe-shaped dish	145.00	90.00	115.00
V-50	Cheese keep	145.00	75.00	115.00
V-52	Coaster	30.00	20.00	25.00
V-55	Coffee pot	425.00	200.00	340.00
V-60	Compote, footed	90.00	45.00	65.00
V-65	Condiment set on tray	135.00	75.00	75.00
V-70	Cream and sugar	65.00	40.00	50.00
V-71	Cream and sugar on tray	120.00	75.00	85.00
V-75	Demi-tasse	45.00	25.00	40.00
V-77	Egg cup, footed	40.00	30.00	35.00
V-80	Hot water jug	180.00	95.00	150.00
V-85	Jam pot with liner	90.00	60.00	65.00
V-90	Jug, 4″	150.00	65.00	135.00
V-91	Jug, 4 1/2″	170.00	75.00	150.00
V-92	Jug, 5″	195.00	85.00	165.00

Cat. No.	Shape	U.S. $	Can. $	U.K. £
V-97	Nut dish	35.00	20.00	25.00
V-201	Plate, 4″ sq.	30.00	20.00	25.00
V-202	Plate, 5″ sq.	35.00	25.00	30.00
V-203	Plate, 6″ sq.	40.00	30.00	35.00
V-204	Plate, 7″ sq.	45.00	35.00	40.00
V-205	Plate, 8″ sq.	50.00	40.00	55.00
V-206	Plate, 9″ sq.	65.00	45.00	65.00
V-207	Plate, 10″ sq.	85.00	50.00	75.00
V-112	Relish dish, small	125.00	75.00	75.00
V-115	Salad bowl, chrome rim	100.00	65.00	65.00
V-117	Salt and pepper	65.00	35.00	45.00
V-118	Salt and pepper on tray	135.00	75.00	85.00
V-120	Sandwich tray, 10″ x 6″	80.00	40.00	50.00
V-121	Sandwich tray, 12″ x 7″	100.00	50.00	65.00
V-125	Sauce boat and liner	125.00	65.00	75.00
V-130	Teacup and saucer	50.00	25.00	40.00
V-135	Teapot, 2 cup	300.00	100.00	210.00
V-136	Teapot, 4 cup	350.00	150.00	265.00
V-137	Teapot, 6 cup	425.00	200.00	315.00
V-140	Teapot, stacking	425.00	300.00	325.00
V-145	Tennis set	75.00	35.00	50.00
V-150	Toast rack, 4 slice	175.00	95.00	125.00
V-151	Toast rack, 2 slice	150.00	65.00	100.00
V-155	Trivet	75.00	30.00	50.00
V-160	Vase, bud	75.00	45.00	55.00

VICTORIAN ROSE

The pattern number is 440, and was registered in Canada in 1953. It was one of the patterns produced by Howard Potteries after the takeover in 1964. This pattern is mentioned on a factory invoice dated 1969.

Cat. No.	Shape	U.S. $	Can. $	U.K. £
VR-04	Bonbon dish	50.00	50.00	40.00
VR-09	Bowl, 5″	50.00	35.00	35.00
VR-14	Bowl, 8″ soup	75.00	60.00	50.00
VR-23	Breakfast set	900.00	725.00	600.00
VR-28	Butter dish	165.00	125.00	100.00
VR-30	Butter pat	45.00	35.00	35.00
VR-35	Cake plate, open handles	165.00	145.00	100.00
VR-36	Cake plate, tab handles	150.00	135.00	100.00
VR-37	Cake plate,8″ sq. pedestal	175.00	160.00	125.00
VR-40	Cake stand, 2 tier	175.00	150.00	125.00
VR-45	Canoe-shaped dish	250.00	195.00	175.00
VR-50	Cheese keep	200.00	175.00	150.00
VR-52	Coaster	40.00	35.00	30.00
VR-55	Coffee pot	750.00	500.00	450.00
VR-60	Compote, footed	135.00	125.00	100.00
VR-65	Condiment set on tray	200.00	150.00	135.00
VR-70	Cream and sugar	100.00	95.00	65.00
VR-71	Cream and sugar on tray	175.00	145.00	135.00
VR-75	Demi-tasse	85.00	55.00	50.00
VR-77	Egg cup, footed	75.00	60.00	50.00
VR-80	Hot water jug	350.00	275.00	225.00
VR-85	Jam pot with liner	150.00	115.00	95.00
VR-90	Jug, 4″	325.00	200.00	160.00
VR-91	Jug, 4 1/2″	375.00	225.00	175.00
VR-92	Jug, 5″	400.00	250.00	190.00
VR-	Lavebo		VERY RARE	
VR-97	Nut dish	45.00	35.00	35.00
VR-201	Plate, 4″ sq.	50.00	35.00	35.00
VR-202	Plate, 5″ sq.	55.00	40.00	40.00
VR-203	Plate, 6″ sq.	60.00	45.00	45.00
VR-204	Plate, 7″ sq.	75.00	50.00	50.00
VR-205	Plate, 8″ sq.	100.00	65.00	65.00
VR-206	Plate, 9″ sq.	120.00	75.00	75.00
VR-207	Plate, 10″ sq.	135.00	95.00	85.00
VR-112	Relish dish, small	150.00	135.00	100.00
VR-115	Salad bowl, chrome rim	125.00	105.00	75.00
VR-117	Salt and pepper	75.00	65.00	50.00
VR-118	Salt and pepper on tray	150.00	115.00	100.00
VR-120	Sandwich tray, 10″ x 6″	100.00	95.00	65.00
VR-121	Sandwich tray, 12″ x 7″	125.00	115.00	100.00
VR-125	Sauce boat and liner	150.00	125.00	75.00
VR-130	Teacup and saucer	95.00	60.00	50.00
VR-135	Teapot, 2 cup	325.00	275.00	225.00
VR-136	Teapot, 4 cup	500.00	350.00	350.00
VR-137	Teapot, 6 cup	600.00	400.00	400.00
VR-140	Teapot, stacking	850.00	575.00	500.00
VR-145	Tennis set	100.00	75.00	65.00
VR-150	Toast rack, 4 slice	200.00	195.00	150.00
VR-151	Toast rack, 2 slice	135.00	145.00	115.00
VR-155	Trivet	100.00	75.00	65.00
VR-160	Vase, bud	125.00	95.00	65.00

WELBECK

The pattern number is 2204, and it was probably introduced in 1934 along with **Hazel** 2208. **Hazel** and **Spring** 2506 are the alternate colourways to **Welbeck**. This pattern was much copied by the Japanese. American collectors place this pattern just below **Julia** in popularity.

Cat. No.	Shape	U.S. $	Can. $	U.K. £
W-04	Bonbon dish	120.00	85.00	80.00
W-09	Bowl, 5"	75.00	60.00	60.00
W-14	Bowl, 8" soup	115.00	90.00	80.00
W-23	Breakfast set	1,500.00	1,000.00	1100.00
W-28	Butter dish	325.00	225.00	225.00
W-30	Butter pat	85.00	75.00	60.00
W-35	Cake plate, open handles	325.00	245.00	225.00
W-36	Cake plate, tab handles	300.00	235.00	205.00
W-37	Cake plate,8" sq. pedestal	300.00	265.00	235.00
W-40	Cake stand, 2 tier	300.00	250.00	235.00
W-45	Canoe-shaped dish	450.00	375.00	325.00
W-50	Cheese keep	400.00	300.00	300.00
W-52	Coaster	85.00	75.00	65.00
W-55	Coffee pot	1,300.00	900.00	925.00
W-60	Compote, footed	250.00	225.00	195.00
W-65	Condiment set on tray	375.00	275.00	275.00
W-70	Cream and sugar	200.00	175.00	150.00
W-71	Cream and sugar on tray	375.00	250.00	285.00
W-75	Demi-tasse	135.00	115.00	95.00
W-77	Egg cup, footed	150.00	110.00	75.00
W-80	Hot water jug	600.00	450.00	400.00
W-85	Jam pot with liner	295.00	200.00	175.00
W-90	Jug, 4"	625.00	350.00	350.00
W-91	Jug, 4 1/2"	700.00	375.00	400.00
W-92	Jug, 5"	775.00	400.00	450.00

Cat. No.	Shape	U.S. $	Can. $	U.K. £
W-97	Nut dish	85.00	750.00	65.00
W-201	Plate, 4" sq.	80.00	60.00	60.00
W-202	Plate, 5" sq.	115.00	65.00	70.00
W-203	Plate, 6" sq.	130.00	75.00	85.00
W-204	Plate, 7" sq.	145.00	95.00	95.00
W-205	Plate, 8" sq.	195.00	115.00	120.00
W-206	Plate, 9" sq.	215.00	135.00	145.00
W-207	Plate, 10" sq.	235.00	150.00	155.00
W-112	Relish dish, small	285.00	225.00	225.00
W-115	Salad bowl, chrome rim	285.00	195.00	225.00
W-117	Salt and pepper	135.00	135.00	120.00
W-118	Salt and pepper on tray	285.00	215.00	195.00
W-120	Sandwich tray, 10" x 6"	200.00	165.00	160.00
W-121	Sandwich tray, 12" x 7"	230.00	195.00	175.00
W-125	Sauce boat and liner	250.00	215.00	185.00
W-130	Teacup and saucer	175.00	125.00	95.00
W-135	Teapot, 2 cup	675.00	500.00	475.00
W-136	Teapot, 4 cup	875.00	650.00	650.00
W-137	Teapot, 6 cup	1150.00	750.00	775.00
W-140	Teapot, stacking	1400.00	950.00	850.00
W-145	Tennis set	160.00	135.00	135.00
W-150	Toast rack, 4 slice	325.00	275.00	260.00
W-151	Toast rack, 2 slice	275.00	235.00	225.00
W-155	Trivet	175.00	135.00	145.00
W-160	Vase, bud	215.00	150.00	145.00

WILD FLOWERS

The pattern number is 3149, and it was probably introduced in 1936. This pattern is difficult to find in North America but it is becoming popular with American collectors.

Cat. No.	Shape	U.S. $	Can. $	U.K. £
WF-04	Bonbon dish	60.00	60.00	40.00
WF-09	Bowl, 5"	50.00	45.00	40.00
WF-14	Bowl, 8" soup	70.00	65.00	55.00
WF-23	Breakfast set	1,100.00	800.00	575.00
WF-28	Butter dish	175.00	150.00	120.00
WF-30	Butter pat	50.00	45.00	35.00
WF-35	Cake plate, open handles	200.00	175.00	120.00
WF-36	Cake plate, tab handles	175.00	165.00	105.00
WF-37	Cake plate,8" sq. pedestal	200.00	185.00	130.00
WF-40	Cake stand, 2 tier	175.00	165.00	125.00
WF-45	Canoe-shaped dish	250.00	225.00	175.00
WF-50	Cheese keep	225.00	195.00	165.00
WF-52	Coaster	45.00	40.00	35.00
WF-55	Coffee pot	900.00	625.00	450.00
WF-60	Compote, footed	150.00	145.00	105.00
WF-65	Condiment set on tray	200.00	165.00	145.00
WF-70	Cream and sugar	100.00	105.00	80.00
WF-71	Cream and sugar on tray	200.00	150.00	145.00
WF-75	Demi-tasse	95.00	60.00	55.00
WF-77	Egg cup, footed	80.00	65.00	50.00
WF-80	Hot water jug	400.00	300.00	185.00
WF-85	Jam pot with liner	150.00	135.00	105.00
WF-90	Jug, 4"	350.00	225.00	135.00
WF-91	Jug, 4 1/2"	400.00	250.00	165.00
WF-92	Jug, 5"	450.00	275.00	185.00
WF-97	Nut dish	50.00	40.00	35.00
WF-201	Plate, 4" sq.	50.00	40.00	40.00
WF-202	Plate, 5" sq.	55.00	45.00	45.00
WF-203	Plate, 6" sq.	65.00	50.00	50.00
WF-204	Plate, 7" sq.	85.00	60.00	55.00
WF-205	Plate, 8" sq.	115.00	75.00	70.00
WF-206	Plate, 9" sq.	135.00	95.00	85.00
WF-207	Plate, 10" sq.	150.00	115.00	95.00
WF-112	Relish dish, small	150.00	145.00	95.00
WF-115	Salad bowl, chrome rim	135.00	115.00	85.00
WF-117	Salt and pepper	75.00	75.00	55.00
WF-118	Salt and pepper on tray	150.00	135.00	105.00
WF-120	Sandwich tray, 10" x 6"	100.00	105.00	70.00
WF-121	Sandwich tray, 12" x 7"	125.00	125.00	80.00
WF-125	Sauce boat and liner	150.00	135.00	105.00
WF-130	Teacup and saucer	95.00	70.00	55.00
WF-135	Teapot, 2 cup	450.00	325.00	225.00
WF-136	Teapot, 4 cup	650.00	400.00	350.00
WF-137	Teapot, 6 cup	850.00	500.00	400.00
WF-140	Teapot, stacking	1,000.00	650.00	550.00
WF-145	Tennis set	100.00	85.00	70.00
WF-150	Toast rack, 4 slice	200.00	195.00	160.00
WF-151	Toast rack, 2 slice	150.00	145.00	120.00
WF-155	Trivet	100.00	85.00	70.00
WF-160	Vase, bud	150.00	115.00	70.00

WINIFRED

Unfortunately we have no information on this pattern at this time.

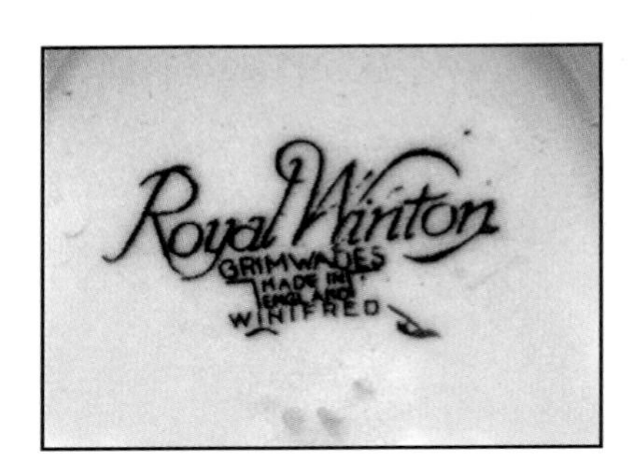

Cat. No.	Shape	U.S. $	Can. $	U.K. £
Wi-04	Bonbon dish	20.00	15.00	20.00
Wi-09	Bowl, 5"	20.00	20.00	20.00
Wi-14	Bowl, 8" soup	30.00	25.00	25.00
Wi-23	Breakfast set	375.00	250.00	295.00
Wi-28	Butter dish	80.00	60.00	60.00
Wi-30	Butter pat	20.00	15.00	20.00
Wi-35	Cake plate, open handles	80.00	65.00	60.00
Wi-36	Cake plate, tab handles	70.00	55.00	55.00
Wi-37	Cake plate, 8" sq. pedestal	80.00	75.00	60.00
Wi-40	Cake stand, 2 tier	80.00	70.00	60.00
Wi-45	Canoe-shaped dish	105.00	75.00	75.00
Wi-50	Cheese keep	95.00	75.00	70.00
Wi-52	Coaster	20.00	20.00	20.00
Wi-55	Coffee pot	300.00	175.00	225.00
Wi-60	Compote, footed	60.00	45.00	45.00
Wi-65	Condiment set on tray	80.00	65.00	60.00
Wi-70	Cream and sugar	45.00	35.00	40.00
Wi-71	Cream and sugar on tray	80.00	65.00	60.00
Wi-75	Demi-tasse	30.00	25.00	25.00
Wi-77	Egg cup, footed	35.00	30.00	25.00
Wi-80	Hot water jug	125.00	95.00	105.00
Wi-85	Jam pot with liner	65.00	50.00	50.00
Wi-90	Jug, 4"	135.00	65.00	75.00
Wi-91	Jug, 4 1/2"	150.00	75.00	100.00
Wi-92	Jug, 5"	165.00	85.00	125.00

Cat. No.	Shape	U.S. $	Can. $	U.K. £
Wi-97	Nut dish	20.00	15.00	20.00
Wi-201	Plate, 4" sq.	20.00	15.00	20.00
Wi-202	Plate, 5" sq.	25.00	20.00	25.00
Wi-203	Plate, 6" sq.	30.00	25.00	30.00
Wi-204	Plate, 7" sq.	40.00	30.00	35.00
Wi-205	Plate, 8" sq.	55.00	35.00	40.00
Wi-206	Plate, 9" sq.	65.00	40.00	45.00
Wi-207	Plate, 10" sq.	75.00	50.00	50.00
Wi-112	Relish dish, small	65.00	50.00	50.00
Wi-115	Salad bowl, chrome rim	80.00	50.00	55.00
Wi-117	Salt and pepper	45.00	35.00	35.00
Wi-118	Salt and pepper on tray	90.00	65.00	60.00
Wi-120	Sandwich tray, 10" x 6"	50.00	35.00	40.00
Wi-121	Sandwich tray, 12" x 7"	60.00	45.00	45.00
Wi-125	Sauce boat and liner	55.00	60.00	40.00
Wi-130	Teacup and saucer	35.00	25.00	30.00
Wi-135	Teapot, 2 cup	150.00	100.00	105.00
Wi-136	Teapot, 4 cup	250.00	125.00	175.00
Wi-137	Teapot, 6 cup	300.00	150.00	200.00
Wi-140	Teapot, stacking	350.00	250.00	250.00
Wi-145	Tennis set	45.00	35.00	35.00
Wi-150	Toast rack, 4 slice	135.00	85.00	100.00
Wi-151	Toast rack, 2 slice	115.00	65.00	85.00
Wi-155	Trivet	45.00	25.00	35.00
Wi-160	Vase, bud	55.00	35.00	40.00

"Royal Winton"

Popular Old English Chintz Designs (a few of many).

FLORAL FEAST 2255 CRANSTONE 2256 SOMERSET 1611

Item No.		Price
021.	"Canoe" Tray	24/- Per doz.
022.	Butter, "Trefu"	4/- ,,
023.	Tray, "Fife" L/s 24/- S/s	21/- ,,
024.	Triple Dish, "Stafford"	21/- ,,
025.	Condiment Set, "Acme" (2 piece on Tray)	14/- ,,
026.	Twin Dish "Stafford"	18/- ,,
027.	Tennis Set, 2 piece, "Ascot" ...	16/- ,,
028.	Toast, Butter and Marmalade "Saville"	15/- ,,
029.	Triple Tray, "Viola"	33/- ,,
030.	Eggset–4 cup, "Saville"	24/- ,,
031.	Individual Breakfast Set, 6 piece, "Athena"	20/- ,,
032.	Cruet Set, "Egg and Clover Leaf"	21/- ,,
033.	Egg-Cruet Set, 5 piece, "Ascot" ...	18/- ,,
034.	Triple Tray, "Gem"	30/- ,,
035.	Egg-Cruet Set, 7 piece, "York" ...	27/- ,,
036.	Cruet Set, "Fife"	27/- ,,
037.	Bed Side Set, 6 piece, "Countess"	48/- ,,
038.	,, ,, ,, 7 piece "Ascot" ...	66/- ,,
039.	,, ,, ,, 7 piece, "York" ...	66/- ,,
01.	4 Compartment Dish, "Ascot" ...	20/- ,,
02.	4 ,, ,, ,, "Oval" ...	24/- ,,
03.	3 ,, ,, ,, "Marina" ...	24/- ,,
	Also 5 Compartment ,, ...	30/- ,,
04.	Mayonnaise Bowl & Stand "Saville"	14/- ,,
	and Ladle ...	4/- ,,
05.	5 Compartment Dish, "Duchess"	27/- ,,
06.	Mayonnaise Bowl & Stand, "Ascot"	14/- ,,
	and Ladle ...	4/- ,,
07.	Marmalade and Stand, "Ascot" ...	15/- ,,
08.	Cheese, "Ascot"	18/- ,,
09.	Covered Butter, "Ascot" L/s 18/- S/s	15/- ,,
010.	Honey, fast stand, "Chelsea" ...	22/- ,,
011.	Nut Dish, "Ascot"	12/- ,,
	and Scoop ...	6/- ,,
012.	Mayonnaise Bowl and Stand, "Norman"	14/- ,,
	and Ladle	4/- ,,
013.	Cheese, No. 3 "Dane"	24/- ,,
014.	Cake Set, 5 piece, "Saville" ...	3/6 Per set
015.	Sandwich Set, 7 piece, 10″×5″ "Ascot" ...	3/5 ,,
016.	Cheese, "Marvel"	18/- Per doz.
017.	Sandwich Set, 7 piece, "Ascot" (12″ Divided Tray & 6″ Actual Plates)	4/9 Per set
018.	Fruit Set, 7 piece, "Stella" ...	5/- ,,
019.	,, ,, 7 piece, "Concave" ...	4/9 ,,
020.	,, ,, 7 piece, "Ascot" ...	4/6 ,,
040.	Sweet, "Holborn" 4″ 10/-, 5″ 11/-, 6″	13/- Per doz.
041.	Sweet, "Bow" S/s 7/-, M/s 7/6, L/s	8/6 ,,
042.	Oatmeal	9/- ,,
043.	Mint Boat and Stand, "Era" ...	12/- ,,
044.	Low Comport, "Ascot"	22/- ,,
045.	Chocolate Comport, "Lily" ...	14/- ,,
	also larger size ...	18/- ,,
046.	Footed Nut, "Bow"	18/- ,,

MARGUERITE 9467

KINVER 2254

JUNE ROSES 2036

Item No.		Price
047.	Jug, "Cambridge" 30/42's ...	4/- Per set
048.	,, "Globe" ,, ...	4/- ,,
049.	Coffee Pot, "Perth"	39/- Per doz
050.	Chocolate Comport, "Greek" ...	14/- ,,
051.	,, ,, "Eton" ...	14/- ,,
052.	Jug, "Duval" 30/42's ...	4/- Per set
053.	,, "Grafton" ,, ...	4/6 ,,
054.	Cake Plate, Handled, "Ascot" ...	18/- Per doz
055.	Coffee Pot, "Norman"	39/- ,,
056.	,, "Greek" 2 pints 45/- 1¼ pints	39/- ,,
057.	Bowl, "Fife"	42/- ,,
058.	Plate, "Ascot" 3″ 4″ 5″ 6″ 7″ 8″ nominal 4/6 6/- 8/- 10/- 13/- 15/-	Per doz
059.	Bowl, "King"	42/- ,,
060.	Teapot, 36's, "Hastings" (1 size)	32/- ,,
061.	Sugar, Tea set size, "Hastings"	Per doz. pairs 18/-
062.	Cream, ,, ,, ,,	
063.	Tea and Saucer, "Hastings" ...	8/6 Per doz
064.	Tea Plate, 4″ nominal, "Ascot" ...	6/- ,,
	Tea Set, 21 piece, "Hastings" with Round or Ascot Plates	10/6 Per set
065.	Sugar, Bridge, "Stuart"	Per doz. pairs 13/-
066.	Cream, ,, ,,	
067.	Teapot, "Countess" 30's 36's 42's 48's 54's 34/- 32/- 30/- 21/- 17/-	Per doz.
068.	Sugar, Bridge, "Countess"	Per doz. pairs 12/-
069.	Cream, ,, ,,	
070.	Sugar, Bridge, "Grecian"	16/-
071.	Cream, ,, ,,	
073.	Sugar, Bridge, "Norman"	12/-
072.	Cream, ,, ,,	
074.	Sugar, Bridge, "Ascot"	12/-
075.	Cream, ,, ,,	
076.	Teapot, "Ascot" 30's 36's 48's 34/- 32/- 21/-	Per doz
078.	Sugar, Bridge, "Hector"	Per doz. pairs 12/-
077.	Cream, ,, ,,	
079.	Teapot Stand, "Ascot"	8/- Per doz
080.	,, ,, Round	9/- ,,
081.	Eggcup, fast stand, Plain	12/- ,,
082.	Eggcup, footed, Plain	4/- ,,
083.	Eggcup, fast stand, "Ascot" ...	12/- ,,
084.	Tea and Saucer, tall, "Ascot" ...	8/6 ,,
	Tea Set, 21 piece, tall, "Ascot" ...	10/6 Per set
085.	Covered Jug, "Sexta" 1 pt. 24/-, ½ pt.	16/- Per doz
086.	Toast Rack, "Queen" 3 bar 10/-, 5 bar	12/- ,,
087.	Covered Jug, "Countess" 1 pt. 24/-, ½ pt.	16/- ,,
088.	Tea and Saucer, "King"	8/6 Per doz
	Teaset, 21 piece, "King"	10/6 Per set
089.	Coffee and Saucer, "Can" ...	8/6 Per doz
090.	Coffee and Saucer, "Ascot" ...	8/6 ,,
	Coffee set, 16 piece, "Can" or "Ascot"	9/6 Per set
091.	Beaker, Handled, "Straight" ...	9/6 Per doz
092.	,, Unhandled, ,, ...	8/6 ,,
093.	Bon-Bon, Handled, "Octagon" S/s 12/- L/s	18/- ,,
094.	,, ,, Unhandled, ,, 10/6	14/- ,,
095.	Covered Muffin, "Countess" ...	24/- ,,

All articles quoted above are illustrated on Supplement "C," and are the same prices in any one design or assorted.

These designs can be finished with Colour or Gilt Edge at the same prices.

GRIMWADES LTD. ∴ STOKE-ON-TRENT.

GRIMWADES LTD., Winton Pottery, STOKE-ON-TRENT
SEXTA 6580 BLUE
ALSO MADE IN PINK, GREEN, MAUVE, GOLDEN YELLOW, & PRIMROSE.
SEXTA 1736.
OXFORD 2030.
CAMBRIDGE 2036.
SYDNEY 6580 PINK
ALSO MADE IN BLUE, MAUVE, GREEN, GOLDEN YELLOW & PRIMROSE.
GRAFTON 6580 MAUVE.
ALSO MADE IN BLUE, PINK, GREEN, GOLDEN YELLOW & PRIMROSE.
OXFORD 2035.
SEXTA 1840.
CAMBRIDGE 10067
OXFORD 6580 PRIMROSE BLACK EDGE
ALSO MADE IN PINK, BLUE, MAUVE, GREEN, GOLDEN YELLOW.
London Showrooms—ATLANTIC HOUSE (3rd Floor by lift), 45 to 50, HOLBORN VIADUCT, E.C.1.

JOHNSON BROTHERS LTD.

Johnson Brothers opened their factory in Hanley in 1883 to produce earthenwares. They became much praised in design books and articles in the 1920s and 1930s for the very plain, often undecorated wares they produced. Johnsons Brothers were not interested in handpainted wares which Clarice Cliff was making a name with or all over transfers such as Royal Winton was becoming known for. In a survey of the pottery industry published in *The Studio* in 1936, Johnsons Brothers are commended: "their aim is to produce earthenware bodies of fine texture and colour and to encourage decoration in printing, lithography and stamping which will show a real appreciation of these more mechanized techniques and enable the artist to produce honest work in the particular idiom and not the 'mass production' travesties of hand-painting to which one is accustomed." Interestingly, it was Gordon Forsyth — who later went to work for Royal Winton as a designer — who praised the firm of Johnson Brothers as an "outstanding example of excellent cheap production."

Johnson Brothers foray into the work of chintz was a pattern called **Rose Chintz** which was sold in great quanties in North America for many years. Advertisements in the 1950s *Crockery and Glass Journal* talk of the "delightful fabric inspired pattern which is a permanent favourite with hostesses. Fifty-piece sets retailed for $29.95 in the United States. Perhaps because of the quality of the production and the popularity of this pattern for so many years, this pattern is still easily found throughout North America.

ROSE CHINTZ

This is not considered a chintz pattern by many chintz collectors but it is bought by them for use as opposed to display and has developed a growing market among this group. This "charming informal chintz pattern" was advertised widely in the *Crockery and Glass Journal* as intended for use in every American home.

Cat. No.	Shape	U.S $	Can. $	U.K. £
RC-09	Bowl, 5"	15.00	10.00	10.00
RC-10	Bowl, 6"	20.00	15.00	15.00
RC-55	Coffee Pot, 6 cup	250.00	175.00	100.00
RC-70	Cream and Sugar	60.00	50.00	30.00
RC-103	Plate, 6 1/2"	15.00	10.00	10.00

Cat. No.	Shape	U.S. $	Can. $	U.K. £
RC-106	Plate, 9"	25.00	25.00	10.00
RC-107	Plate, 10"	35.00	30.00	15.00
RC-130	Teacup and saucer	30.00	25.00	15.00
RC-137	Teapot, 6 cup	225.00	150.00	95.00

JAMES KENT, LTD.

James Kent, Ltd. was another of those Staffordshire factories that tried to serve as many mid- or low-priced markets as they could identify. As reported in the 1935 *Pottery Gazette*, Old Foley Pottery at Longton was one of the oldest factories in the potteries. John Wesley preached from the steps of the old house that was incorporated into the James Kent factory on his visit to the potteries in 1790. James Kent took over the factory in 1897 and for more than forty years continued to produce earthenwares which "catered for expressed needs." His three sons helped him to keep in touch with modern movements and the *Gazette* reported the Kent range to be thoroughly up to date.

After this extended report there is remarkably little reference to James Kent in any of the trade publications. In 1939 there is a report of **Du Barry** being presented in the London showrooms. In 1941 Goodwin Johnson Inc. of New York City advertised for sale the following James Kent chintzes: **Harmony, Apple Blossom, Capri, Hydrangea, Du Barry, Pearl Delight, Mille Fleurs,** and **Rosalynde.** Later that year, they took out a full page advertisement showing a wide range of James Kent chintzes including mayonnaise bowls with ladles and nut dishes with scoops similar in shape to Grimwades. Ebeling & Reuss Co., with headquarters in Philadelphia, were the American distributors for Royal Winton and they also appear to have taken on James Kent in 1942. In April 1942 they advertised the six Kent chintz patterns in four place settings to the trade at $17.95. In 1949 they offered open stock in dinnerware and gift items in **Apple Blossom**; cups and saucers were $10.00 per dozen and luncheon plates $12.00 per dozen wholesale. By 1950 Ebeling & Reuss were urging retailers to stock up on assorted **Rosalynde**, offering coffee pots at $33.00 a dozen and small teapots at $24.00 a dozen. In January, 1951 *The Gift Buyer* reported that Miss Ruth Kent had toured Canada to study the methods and requirements of pottery merchandising in Canada. Her 87-year-old father was still chairman and her brothers Phillip and Peter joint managing directors while Ruth served as Sales Director. The next report about the factory came in the 1958 *Gazette* and mentioned four new James Kent chintzes, including **Tapestry**, on display at the Blackpool Gift Fair.

We were fortunate to be able to spend a morning with one of Jimmy Kent's workers. Mrs. Doreen Donegan worked at James Kent in the 1930s, which she described as "hard work for small wages." She joined the factory in 1935 at the age of 16 and was paid 5 shillings and 9 pence a week. She remembers the women who worked on chintz were considered a little above the others. Two slightly stand-offish sisters called Ada and Maude Kent (no relation) did nearly all of the chintzware for many years. "Since you went onto piece work after a training period and chintz was much harder to do everyone wanted to be paid more for doing chintz. I was never able to do teapots . . . they were beyond me." Doreen described cutting out all the little notches for the ruffled sweet dishes and how often the girls cut their fingers while they were working. She said that employees were allowed to buy "thirds" not "seconds" — the difference being that the thirds had obvious chips or cracks. When we asked about day after day of applying transfers, Doreen looked surprised and explained, "I couldn't grumble because I was working." After Jimmy Kent the factory was run by his son Peter and then by Peter's sister, Ruth Kent. By all accounts, Ruth Kent, who had never expected to be running the factory, did a splendid job and was well regarded throughout the potteries.

After being bought and sold several times through the 1980s, the firm went into receivership in 1989 and was bought by M.R. Hadida Ltd., a bathroom furnishings company and owner of Hadida Fine Bone China Ltd. For a brief time in 1985 James Kent made **Du Barry** once again, but the backstamp is very clear: "MIKASA Semi Porcelain Dubarry James Kent England."

Shortly after the first edition came out, we had a reply to our letter to Miss Ruth Kent: "Regarding the chintz patterns produced by our company, there was also another one called **Lichfield**. As far as I can remember **Du Barry** was the first produced around 1934/5 and the others followed; **Du Barry** and **Rosalynde** being the most popular. I do not remember the names of the designers. **Du Barry** remained in production up to 1980 but it was slow to produce and costly. I hope this information may be of some use to you."

APPLE BLOSSOM

This pattern was introduced in the 1930s and exported in quantity to North America before and after the war. Complete dinner services still turn up occasionally in North America.

Cat. No.	Shape	U.S $	Can. $	U.K. £
AB-04	Bonbon dish	50.00	60.00	35.00
AB-10	Bowl, 6"	50.00	50.00	35.00
AB-15	Bowl, 9"	150.00	105.00	85.00
AB-23	Breakfast set	800.00	700.00	450.00
AB-28	Butter dish	150.00	145.00	100.00
AB-36	Cake plate, square, 11"	125.00	125.00	75.00
AB-55	Coffee pot, 4 cup	600.00	500.00	350.00
AB-60	Compote, footed	115.00	95.00	75.00
AB-65	Condiment set on tray	200.00	175.00	115.00
AB-70	Cream and sugar	125.00	95.00	75.00
AB-71	Cream and sugar on tray	175.00	145.00	125.00
AB-75	Demi-tasse	65.00	50.00	40.00
AB-85	Jam pot	125.00	125.00	75.00

Cat. No.	Shape	U.S. $	Can. $	U.K. £
AB-97	Nut dish	50.00	40.00	30.00
AB-103	Plate, 6 1/2"	60.00	50.00	35.00
AB-106	Plate, 9"	100.00	95.00	65.00
AB-112	Relish dish	125.00	125.00	75.00
AB-117	Salt and pepper	75.00	80.00	45.00
AB-118	Salt and pepper on tray	150.00	135.00	90.00
AB-120	Sandwich tray	100.00	110.00	65.00
AB-130	Teacup and saucer	75.00	60.00	45.00
AB-136	Teapot, 4 cup	550.00	300.00	325.00
AB-137	Teapot, 6 cup	650.00	400.00	400.00
AB-150	Toast rack, 4 slice	200.00	165.00	125.00
AB-160	Vase, bud	95.00	95.00	50.00

CRAZY PAVING

The pattern number is 2839.

Cat. No.	Shape	U.S $	Can. $	U.K. £
CP-04	Bonbon dish	45.00	30.00	30.00
CP-10	Bowl, 6 1/2"	45.00	25.00	30.00
CP-15	Bowl, 9"	125.00	75.00	75.00
CP-23	Breakfast set	800.00	500.00	420.00
CP-28	Butter dish	125.00	95.00	80.00
CP-36	Cake plate, square, 11"	100.00	85.00	60.00
CP-55	Coffee pot, 4 cup	500.00	300.00	315.00
CP-60	Compote, footed	100.00	65.00	65.00
CP-65	Condiment set on tray	165.00	115.00	105.00
CP-70	Cream and sugar	100.00	65.00	65.00
CP-71	Cream and sugar on tray	150.00	95.00	95.00
CP-75	Demi-tasse	55.00	40.00	35.00
CP-85	Jam pot	100.00	95.00	70.00

Cat. No.	Shape	U.S. $	Can. $	U.K. £
CP-97	Nut dish	40.00	25.00	25.00
CP-103	Plate, 6 1/2"	45.00	35.00	30.00
CP-106	Plate, 9"	75.00	65.00	50.00
CP-112	Relish dish	100.00	95.00	65.00
CP-117	Salt and pepper	65.00	55.00	40.00
CP-118	Salt and pepper on tray	135.00	105.00	90.00
CP-120	Sandwich tray	85.00	75.00	50.00
CP-130	Teacup and saucer	65.00	45.00	45.00
CP-136	Teapot, 4 cup	450.00	225.00	290.00
CP-137	Teapot, 6 cup	550.00	275.00	340.00
CP-150	Toast rack, 4 slice	200.00	125.00	130.00
CP-160	Vase, bud	85.00	75.00	50.00

DU BARRY

This pattern was in the London showrooms in 1938 and exported in quantity to North America before and after the war. Complete dinner services still turn up occasionally in North America. It was reproduced briefly in 1985, but clearly marked MIKASA. According to Miss Ruth Kent, **Du Barry** was first produced around 1934/35 and remained in production up to 1980, "but it was slow to produce and costly."

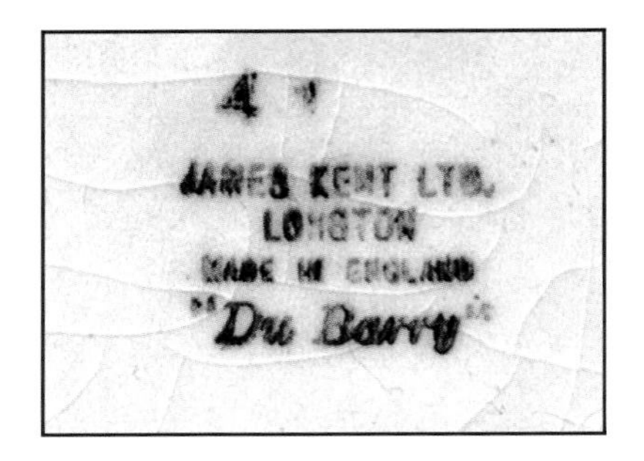

Cat. No.	Shape	U.S $	Can. $	U.K. £
D-04	Bonbon dish	50.00	60.00	35.00
D-10	Bowl, 6"	50.00	50.00	35.00
D-15	Bowl, 9"	150.00	105.00	95.00
D-23	Breakfast set	850.00	700.00	525.00
D-28	Butter dish	150.00	145.00	110.00
D-36	Cake plate, square, 11"	125.00	125.00	85.00
D-55	Coffee pot, 4 cup	700.00	500.00	500.00
D-60	Compote, footed	115.00	95.00	85.00
D-65	Condiment set on tray	200.00	175.00	125.00
D-70	Cream and sugar	100.00	95.00	70.00
D-71	Cream and sugar on tray	175.00	145.00	110.00
D-75	Demi-tasse	65.00	50.00	45.00
D-	Honey Pot		VERY RARE	

Cat. No.	Shape	U.S. $	Can. $	U.K. £
D-85	Jam pot	125.00	125.00	85.00
D-97	Nut dish	50.00	40.00	30.00
D-103	Plate, 6 1/2"	60.00	50.00	35.00
D-106	Plate, 9"	100.00	95.00	70.00
D-112	Relish dish	125.00	125.00	85.00
D-117	Salt and pepper	75.00	80.00	50.00
D-118	Salt and pepper on tray	150.00	135.00	95.00
D-120	Sandwich tray	100.00	110.00	65.00
D-130	Teacup and saucer	75.00	60.00	50.00
D-136	Teapot, 4 cup	550.00	300.00	350.00
D-137	Teapot, 6 cup	650.00	400.00	450.00
D-150	Toast rack, 4 slice	225.00	165.00	135.00
D-160	Vase, bud	125.00	95.00	60.00

FLORITA

The pattern number is 5008, and the pattern was probably introduced in early 1958. It is very popular with North American collectors. Because the blue tends to fade, the more vivid the colour, the higher the price.

Cat. No.	Shape	U.S $	Can. $	U.K. £
F-04	Bonbon dish	60.00	70.00	40.00
F-10	Bowl, 6"	60.00	60.00	40.00
F-15	Bowl, 9"	165.00	125.00	110.00
F-23	Breakfast set	1,000.00	800.00	525.00
F-28	Butter dish	165.00	175.00	110.00
F-36	Cake plate, square, 11"	150.00	150.00	95.00
F-55	Coffee pot, 4 cup	750.00	650.00	500.00
F-60	Compote, footed	125.00	125.00	85.00
F-65	Condiment set on tray	225.00	200.00	135.00
F-70	Cream and sugar	125.00	110.00	85.00
F-71	Cream and sugar on tray	200.00	175.00	125.00
F-75	Demi-tasse	75.00	60.00	50.00
F-85	Jam Pot	150.00	145.00	110.00

Cat. No.	Shape	U.S. $	Can. $	U.K. £
F-97	Nut dish	50.00	50.00	35.00
F-103	Plate, 6 1/2"	65.00	60.00	45.00
F-106	Plate, 9"	100.00	110.00	70.00
F-112	Relish dish	150.00	150.00	95.00
F-117	Salt and pepper	75.00	95.00	55.00
F-118	Salt and pepper on tray	165.00	165.00	110.00
F-120	Sandwich tray	115.00	125.00	85.00
F-130	Teacup and saucer	75.00	75.00	55.00
F-136	Teapot, 4 cup	600.00	450.00	400.00
F-137	Teapot, 6 cup	700.00	550.00	475.00
F-150	Toast rack, 4 slice	225.00	195.00	150.00
F-160	Vase, bud	125.00	125.00	60.00

HARMONY

This chintz pattern was an uncontrolled pattern and was used by a number of companies, including A.G. Richardson pattern number 3275, and Hollinshead & Kirkham. The Czechoslovakian version of this pattern is called **Chelsea**.

Cat. No.	Shape	U.S $	Can. $	U.K. £
Ha-04	Bonbon dish	35.00	30.00	25.00
Ha-10	Bowl, 6″	40.00	25.00	30.00
Ha-15	Bowl, 9″	90.00	75.00	70.00
Ha-23	Breakfast set	500.00	500.00	350.00
Ha-28	Butter dish	90.00	95.00	70.00
Ha-36	Cake plate, square, 11″	90.00	85.00	70.00
Ha-55	Coffee pot, 4 cup	400.00	300.00	325.00
Ha-60	Compote, footed	65.00	65.00	55.00
Ha-65	Condiment set on tray	115.00	115.00	90.00
Ha-70	Cream and sugar	65.00	65.00	50.00
Ha-71	Cream and sugar on tray	105.00	95.00	85.00
Ha-75	Demi-tasse	40.00	40.00	35.00
Ha-85	Jam pot	90.00	95.00	65.00

Cat. No.	Shape	U.S. $	Can. $	U.K. £
Ha-97	Nut dish	40.00	25.00	30.00
Ha-103	Plate, 6 1/2″	35.00	35.00	25.00
Ha-106	Plate, 9″	55.00	65.00	40.00
Ha-112	Relish dish	65.00	95.00	55.00
Ha-117	Salt and pepper	55.00	55.00	40.00
Ha-118	Salt and pepper on tray	100.00	95.00	80.00
Ha-120	Sandwich tray	65.00	75.00	50.00
Ha-130	Teacup and saucer	45.00	45.00	35.00
Ha-136	Teapot, 4 cup	325.00	200.00	275.00
Ha-137	Teapot, 6 cup	400.00	250.00	325.00
Ha-150	Toast rack, 4 slice	135.00	110.00	95.00
Ha-160	Vase, bud	65.00	70.00	45.00

HYDRANGEA (WHITE)

This pattern is the most sought after James Kent pattern in North America. The pattern was also available with a black background, but this version is much preferred. Hydrangea cups and saucers were advertised for sale by Bullocks, Los Angeles in 1941 for 75¢ each.

Cat. No.	Shape	U.S $	Can. $	U.K. £
Hy-04	Bonbon dish	65.00	70.00	40.00
Hy-10	Bowl, 6″	75.00	60.00	45.00
Hy-15	Bowl, 9″	175.00	125.00	105.00
Hy-23	Breakfast set	1,000.00	800.00	525.00
Hy-28	Butter dish	175.00	175.00	105.00
Hy-36	Cake plate, square, 11″	150.00	150.00	90.00
Hy-55	Coffee pot, 4 cup	750.00	650.00	475.00
Hy-60	Compote, footed	135.00	125.00	90.00
Hy-65	Condiment set on tray	225.00	200.00	145.00
Hy-70	Cream and sugar	125.00	115.00	80.00
Hy-71	Cream and sugar on tray	200.00	185.00	135.00
Hy-75	Demi-tasse	75.00	60.00	50.00
Hy-85	Jam pot	150.00	145.00	95.00

Cat. No.	Shape	U.S. $	Can. $	U.K. £
Hy-97	Nut dish	50.00	50.00	35.00
Hy-103	Plate, 6 1/2″	75.00	60.00	50.00
Hy-106	Plate, 9″	125.00	110.00	80.00
Hy-112	Relish dish	150.00	150.00	90.00
Hy-117	Salt and pepper	100.00	95.00	65.00
Hy-118	Salt and pepper on tray	175.00	165.00	105.00
Hy-120	Sandwich tray	125.00	130.00	80.00
Hy-130	Teacup and saucer	85.00	75.00	55.00
Hy-136	Teapot, 4 cup	725.00	450.00	425.00
Hy-137	Teapot, 6 cup	825.00	550.00	475.00
Hy-150	Toast rack, 4 slice	250.00	200.00	160.00
Hy-160	Vase, bud	125.00	125.00	70.00

HYDRANGEA (BLACK)

This pattern is the alternate colourway to **Hydrangea** but it is not popular with North American collectors.

Cat. No.	Shape	U.S $	Can. $	U.K. £
HyB-04	Bonbon dish	35.00	30.00	25.00
HyB-10	Bowl, 6″	40.00	25.00	30.00
HyB-15	Bowl, 9″	90.00	75.00	65.00
HyB-23	Breakfast set	500.00	500.00	365.00
HyB-28	Butter dish	90.00	95.00	70.00
HyB-36	Cake plate, square, 11″	80.00	85.00	50.00
HyB-55	Coffee pot, 4 cup	400.00	300.00	325.00
HyB-60	Compote, footed	70.00	65.00	55.00
HyB-65	Condiment set on tray	115.00	115.00	90.00
HyB-70	Cream and sugar	65.00	70.00	50.00
HyB-71	Cream and sugar on tray	105.00	115.00	80.00
HyB-75	Demi-tasse	40.00	40.00	35.00
HyB-85	Jam pot	90.00	95.00	70.00

Cat. No.	Shape	U.S. $	Can. $	U.K. £
HyB-97	Nut dish	40.00	25.00	30.00
HyB-103	Plate, 6 1/2″	40.00	35.00	25.00
HyB-106	Plate, 9″	55.00	65.00	40.00
HyB-112	Relish dish	75.00	95.00	55.00
HyB-117	Salt and pepper	50.00	55.00	40.00
HyB-118	Salt and pepper on tray	100.00	105.00	80.00
HyB-120	Sandwich tray	65.00	75.00	45.00
HyB-130	Teacup and saucer	50.00	45.00	35.00
HyB-136	Teapot, 4 cup	325.00	225.00	275.00
HyB-137	Teapot, 6 cup	400.00	275.00	325.00
HyB-150	Toast rack, 4 slice	135.00	115.00	90.00
HyB-160	Vase, bud	65.00	75.00	45.00

LICHFIELD

Although this pattern was exported to North America in the 1940s in quantity, it is not popular with American collectors. Miss Ruth Kent said in a letter dated April 15, 1996 that this was definitely considered one of the Kent chintz patterns, however.

Cat. No.	Shape	U.S $	Can. $	U.K. £
L-04	Bonbon dish	35.00	25.00	25.00
L-10	Bowl, 6″	40.00	20.00	30.00
L-15	Bowl, 9″	90.00	65.00	65.00
L-23	Breakfast set	500.00	450.00	325.00
L-28	Butter dish	90.00	85.00	65.00
L-36	Cake plate, square, 11″	90.00	75.00	65.00
L-55	Coffee pot, 4 cup	400.00	275.00	300.00
L-60	Compote, footed	65.00	60.00	50.00
L-65	Condiment set on tray	115.00	105.00	80.00
L-70	Cream and sugar	65.00	50.00	45.00
L-71	Cream and sugar on tray	105.00	85.00	75.00
L-75	Demi-tasse	40.00	35.00	30.00
L-85	Jam pot	90.00	85.00	60.00

Cat. No.	Shape	U.S. $	Can. $	U.K. £
L-97	Nut dish	40.00	20.00	30.00
L-103	Plate, 6 1/2″	35.00	30.00	25.00
L-106	Plate, 9″	55.00	50.00	40.00
L-112	Relish dish	65.00	75.00	50.00
L-117	Salt and pepper	55.00	45.00	35.00
L-118	Salt and pepper on tray	100.00	75.00	75.00
L-120	Sandwich tray	65.00	60.00	45.00
L-130	Teacup and saucer	45.00	35.00	30.00
L-136	Teapot, 4 cup	325.00	200.00	250.00
L-137	Teapot, 6 cup	400.00	250.00	300.00
L-150	Toast rack, 4 slice	135.00	100.00	90.00
L-160	Vase, bud	65.00	60.00	40.00

MARIGOLD

We currently have no information available on this pattern.

Cat. No.	Shape	U.S $	Can. $	U.K. £
Mg-04	Bonbon dish	40.00	30.00	25.00
Mg-10	Bowl, 6″	45.00	25.00	30.00
Mg-15	Bowl, 9″	100.00	75.00	65.00
Mg-23	Breakfast set	550.00	500.00	325.00
Mg-28	Butter dish	100.00	95.00	70.00
Mg-36	Cake plate, square, 11″	90.00	85.00	50.00
Mg-55	Coffee pot, 4 cup	450.00	300.00	325.00
Mg-60	Compote, footed	80.00	65.00	55.00
Mg-65	Condiment set on tray	135.00	115.00	90.00
Mg-70	Cream and sugar	75.00	65.00	45.00
Mg-71	Cream and sugar on tray	125.00	105.00	80.00
Mg-75	Demi-tasse	45.00	40.00	35.00
Mg-85	Jam pot	100.00	95.00	70.00

Cat. No.	Shape	U.S. $	Can. $	U.K. £
Mg-97	Nut dish	45.00	25.00	30.00
Mg-103	Plate, 6 1/2″	40.00	35.00	25.00
Mg-106	Plate, 9″	65.00	65.00	40.00
Mg-112	Relish dish	85.00	95.00	55.00
Mg-117	Salt and pepper	60.00	55.00	40.00
Mg-118	Salt and pepper on tray	115.00	105.00	80.00
Mg-120	Sandwich tray	75.00	75.00	45.00
Mg-130	Teacup and saucer	50.00	45.00	35.00
Mg-136	Teapot, 4 cup	375.00	225.00	275.00
Mg-137	Teapot, 6 cup	450.00	275.00	325.00
Mg-150	Toast rack, 4 slice	150.00	115.00	95.00
Mg-160	Vase, bud	65.00	75.00	45.00

MILLE FLEURS

This pattern was an uncontrolled pattern and was used by a number of companies, including A.G. Richardson pattern number 5007 and Elijah Cotton, who called it **Marigold**. It was also produced in Czechoslovakia. A 1941 American advertisement by Bullock's of Los Angeles offered **Mille Fleurs** cups and saucers for sale at 75¢ each.

Cat. No.	Shape	U.S $	Can. $	U.K. £
MF-04	Bonbon dish	50.00	30.00	30.00
MF-10	Bowl, 6"	50.00	25.00	30.00
MF-15	Bowl, 9"	115.00	75.00	75.00
MF-23	Breakfast set	650.00	500.00	425.00
MF-28	Butter dish	125.00	95.00	80.00
MF-36	Cake plate, square, 11"	125.00	85.00	80.00
MF-55	Coffee pot, 4 cup	550.00	300.00	375.00
MF-60	Compote, footed	100.00	65.00	65.00
MF-65	Condiment set on tray	175.00	115.00	105.00
MF-70	Cream and sugar	85.00	65.00	50.00
MF-71	Cream and sugar on tray	150.00	105.00	90.00
MF-75	Demi-tasse	60.00	40.00	40.00
MF-85	Jam pot	110.00	95.00	70.00
MF-97	Nut dish	45.00	25.00	30.00
MF-103	Plate, 6 1/2"	50.00	35.00	30.00
MF-106	Plate, 9"	85.00	65.00	50.00
MF-112	Relish dish	100.00	95.00	70.00
MF-117	Salt and pepper	75.00	55.00	50.00
MF-118	Salt and pepper on tray	135.00	105.00	95.00
MF-120	Sandwich tray	85.00	75.00	50.00
MF-130	Teacup and saucer	65.00	45.00	45.00
MF-136	Teapot, 4 cup	450.00	225.00	325.00
MF-137	Teapot, 6 cup	550.00	275.00	375.00
MF-150	Toast rack, 4 slice	200.00	115.00	120.00
MF-160	Vase, bud	70.00	75.00	50.00

PRIMULA

We currently have no information available on this pattern.

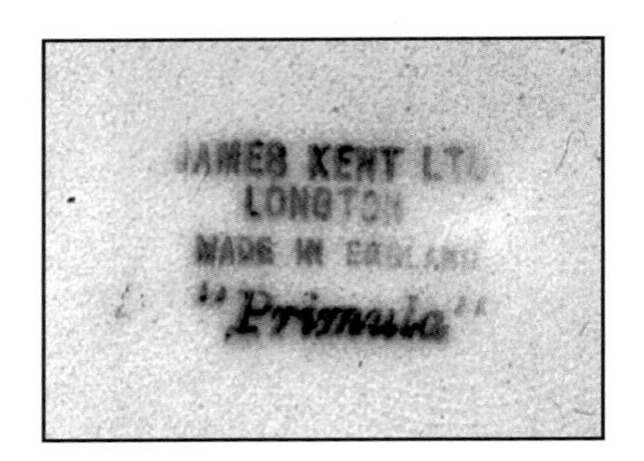

Cat. No.	Shape	U.S $	Can. $	U.K. £
Pr-04	Bonbon dish	50.00	30.00	35.00
Pr-10	Bowl, 6"	50.00	30.00	35.00
Pr-15	Bowl, 9"	115.00	75.00	80.00
Pr-23	Breakfast set	650.00	500.00	440.00
Pr-28	Butter dish	125.00	90.00	85.00
Pr-36	Cake plate, square, 11"	120.00	85.00	85.00
Pr-55	Coffee pot, 4 cup	550.00	300.00	375.00
Pr-60	Compote, footed	100.00	65.00	75.00
Pr-65	Condiment set on tray	175.00	125.00	110.00
Pr-70	Cream and sugar	100.00	65.00	75.00
Pr-71	Cream and sugar on tray	150.00	105.00	95.00
Pr-75	Demi-tasse	60.00	40.00	45.00
Pr-85	Jam pot	110.00	95.00	75.00

Cat. No.	Shape	U.S. $	Can. $	U.K. £
Pr-97	Nut dish	45.00	25.00	35.00
Pr-103	Plate, 6 1/2"	50.00	35.00	35.00
Pr-106	Plate, 9"	85.00	65.00	55.00
Pr-112	Relish dish	105.00	95.00	75.00
Pr-117	Salt and pepper	75.00	55.00	50.00
Pr-118	Salt and pepper on tray	135.00	95.00	95.00
Pr-120	Sandwich tray	85.00	75.00	55.00
Pr-130	Teacup and saucer	65.00	45.00	45.00
Pr-136	Teapot, 4 cup	450.00	225.00	325.00
Pr-137	Teapot, 6 cup	550.00	275.00	375.00
Pr-150	Toast rack, 4 slice	200.00	115.00	135.00
Pr-160	Vase, bud	75.00	75.00	55.00

RAPTURE

The pattern number is 3007.

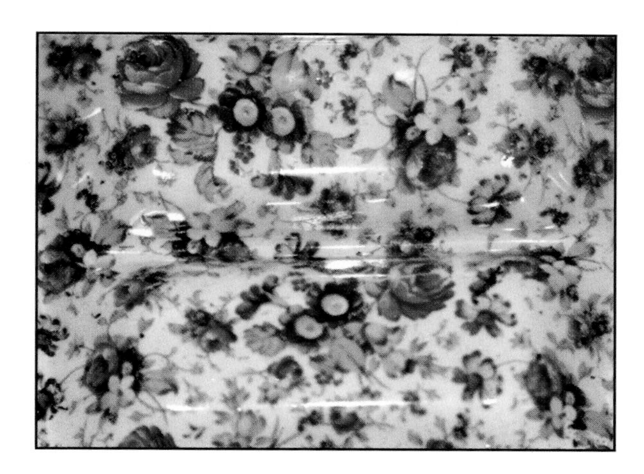

Cat. No.	Shape	U.S $	Can. $	U.K. £
Ra-04	Bonbon dish	40.00	30.00	25.00
Ra-10	Bowl, 6″	45.00	25.00	30.00
Ra-15	Bowl, 9″	100.00	75.00	65.00
Ra-23	Breakfast set	550.00	500.00	350.00
Ra-28	Butter dish	100.00	95.00	65.00
Ra-36	Cake plate, square, 11″	100.00	85.00	65.00
Ra-55	Coffee pot, 4 cup	450.00	300.00	300.00
Ra-60	Compote, footed	80.00	65.00	50.00
Ra-65	Condiment set on tray	135.00	115.00	85.00
Ra-70	Cream and sugar	75.00	65.00	45.00
Ra-71	Cream and sugar on tray	125.00	105.00	75.00
Ra-75	Demi-tasse	45.00	40.00	30.00
Ra-85	Jam pot	100.00	95.00	65.00

Cat. No.	Shape	U.S. $	Can. $	U.K. £
Ra-97	Nut dish	45.00	25.00	30.00
Ra-103	Plate, 6 1/2″	40.00	35.00	25.00
Ra-106	Plate, 9″	65.00	65.00	40.00
Ra-112	Relish dish	85.00	95.00	50.00
Ra-117	Salt and pepper	60.00	55.00	35.00
Ra-118	Salt and pepper on tray	115.00	95.00	75.00
Ra-120	Sandwich tray	75.00	75.00	45.00
Ra-140	Stacking Teapot		Rare	
Ra-130	Teacup and saucer	50.00	45.00	30.00
Ra-136	Teapot, 4 cup	375.00	225.00	250.00
Ra-137	Teapot, 6 cup	450.00	275.00	300.00
Ra-150	Toast rack, 4 slice	150.00	115.00	85.00
Ra-160	Vase, bud	65.00	70.00	40.00

ROCHELLE

Unfortunately we have no information on this pattern at this time.

Rochelle Ware
James Kent, Ltd.
FENTON, ENGLAND.

Cat. No.	Shape	U.S $	Can. $	U.K. £
Roc-04	Bonbon dish	35.00	25.00	25.00
Roc-10	Bowl, 6″	40.00	20.00	30.00
Roc-15	Bowl, 9″	90.00	65.00	70.00
Roc-23	Breakfast set	500.00	450.00	350.00
Roc-28	Butter dish	90.00	85.00	70.00
Roc-36	Cake plate, square, 11″	90.00	75.00	70.00
Roc-55	Coffee pot, 4 cup	400.00	300.00	325.00
Roc-60	Compote, footed	65.00	60.00	55.00
Roc-65	Condiment set on tray	115.00	105.00	90.00
Roc-70	Cream and sugar	65.00	60.00	50.00
Roc-71	Cream and sugar on tray	105.00	95.00	85.00
Roc-75	Demi-tasse	40.00	35.00	35.00
Roc-85	Jam pot	90.00	85.00	65.00

Cat. No.	Shape	U.S. $	Can. $	U.K. £
Roc-97	Nut dish	40.00	20.00	30.00
Roc-103	Plate, 6 1/2″	35.00	30.00	25.00
Roc-106	Plate, 9″	55.00	60.00	40.00
Roc-112	Relish dish	65.00	85.00	55.00
Roc-117	Salt and pepper	55.00	50.00	40.00
Roc-118	Salt and pepper on tray	100.00	90.00	80.00
Roc-120	Sandwich tray	65.00	65.00	50.00
Roc-130	Teacup and saucer	45.00	35.00	35.00
Roc-136	Teapot, 4 cup	325.00	200.00	275.00
Roc-137	Teapot, 6 cup	400.00	250.00	325.00
Roc-150	Toast rack, 4 slice	135.00	105.00	95.00
Roc-160	Vase, bud	65.00	60.00	45.00

ROSALYNDE

The pattern number is 2662. This pattern was introduced in the 1930s and exported in quantity to North America before and after the war. Complete dinner services still turn up occasionally in North America. Miss Ruth Kent remembers **Rosalynde** as one of the most popular patterns produced by her factory.

Cat. No.	Shape	U.S $	Can. $	U.K. £
Ro-04	Bonbon dish	60.00	65.00	35.00
Ro-10	Bowl, 6″	60.00	55.00	35.00
Ro-15	Bowl, 9″	165.00	115.00	105.00
Ro-23	Breakfast set	800.00	750.00	525.00
Ro-28	Butter dish	165.00	150.00	105.00
Ro-36	Cake plate, square, 11″	150.00	135.00	90.00
Ro-55	Coffee pot, 4 cup	750.00	550.00	525.00
Ro-60	Compote, footed	125.00	105.00	80.00
Ro-65	Condiment set on tray	225.00	185.00	160.00
Ro-70	Cream and sugar	125.00	105.00	80.00
Ro-71	Cream and sugar on tray	200.00	165.00	125.00
Ro-75	Demi-tasse	75.00	55.00	50.00
Ro-85	Jam pot	150.00	135.00	90.00

Cat. No.	Shape	U.S. $	Can. $	U.K. £
Ro-97	Nut dish	50.00	45.00	35.00
Ro-103	Plate, 6 1/2″	65.00	55.00	40.00
Ro-106	Plate, 9″	110.00	105.00	65.00
Ro-112	Relish dish	150.00	115.00	90.00
Ro-117	Salt and pepper	80.00	85.00	50.00
Ro-118	Salt and pepper on tray	165.00	150.00	105.00
Ro-120	Sandwich tray	110.00	115.00	70.00
Ro-130	Teacup and saucer	80.00	65.00	55.00
Ro-136	Teapot, 4 cup	600.00	325.00	400.00
Ro-137	Teapot, 6 cup	700.00	425.00	475.00
Ro-150	Toast rack, 4 slice	225.00	175.00	145.00
Ro-160	Vase, bud	90.00	100.00	60.00

SILVERDALE

The James Kent pattern number is 1097, but this pattern has also been found with a Royal Winton backstamp.

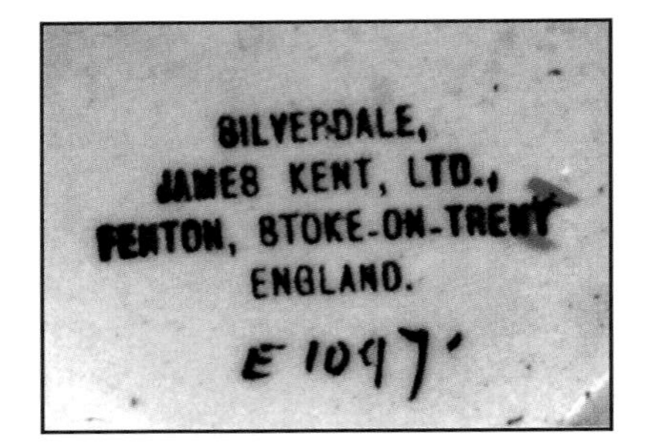

Cat. No.	Shape	U.S $	Can. $	U.K. £
S-04	Bonbon dish	30.00	25.00	20.00
S-10	Bowl, 6″	35.00	20.00	20.00
S-15	Bowl, 9″	75.00	65.00	45.00
S-23	Breakfast set	450.00	450.00	300.00
S-28	Butter dish	100.00	85.00	60.00
S-36	Cake plate, square, 11″	75.00	75.00	45.00
S-55	Coffee pot, 4 cup	400.00	275.00	250.00
S-60	Compote, footed	75.00	55.00	45.00
S-65	Condiment set on tray	135.00	105.00	85.00
S-70	Cream and sugar	65.00	60.00	40.00
S-71	Cream and sugar on tray	115.00	95.00	75.00
S-75	Demi-tasse	40.00	35.00	25.00
S-85	Jam pot	85.00	80.00	50.00

Cat. No.	Shape	U.S. $	Can. $	U.K. £
S-97	Nut dish	35.00	20.00	20.00
S-103	Plate, 6 1/2″	35.00	30.00	20.00
S-106	Plate, 9″	75.00	55.00	45.00
S-112	Relish dish	75.00	75.00	45.00
S-117	Salt and pepper	50.00	55.00	35.00
S-118	Salt and pepper on tray	110.00	85.00	65.00
S-120	Sandwich tray	60.00	65.00	35.00
S-130	Teacup and saucer	45.00	40.00	30.00
S-136	Teapot, 4 cup	325.00	200.00	200.00
S-137	Teapot, 6 cup	395.00	250.00	225.00
S-150	Toast rack, 4 slice	125.00	105.00	75.00
S-160	Vase, bud	65.00	60.00	40.00

TAPESTRY

The pattern number is 5615, and the pattern was introduced at the gift show in Blackpool in 1958. This pattern was used by a number of factories in the 1950s including Rosina on bone china.

Cat. No.	Shape	U.S $	Can. $	U.K. £
Tp-04	Bonbon dish	50.00	30.00	30.00
Tp-10	Bowl, 6″	50.00	25.00	30.00
Tp-15	Bowl, 9″	115.00	85.00	75.00
Tp-23	Breakfast set	650.00	550.00	400.00
Tp-28	Butter dish	125.00	105.00	75.00
Tp-36	Cake plate, square, 11″	125.00	95.00	75.00
Tp-55	Coffee pot, 4 cup	550.00	325.00	350.00
Tp-60	Compote, footed	100.00	75.00	65.00
Tp-65	Condiment set on tray	175.00	125.00	100.00
Tp-70	Cream and sugar	100.00	75.00	65.00
Tp-71	Cream and sugar on tray	150.00	125.00	85.00
Tp-75	Demi-tasse	60.00	45.00	35.00
Tp-85	Jam pot	110.00	105.00	65.00

Cat. No.	Shape	U.S. $	Can. $	U.K. £
Tp-97	Nut dish	45.00	30.00	30.00
Tp-103	Plate, 6 1/2″	50.00	40.00	30.00
Tp-106	Plate, 9″	85.00	75.00	50.00
Tp-112	Relish dish	100.00	105.00	65.00
Tp-117	Salt and pepper	75.00	65.00	45.00
Tp-118	Salt and pepper on tray	135.00	115.00	85.00
Tp-120	Sandwich tray	85.00	85.00	50.00
Tp-130	Teacup and saucer	65.00	50.00	40.00
Tp-136	Teapot, 4 cup	450.00	250.00	300.00
Tp-137	Teapot, 6 cup	550.00	300.00	350.00
Tp-150	Toast rack, 4 slice	200.00	125.00	115.00
Tp-160	Vase, bud	85.00	80.00	50.00

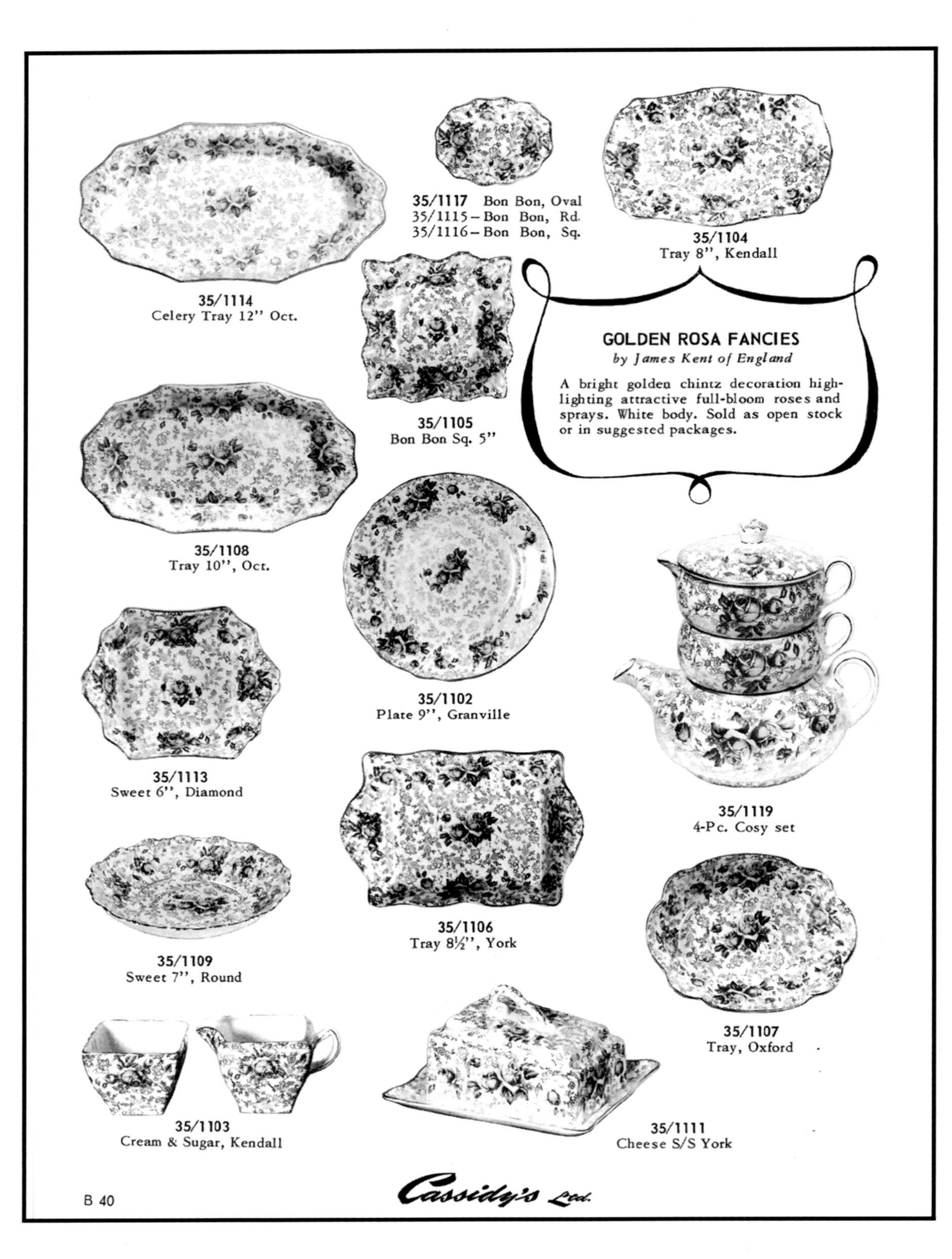

35/1114
Celery Tray 12" Oct.

35/1117 Bon Bon, Oval
35/1115 – Bon Bon, Rd.
35/1116 – Bon Bon, Sq.

35/1104
Tray 8", Kendall

35/1105
Bon Bon Sq. 5"

GOLDEN ROSA FANCIES

by James Kent of England

A bright golden chintz decoration highlighting attractive full-bloom roses and sprays. White body. Sold as open stock or in suggested packages.

35/1108
Tray 10", Oct.

35/1102
Plate 9", Granville

35/1119
4-Pc. Cosy set

35/1113
Sweet 6", Diamond

35/1106
Tray 8½", York

35/1109
Sweet 7", Round

35/1107
Tray, Oxford

35/1103
Cream & Sugar, Kendall

35/1111
Cheese S/S York

W.R. MIDWINTER LTD.

William Robinson Midwinter spent 18 years working for the head of Royal Doulton and selling "seconds" at night and on weekends. By 1910 he had saved 50 pounds and was ready to set up his own business at Bournes Bank Pottery in Burslem. The factory turned out very much the same product lines as every other small pottery in Staffordshire, and it prospered. After buying up the Albion Pottery and Stewart Maddock Ltd., Midwinter increased production and began to produce tablewares in addition to teawares and toiletwares. For the most part the patterns were the traditional florals produced by the other factories.

According to Allan Peat, author of *Midwinter: A Collectors' Guide,* the Midwinter factory worked on the basis of one new pattern a week and Roy Midwinter, William's son, set off for North America in 1952 with a number of recent designs. Colonel Keene, the legendary buyer for Eaton's of Canada, is reported to have said, "Get that... stuff out of here," and his colleague at Robert Simpson of Canada, Maurice Pickles, concurred. Asked for advice, Colonel Keene directed Roy Midwinter to the American West Coast and designers like Eva Zeisal. Roy shipped samples home from California and helped to change the design direction not only of Midwinter but of the Potteries as well.

Midwinter became renowned for their risk taking in leading the way in modern design in Staffordshire. Their designs by Jessie Tait, Terence Conran, Sir Hugh Casson and David Queensberry have found their way into most museums of modern design. Roy Midwinter never lost sight of the traditional markets, however, and he was careful to continue to cater to them. The Midwinter chintzes are part of this traditional market and they warrant exactly one line in Allan Peat's book on Midwinter.

Although the whole factory was modernized and a decorating department opened, the printing shop was still used principally for traditional printed patterns such as **Springtime.** Several Midwinter advertisements from the mid 1940s feature **Springtime** as a controlled Midwinter chintz. The only other reference to **Springtime** is in the pattern information from *The Midwinter Trade Price Book,* which states that the pattern was discontinued in 1974 on the Fine shape. Since this shape is chunky and seemingly unsuited to chintz, one wonders if **Springtime** was now a different pattern. This could account for chintz pieces with the name **Brama** clearly marked on **Springtime** chintz and for backstamps which date to the late 1940s and the 1950s.

An advertisement appeared in May 1949 for a "new Wilkinson production of superb colour and charm..." and the pattern was called **Lorna Doone**. This identical pattern appears frequently with the Midwinter Stylecraft backstamp. In fact, Midwinter bought Wilkinson from Clarice Cliff in 1964 and presumably took over the pattern. It is an excellent example of a transitional period in design. The Midwinter **Lorna Doone** range is a strange amalgam of traditional decoration and modern styling. Most of the line was in some way fitted with chrome handles or chrome bases. Neither the shapes nor the fittings were particularly well-suited to chintz. Some pieces have a Midwinter backstamp with the name **Bird Chintz** underneath so perhaps at some point the factory renamed their patterns.

In 1968 Midwinter merged with J & G Meakin Ltd., and in 1970 the combined company was taken over by the Wedgwood Group.

BRAMA

This was a pattern controlled to Midwinter as **Springtime** and advertised as such before and after the Second World War. It is unclear when and why the name was changed to **Brama**.

Cat. No.	Shape	U.S. $	Can. $	U.K. £
Br-170	Biscuit barrel	450.00	350.00	250.00
Br-04	Bonbon dish	60.00	45.00	35.00
Br-40	Cake plate, 2 tier	125.00	95.00	75.00
Br-41	Cake plate, 3 tier	175.00	125.00	125.00
Br-42	Cake plate, with server	175.00	150.00	125.00
Br-43	Cake stand, chrome handle	100.00	75.00	65.00
Br-44	Cake stand, chrome base	100.00	75.00	65.00

Cat. No.	Shape	U.S. $	Can. $	U.K. £
Br-65	Condiment set on tray	200.00	150.00	125.00
Br-85	Jam pot with liner	125.00	115.00	75.00
Br-103	Plate, 6"	75.00	50.00	45.00
Br-106	Plate, 9"	125.00	75.00	75.00
Br-120	Sandwich tray	150.00	125.00	85.00
Br-169	Sugar shaker	300.00	225.00	150.00
Br-130	Teacup and saucer	85.00	55.00	50.00

CORAL

We currently have no information available on this pattern.

Midwinter
Stylecraft
STAFFORDSHIRE ENGLAND
FASHION SHAPE
3-66

Cat. No.	Shape	U.S. $	Can. $	U.K. £
C-170	Biscuit barrel	450.00	350.00	250.00
C-04	Bonbon dish	50.00	45.00	30.00
C-40	Cake plate, 2 tier	125.00	95.00	75.00
C-41	Cake plate, 3 tier	175.00	125.00	125.00
C-42	Cake plate, with server	175.00	150.00	125.00
C-43	Cake stand, chrome handle	100.00	75.00	50.00
C-44	Cake stand, chrome base	85.00	75.00	50.00
C-65	Condiment set on tray	175.00	145.00	125.00
C-85	Jam pot with liner	100.00	110.00	65.00
C-103	Plate, 6″	60.00	45.00	35.00
C-106	Plate, 9″	115.00	70.00	75.00
C-120	Sandwich tray	125.00	110.00	75.00
C-169	Sugar shaker	275.00	225.00	150.00
C-130	Teacup and saucer	85.00	50.00	50.00

LORNA DOONE

This pattern can be found in the A.J. Wilkinson Clarice Cliff archive from the late 1940s. Some pieces have been found with a "Royal Staffordshire Ceramics by Clarice Cliff" backstamp. We assume that any piece of **Lorna Doone** with a Midwinter backstamp must have been produced after the 1964 takeover of Wilkinsons. At some point Midwinter changed the name and pieces appear with the backstamp pattern name **Bird Chintz**. This pattern was also produced by Barker Brothers and other Staffordshire factories.

Cat. No.	Shape	U.S. $	Can. $	U.K. £
LD-170	Biscuit barrel	400.00	275.00	225.00
LD-04	Bonbon dish	40.00	35.00	25.00
LD-40	Cake plate, 2 tier	110.00	75.00	65.00
LD-41	Cake plate, 3 tier	150.00	95.00	100.00
LD-42	Cake plate, with server	150.00	115.00	100.00
LD-43	Cake stand, chrome handle	85.00	60.00	50.00
LD-44	Cake stand, chrome base	75.00	60.00	45.00
LD-	Candlestick		RARE	
LD-65	Condiment set on tray	150.00	95.00	100.00
LD-85	Jam pot with liner	95.00	75.00	60.00
LD-103	Plate, 6"	50.00	35.00	30.00
LD-106	Plate, 9"	100.00	55.00	65.00
LD-120	Sandwich tray	100.00	75.00	65.00
LD-169	Sugar shaker	250.00	175.00	150.00
LD-130	Teacup and saucer	75.00	40.00	45.00
LD-160	Vase		RARE	

MYOTT SON & COMPANY

Although the original pottery was established in the early nineteenth century, when Ashley Myott inherited the chairmanship at 19 years of age, he and his brother Sydney built up the business into a worldwide concern. The factory tried to produce a little of everything in earthenware. They produced some extreme shapes with vivid handpainting during the 1920s and 1930s in competition with Newport Pottery. They produced art pottery in the Carlton ware mould but not of the same quality. They used a wide variety of prints and enamels on their tablewares during the 1930s, and the company registered almost 500 different patterns between the years 1933 and 1935. Myott were not known for their chintzes, but obviously did not want to let a potential market go completely unaddressed. A couple of Myott chintzes have come to light, but there may well be others. The **Summer Flower** pattern seems to date from the 1930s.

The factory passed out of family hands some years after the war and eventually amalgamated with Alfred Meakin Pottery. There was a dreadful fire in 1949 and all the records and pattern books from the Myott factory were destroyed. The Churchill Group took over the combined company in 1991.

"SPRING FLOWER"

The pattern number is 3005. This pattern appears to have been used for complete dinner services. The handles of the teapots and coffee pots are painted bright orange and black.

Backstamp not available
at
press time

Cat. No.	Shape	U.S. $	Can. $	U.K. £
SF-55	Coffee pot, 6 cup	500.00	375.00	350.00
SF-70	Cream and sugar	135.00	75.00	85.00
SF-95	Jug, 7" straight-sided	300.00	175.00	200.00
SF-103	Plate, 6"	60.00	50.00	35.00
SF-104	Plate, 7"	75.00	60.00	45.00
SF-106	Plate, 9"	125.00	75.00	75.00
SF-130	Teacup and saucer	75.00	55.00	45.00
SF-137	Teapot, 6 cup	450.00	350.00	300.00

SUMMER FLOWER

We currently have no information available on this pattern.

Cat. No.	Shape	U.S. $	Can. $	U.K. £
SuF-55	Coffee pot, 6 cup	500.00	360.00	350.00
SuF-70	Cream and sugar	135.00	70.00	85.00
SuF-95	Jug, 7" straight-sided	300.00	165.00	200.00
SuF-103	Plate, 6"	60.00	45.00	35.00
SuF-104	Plate, 7"	75.00	55.00	45.00
SuF-106	Plate, 9"	125.00	70.00	75.00
SuF-130	Teacup and saucer	75.00	50.00	45.00
SuF-137	Teapot, 6 cup	450.00	340.00	300.00

9/1121
4-Pc. Cruet Set
Nantwich FANCIES
by ROYAL WINTON
An appealing chintz decoration of multi-colored floral sprays in soft tones of blue, yellow, pink and green on a black background. Heavy gold trim.
9/1101
Cup and Saucer
9/1110
Comport 6½''
9/1114
Covered Butter 6''
9/1103
Plate, Square, 10''
9/1102
Plate, Square, 9''
9/1115
Cheese dish 6''
9/1107 – Tray, Peebles 9''
9/1118
Sandwich tray 12''
9/1112
Celery Tray 11''
9/1104
Sugar and Cream
9/1124
23-Pc. Tea Set
9/1123
16-Pc. Coffee Set
9/1108
Tray, Malta 10''
9/1119
Fruit bowl 8''
B 44
Cassidy's Ltd.

A.G. RICHARDSON & CO. LTD. (CROWN DUCAL)

In 1915 at the Gordon Pottery, Tunstall, Albert Goodwin Richardson formed A.G. Richardson & Co. Ltd. with the stated intention of producing good quality earthenware under the trade name "Crown Ducal." The early production included Victorian silver luster ware and black groundlay decoration. The first chintz pattern produced by Richardson was in 1918 and was numbered A500. The pattern book started at A1 and by 1931 had reached A2000, when the "A" was dropped. In 1919 *The Pottery and Glass Record* noted two new Ducal chintzes, **Rose and Motifs** A601 and **Delhi** A617. According to this report, vases were made from 4 1/2 inches up to 12 inches and the flower pots came in four sizes.

In 1919 Albert Richardson left Richardsons, and Harry Taylor, owner of Universal Transfer Company, Burslem, bought a major interest in the company. Universal, Rataud, and the Chromo Transfer Company supplied most of Richardson's lithographs.

Maddock & Miller, the New York importers, agreed to represent Richardsons in the United States and sales grew rapidly. Crown Ducal is mentioned in *The Pottery Glass & Brass Salesman* in June 1920 and frequently thereafter. Chintzware was particularly popular with the American public, and Richardson's expanded the line to include teaware in 1921. Again with the urging of America, Richardson's expanded their line in 1925 to include dinnerware for the first time. All-over patterns like **Blue Chintz** A1885 and **Florida** A1257 (known to many American collectors as **Mauve Crown Ducal**) were advertised in 1926 and much admired. In 1928 they offered six "delightful new chintz patterns on square or octagonal plates, tea and breakfast sets, full dinner services, fancy pieces and salad sets." According to the American *Crockery & Glass Journal* these lines were "planned to harmonize with the trend of interior decoration today."

By 1929 the *Brass Salesman* had published a two-page story on the success of A.G. Richardson in America. They said the thrifty American housewife loved Crown Ducal, which duplicated bone china in terms of quality but cost $100 compared to $500 for a china service of equal charm. Richardson's led the way in adapting designs which had previously been reserved for fine china to earthenware. "The great success of the Crown Ducal ware surely proves that people of moderate means as well as the wealthier class prefer to have good-looking belongings in table service, even if the price is necessarily slightly higher than that of uninspired thick potteries." They were praised in English publications as well. The 1932 *Pottery Gazette* commented that they were reliable without being high-priced and exclusive and noted their ability to lead rather than follow the other potteries. *The Pottery and Glass Record* made a similar point in 1935: "In these days when the artistic standard of the people is high, it is comforting to know that by dealing with Messrs. A. G. Richardson, a smart and well equipped table does not depend on whether or not one has a big income."

The company purchased a second potbank, Britannia Pottery at Cobridge, to cope with increased production. Although Harold Holdcroft joined the design staff in 1928 and is said to be responsible for many of the firm's lithographic patterns, most of the exotic chintzes were already in production by that time and he was gone by 1934. Charlotte Rhead joined them as a designer in 1931 and stayed for the next eleven years. Many wonderful designs were produced over the next few years but there seems to be a gap of close to ten years before the next group of chintz designs were produced at Richardson. **Primrose**, **Peony**, **Pansy**, and **Priscilla** were all designed late in the 1930s, but none achieved the popularity of the earlier chintzes. The deep ivory glaze base colour which was developed at Richardsons in 1931 was used for all the later chintzes. Richardson's were still producing chintzes in 1940 but wartime restrictions drastically reduced the output of decorated ware.

Although there is no mention of Crown Ducal chintzes in the American trade magazines after the war, a reporter for *The Pottery and Glass Record*, on a visit to the works at Cobridge in 1955 commended the earthenware as being "of very fine quality . . . an all-over engraving of a conventionalized bird and flowers in blue, mauve or pink is a magnificent reminder of Victorian plenitude." This would suggest that Crown Ducal chintzes were still being produced in the 1950s.

Like all too many potteries during these years, A.G. Richardson could not survive alone and they were acquired by Enoch Wedgwood (Tunstall) Ltd. in 1974 which in turn were taken over by the Wedgwood Group in 1980 and renamed the Unicorn Pottery.

Thanks in part to the detective work and perseverance of Gerrard Shaw, who has recently completed his manuscript on the A. G. Richardson factory, some of the pattern books have been located in the City Museum in Stoke-on-Trent. Gerrard, Dora Shaw and Ivy Mayer went through the pattern books for us and recorded and photographed any chintz patterns they could find. Interestingly only five or six of the patterns were in the pattern books including **Peony** pattern number 5008, and **"Spring Blossom,"** pattern number 3271.

ASCOT

This pattern was introduced in the United States in 1926.

Cat. No.	Shape	U.S. $	Can. $	U.K. £
As-17	Bowl, lily 12″	100.00	75.00	65.00
As-22	Bowl, octagonal, 7″	255.00	150.00	175.00
As-24	Bowl, octagonal, 8″	300.00	175.00	200.00
As-53	Coffee pot, 3 cup	550.00	300.00	350.00
As-65	Condiment set	165.00	95.00	100.00
As-70	Cream and sugar	115.00	75.00	75.00
As-75	Demi-tasse	65.00	45.00	40.00
As-85	Jam pot	100.00	65.00	65.00
As-95	Jug, 5″	250.00	95.00	150.00
As-96	Jug, 7″	325.00	115.00	175.00

Cat. No.	Shape	U.S. $	Can. $	U.K. £
As-402	Plate, octagonal, 5″	65.00	25.00	40.00
As-406	Plate, octagonal, 9″	100.00	50.00	65.00
As-407	Plate, octagonal, 10″	125.00	65.00	75.00
As-130	Teacup and saucer	75.00	35.00	45.00
As-135	Teapot, 2 cup	375.00	175.00	250.00
As-136	Teapot, 4 cup	475.00	250.00	300.00
As-160	Vase, bud	100.00	65.00	65.00
As-163	Vase, spill, 8″	165.00	95.00	100.00
As-162	Vase, trumpet 6″	135.00	75.00	80.00
As-165	Vase, 9″	225.00	135.00	150.00

BLUE CHINTZ

The pattern number is 1185. This chintz pattern was introduced in the United States in 1926 and continued in production for many years. We have named the identical pattern without the bird **"Spring Blossom"** (see page 156) because it tends to sell for less than the **Blue Chintz**.

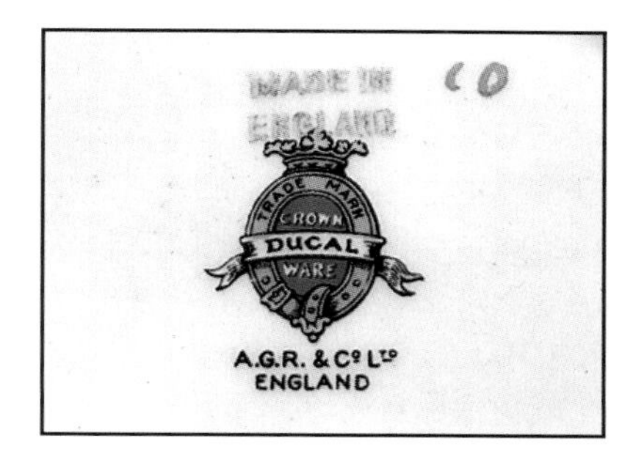

Cat. No.	Shape	U.S. $	Can. $	U.K. £
BC-17	Bowl, lily 12″	125.00	125.00	75.00
BC-22	Bowl, octagonal, 7″	300.00	225.00	200.00
BC-24	Bowl, octagonal, 8″	350.00	275.00	250.00
BC-	Candlesticks		VERY RARE	
BC-53	Coffee pot, 3 cup	650.00	500.00	400.00
BC-65	Condiment set	200.00	150.00	115.00
BC-70	Cream and sugar	135.00	110.00	85.00
BC-	Cruet set		VERY RARE	
BC-75	Demi-tasse	75.00	65.00	45.00
BC-85	Jam pot	125.00	95.00	75.00
BC-95	Jug, 5″	275.00	195.00	150.00

Cat. No.	Shape	U.S. $	Can. $	U.K. £
BC-96	Jug, 7″	350.00	225.00	175.00
BC-402	Plate, octagonal, 5″	75.00	50.00	45.00
BC-406	Plate, octagonal, 9″	125.00	85.00	75.00
BC-407	Plate, octagonal, 10″	150.00	95.00	90.00
BC-130	Teacup and saucer	85.00	60.00	50.00
BC-135	Teapot, 2 cup	450.00	300.00	300.00
BC-136	Teapot, 4 cup	550.00	425.00	350.00
BC-160	Vase, bud	125.00	125.00	75.00
BC-163	Vase, spill, 8″	200.00	165.00	115.00
BC-162	Vase, trumpet 6″	165.00	145.00	100.00
BC-165	Vase, 9″	275.00	195.00	175.00

CANTON

This chintz-like pattern was produced by a number of companies.

Cat. No.	Shape	U.S. $	Can. $	U.K. £
C-17	Bowl, lily 12″	90.00	65.00	65.00
C-22	Bowl, octagonal, 7″	200.00	125.00	150.00
C-24	Bowl, octagonal, 8″	225.00	145.00	175.00
C-53	Coffee pot, 3 cup	425.00	275.00	300.00
C-65	Condiment set	150.00	85.00	90.00
C-70	Cream and sugar	90.00	65.00	60.00
C-75	Demi-tasse	45.00	35.00	35.00
C-85	Jam pot	90.00	60.00	65.00
C-95	Jug, 5″	125.00	85.00	75.00
C-96	Jug, 7″	150.00	95.00	90.00
C-402	Plate, octagonal, 5″	45.00	25.00	35.00
C-406	Plate, octagonal, 9″	75.00	50.00	65.00
C-407	Plate, octagonal, 10″	95.00	60.00	65.00
C-130	Teacup and saucer	55.00	35.00	40.00
C-135	Teapot, 2 cup	295.00	150.00	225.00
C-136	Teapot, 4 cup	350.00	175.00	250.00
C-160	Vase, bud	90.00	60.00	65.00
C-163	Vase, spill, 8″	135.00	95.00	90.00
C-162	Vase, trumpet 6″	115.00	75.00	75.00
C-165	Vase, 9″	175.00	125.00	150.00

DELHI

This was one of the earlier of the Crown Ducal chintzes, pattern number A617 and was introduced in 1918. It has been found on a limited range of vases and toiletware as well as plates and teapots.

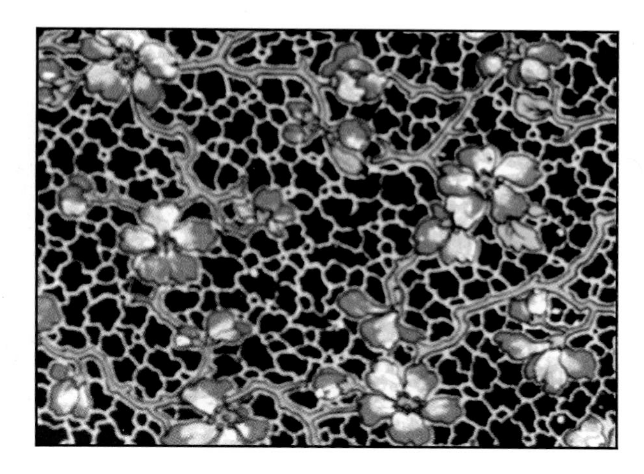

Cat. No.	Shape	U.S. $	Can. $	U.K. £
Dh-95	Jug, 5″	125.00	95.00	75.00
Dh-96	Jug, 7″	150.00	125.00	90.00
Dh-406	Plate, octagonal, 9″	90.00	75.00	55.00
Dh-135	Teapot, 2 cup	295.00	175.00	175.00

Cat. No.	Shape	U.S. $	Can. $	U.K. £
Dh-160	Vase, bud	90.00	75.00	65.00
Dh-163	Vase, spill, 8″	135.00	125.00	75.00
Dh-162	Vase, trumpet 6″	115.00	105.00	65.00
Dh-165	Vase, 9″	180.00	150.00	125.00

FESTIVAL

This pattern was introduced in the United States around 1926.

Cat. No.	Shape	U.S. $	Can. $	U.K. £
Fe-17	Bowl, lily 12″	100.00	75.00	65.00
Fe-22	Bowl, octagonal, 7″	250.00	125.00	175.00
Fe-24	Bowl, octagonal, 8″	300.00	145.00	200.00
Fe-53	Coffee pot, 3 cup	550.00	300.00	350.00
Fe-65	Condiment set	165.00	95.00	100.00
Fe-70	Cream and sugar	115.00	75.00	75.00
Fe-75	Demi-tasse	65.00	45.00	40.00
Fe-85	Jam pot	100.00	70.00	65.00
Fe-95	Jug, 5″	250.00	110.00	125.00
Fe-96	Jug, 7″	325.00	135.00	150.00

Cat. No.	Shape	U.S. $	Can. $	U.K. £
Fe-402	Plate, octagonal, 5″	65.00	25.00	40.00
Fe-406	Plate, octagonal, 9″	100.00	50.00	65.00
Fe-407	Plate, octagonal, 10″	125.00	65.00	75.00
Fe-	Rose Bowl	EXTREMELY RARE		
Fe-130	Teacup and saucer	75.00	35.00	45.00
Fe-135	Teapot, 2 cup	375.00	200.00	250.00
Fe-136	Teapot, 4 cup	475.00	250.00	300.00
Fe-160	Vase, bud	100.00	65.00	65.00
Fe-163	Vase, spill, 8″	165.00	95.00	125.00
Fe-162	Vase, trumpet 6″	135.00	75.00	75.00
Fe-165	Vase, 9″	250.00	125.00	150.00

FLORIDA

This chintz pattern was advertised in the United States in 1925 and was described as "a wordless song of the tropics." American collectors know this pattern as "**Mauve Crown Ducal**" and it is the most popular Crown Ducal pattern in the United States.

Cat. No.	Shape	U.S. $	Can. $	U.K. £
Fd-170	Biscuit Barrel	EXTREMELY RARE		
Fd-17	Bowl, lily 12"	165.00	135.00	100.00
Fd-22	Bowl, octagonal, 7"	400.00	235.00	275.00
Fd-24	Bowl, octagonal, 8"	450.00	295.00	300.00
Fd-53	Coffee pot, 3 cup	900.00	500.00	600.00
Fd-65	Condiment set	250.00	150.00	175.00
Fd-70	Cream and sugar	175.00	115.00	100.00
Fd-75	Demi-tasse	115.00	75.00	65.00
Fd-85	Jam pot	165.00	95.00	100.00
Fd-95	Jug, 5"	350.00	215.00	200.00
Fd-96	Jug, 7"	400.00	250.00	225.00

Cat. No.	Shape	U.S. $	Can. $	U.K. £
Fd-	Mayonnaise bowl	EXTREMELY RARE		
Fd-402	Plate, octagonal, 5"	100.00	50.00	65.00
Fd-406	Plate, octagonal, 9"	160.00	95.00	100.00
Fd-407	Plate, octagonal, 10"	175.00	125.00	125.00
Fd-130	Teacup and saucer	125.00	65.00	65.00
Fd-135	Teapot, 2 cup	575.00	350.00	375.00
Fd-136	Teapot, 4 cup	800.00	450.00	450.00
Fd-160	Vase, bud	160.00	135.00	125.00
Fd-163	Vase, spill, 8"	250.00	175.00	175.00
Fd-162	Vase, trumpet 6"	200.00	150.00	150.00
Fd-165	Vase, 9"	350.00	215.00	450.00

"GREY FRUIT"

Unfortunately we have no information available on this pattern at this time.

Cat. No.	Shape	U.S. $	Can. $	U.K. £
GF-17	Bowl, lily 12"	100.00	75.00	65.00
GF-22	Bowl, octagonal, 7"	225.00	115.00	150.00
GF-24	Bowl, octagonal, 8"	250.00	135.00	175.00
GF-53	Coffee pot, 3 cup	475.00	275.00	300.00
GF-65	Condiment set	150.00	75.00	90.00
GF-70	Cream and sugar	100.00	65.00	65.00
GF-75	Demi-tasse	50.00	45.00	35.00
GF-85	Jam pot	100.00	65.00	65.00
GF-95	Jug, 5"	150.00	95.00	90.00
GF-96	Jug, 7"	175.00	115.00	100.00

Cat. No.	Shape	U.S. $	Can. $	U.K. £
GF-402	Plate, octagonal, 5"	50.00	25.00	35.00
GF-406	Plate, octagonal, 9"	100.00	50.00	65.00
GF-407	Plate, octagonal, 10"	100.00	65.00	65.00
GF-130	Teacup and saucer	65.00	35.00	40.00
GF-135	Teapot, 2 cup	325.00	175.00	225.00
GF-136	Teapot, 4 cup	400.00	225.00	275.00
GF-160	Vase, bud	100.00	65.00	65.00
GF-163	Vase, spill, 8"	150.00	95.00	85.00
GF-162	Vase, trumpet 6"	125.00	75.00	75.00
GF-165	Vase, 9"	200.00	125.00	150.00

IVORY CHINTZ

The pattern number is A500 and this is considered the first Crown Ducal chintz and was designed in 1918. This chintz pattern was introduced into the United States early in the 1920s and is found on a very wide variety of shapes and sizes of vases and bowls.

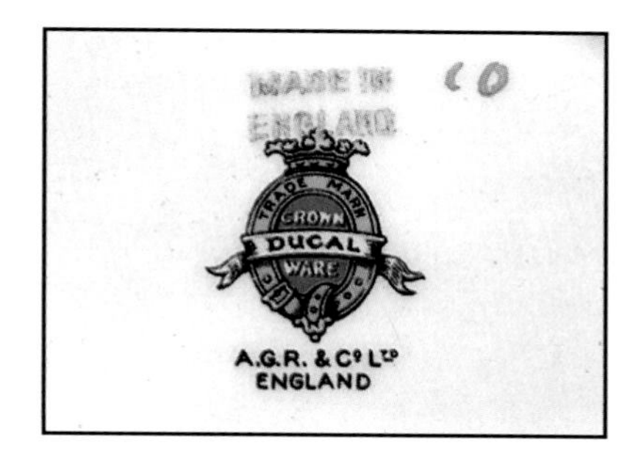

Cat. No.	Shape	U.S. $	Can. $	U.K. £
IC-17	Bowl, lily 12″	125.00	125.00	75.00
IC-22	Bowl, octagonal, 7″	300.00	225.00	200.00
IC-24	Bowl, octagonal, 8″	350.00	275.00	250.00
IC-53	Coffee pot, 3 cup	650.00	500.00	400.00
IC-60	Compore, Footed		VERY RARE	
IC-65	Condiment set	200.00	150.00	150.00
IC-70	Cream and sugar	135.00	115.00	85.00
IC-75	Demi-tasse	75.00	70.00	45.00
IC-85	Jam pot	125.00	95.00	75.00
IC-	Jardinere		EXTREMELY RARE	
IC-95	Jug, 5″	275.00	195.00	175.00
IC-96	Jug, 7″	350.00	225.00	175.00
IC-402	Plate, octagonal, 5″	75.00	50.00	45.00
IC-406	Plate, octagonal, 9″	125.00	95.00	75.00
IC-407	Plate, octagonal, 10″	150.00	115.00	85.00
IC-130	Teacup and saucer	95.00	60.00	50.00
IC-135	Teapot, 2 cup	450.00	300.00	300.00
IC-136	Teapot, 4 cup	550.00	400.00	350.00
IC-160	Vase, bud	125.00	125.00	75.00
IC-163	Vase, spill, 8″	200.00	165.00	150.00
IC-162	Vase, trumpet 6″	165.00	145.00	125.00
IC-165	Vase, 9″	275.00	195.00	175.00

"IVORY FRUIT"

Unfortunately, we have no information on this pattern at this time.

Cat. No.	Shape	U.S. $	Can. $	U.K. £
IF-17	Bowl, lily 12″	100.00	75.00	65.00
IF-22	Bowl, octagonal, 7″	225.00	125.00	150.00
IF-24	Bowl, octagonal, 8″	250.00	145.00	150.00
IF-53	Coffee pot, 3 cup	475.00	300.00	300.00
IF-65	Condiment set	150.00	85.00	85.00
IF-70	Cream and sugar	100.00	75.00	65.00
IF-75	Demi-tasse	50.00	45.00	35.00
IF-85	Jam pot	100.00	65.00	65.00
IF-95	Jug, 5″	150.00	95.00	85.00
IF-96	Jug, 7″	175.00	125.00	100.00

Cat. No.	Shape	U.S. $	Can. $	U.K. £
IF-402	Plate, octagonal, 5″	50.00	30.00	35.00
IF-406	Plate, octagonal, 9″	100.00	60.00	65.00
IF-407	Plate, octagonal, 10″	110.00	75.00	65.00
IF-130	Teacup and saucer	65.00	35.00	40.00
IF-135	Teapot, 2 cup	325.00	200.00	225.00
IF-136	Teapot, 4 cup	400.00	275.00	275.00
IF-160	Vase, bud	100.00	65.00	65.00
IF-163	Vase, spill, 8″	150.00	95.00	85.00
IF-162	Vase, trumpet 6″	125.00	75.00	75.00
IF-165	Vase, 9″	200.00	135.00	125.00

MARIGOLD

This pattern is most often found on vases and rose bowls.

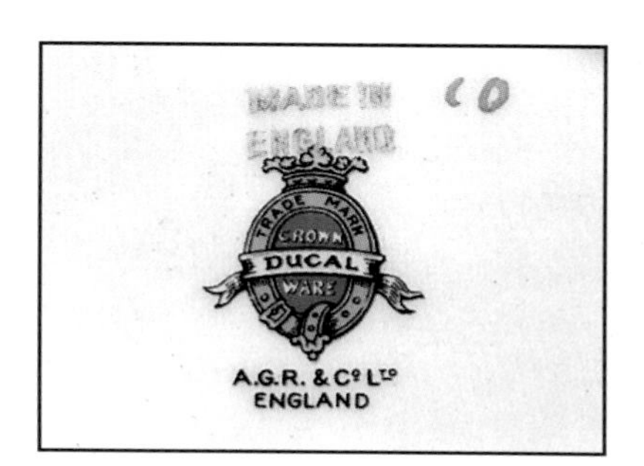

Cat. No.	Shape	U.S. $	Can. $	U.K. £
MgR-17	Bowl, lily 12″	100.00	75.00	65.00
MgR-22	Bowl, octagonal, 7″	250.00	125.00	175.00
MgR-24	Bowl, octagonal, 8″	300.00	145.00	200.00
MgR-	Candlesticks		VERY RARE	
MgR-53	Coffee pot, 3 cup	550.00	325.00	350.00
MgR-65	Condiment set	165.00	95.00	100.00
MgR-70	Cream and sugar	100.00	75.00	65.00
MgR-75	Demi-tasse	115.00	50.00	75.00
MgR-85	Jam pot	100.00	75.00	65.00
MgR-95	Jug, 5″	200.00	115.00	150.00
MgR-96	Jug, 7″	225.00	145.00	150.00

Cat. No.	Shape	U.S. $	Can. $	U.K. £
MgR-402	Plate, octagonal, 5″	65.00	35.00	40.00
MgR-406	Plate, octagonal, 9″	100.00	55.00	65.00
MgR-407	Plate, octagonal, 10″	125.00	70.00	75.00
MgR-130	Teacup and saucer	70.00	35.00	45.00
MgR-135	Teapot, 2 cup	375.00	200.00	450.00
MgR-136	Teapot, 4 cup	465.00	275.00	300.00
MgR-160	Vase, bud	100.00	65.00	65.00
MgR-163	Vase, spill, 8″	165.00	95.00	100.00
MgR-162	Vase, trumpet 6″	135.00	75.00	85.00
MgR-165	Vase, 9″	225.00	135.00	150.00

"MAUVE CHINTZ"

This pattern was not a controlled pattern and was used by a number of companies.

Cat. No.	Shape	U.S. $	Can. $	U.K. £
MC-17	Bowl, lily 12″	100.00	75.00	65.00
MC-22	Bowl, octagonal, 7″	225.00	125.00	150.00
MC-24	Bowl, octagonal, 8″	250.00	145.00	175.00
MC-53	Coffee pot, 3 cup	475.00	275.00	300.00
MC-65	Condiment set	150.00	85.00	90.00
MC-70	Cream and sugar	100.00	65.00	65.00
MC-75	Demi-tasse	50.00	35.00	35.00
MC-85	Jam pot	100.00	60.00	65.00
MC-95	Jug, 5″	150.00	85.00	85.00
MC-96	Jug, 7″	175.00	105.00	125.00

Cat. No.	Shape	U.S. $	Can. $	U.K. £
MC-402	Plate, octagonal, 5″	50.00	25.00	35.00
MC-406	Plate, octagonal, 9″	100.00	50.00	65.00
MC-407	Plate, octagonal, 10″	100.00	60.00	65.00
MC-130	Teacup and saucer	65.00	35.00	40.00
MC-135	Teapot, 2 cup	325.00	175.00	225.00
MC-136	Teapot, 4 cup	400.00	250.00	275.00
MC-160	Vase, bud	100.00	65.00	65.00
MC-163	Vase, spill, 8″	150.00	85.00	85.00
MC-162	Vase, trumpet 6″	125.00	75.00	75.00
MC-165	Vase, 9″	200.00	125.00	125.00

PANSY

This pattern is difficult to find in the United States but more common in Australia and New Zealand. According to the *Pottery Gazette,* November 1938, this pattern was introduced earlier that year.

Cat. No.	Shape	U.S. $	Can. $	U.K. £
PaR-17	Bowl, lily 12″	100.00	85.00	65.00
PaR-22	Bowl, octagonal, 7″	255.00	145.00	175.00
PaR-24	Bowl, octagonal, 8″	300.00	175.00	200.00
PaR-53	Coffee pot, 3 cup	550.00	325.00	350.00
PaR-65	Condiment set	165.00	105.00	100.00
PaR-70	Cream and sugar	115.00	85.00	75.00
PaR-75	Demi-tasse	65.00	50.00	40.00
PaR-85	Jam pot	100.00	75.00	65.00
PaR-95	Jug, 5″	250.00	125.00	150.00
PaR-96	Jug, 7″	325.00	145.00	175.00

Cat. No.	Shape	U.S. $	Can. $	U.K. £
PaR-402	Plate, octagonal, 5″	65.00	30.00	40.00
PaR-406	Plate, octagonal, 9″	100.00	65.00	65.00
PaR-407	Plate, octagonal, 10″	125.00	75.00	75.00
PaR-130	Teacup and saucer	75.00	40.00	45.00
PaR-135	Teapot, 2 cup	375.00	225.00	250.00
PaR-136	Teapot, 4 cup	475.00	300.00	300.00
PaR-160	Vase, bud	100.00	75.00	65.00
PaR-163	Vase, spill, 8″	165.00	115.00	100.00
PaR-162	Vase, trumpet 6″	135.00	95.00	80.00
PaR-165	Vase, 9″	225.00	145.00	150.00

PEONY

The pattern number is 5008 and can be dated to 1937. It is recorded in the pattern books as being produced on the Victory shape. This pattern is becoming very popular in North America.

Cat. No.	Shape	U.S. $	Can. $	U.K. £
Py-17	Bowl, lily 12″	125.00	125.00	75.00
Py-22	Bowl, octagonal, 7″	300.00	250.00	200.00
Py-24	Bowl, octagonal, 8″	350.00	300.00	250.00
Py-53	Coffee pot, 3 cup	650.00	575.00	400.00
Py-65	Condiment set	200.00	150.00	115.00
Py-70	Cream and sugar	135.00	115.00	85.00
Py-75	Demi-tasse	75.00	70.00	45.00
Py-85	Jam pot	125.00	115.00	75.00
Py-95	Jug, 5″	275.00	225.00	150.00
Py-96	Jug, 7″	350.00	275.00	175.00

Cat. No.	Shape	U.S. $	Can. $	U.K. £
Py-402	Plate, octagonal, 5″	75.00	50.00	45.00
Py-406	Plate, octagonal, 9″	125.00	95.00	75.00
Py-407	Plate, octagonal, 10″	150.00	125.00	90.00
Py-	Salad Bowl		VERY RARE	
Py-130	Teacup and saucer	85.00	65.00	50.00
Py-135	Teapot, 2 cup	450.00	350.00	300.00
Py-136	Teapot, 4 cup	550.00	450.00	350.00
Py-160	Vase, bud	125.00	125.00	75.00
Py-163	Vase, spill, 8″	200.00	165.00	115.00
Py-162	Vase, trumpet 6″	165.00	150.00	100.00
Py-165	Vase, 9″	275.00	225.00	175.00

"PINK CHINTZ"

This chintz pattern was probably introduced into the United States in 1928.

Cat. No.	Shape	U.S. $	Can. $	U.K. £
PC-17	Bowl, lily 12"	100.00	115.00	65.00
PC-22	Bowl, octagonal, 7"	275.00	225.00	175.00
PC-24	Bowl, octagonal, 8"	325.00	275.00	200.00
PC-53	Coffee pot, 3 cup	700.00	450.00	375.00
PC-65	Condiment set	175.00	145.00	125.00
PC-70	Cream and sugar	125.00	105.00	75.00
PC-75	Demi-tasse	65.00	65.00	40.00
PC-85	Jam pot	115.00	90.00	75.00
PC-95	Jug, 5"	325.00	175.00	150.00
PC-96	Jug, 7"	400.00	200.00	175.00

Cat. No.	Shape	U.S. $	Can. $	U.K. £
PC-402	Plate, octagonal, 5"	65.00	50.00	40.00
PC-406	Plate, octagonal, 9"	115.00	85.00	75.00
PC-407	Plate, octagonal, 10"	135.00	100.00	85.00
PC-130	Teacup and saucer	90.00	60.00	45.00
PC-135	Teapot, 2 cup	400.00	325.00	250.00
PC-136	Teapot, 4 cup	500.00	425.00	350.00
PC-160	Vase, bud	125.00	125.00	75.00
PC-163	Vase, spill, 8"	175.00	165.00	125.00
PC-162	Vase, trumpet 6"	150.00	145.00	90.00
PC-165	Vase, 9"	250.00	225.00	175.00

PRIMULA

This chintz pattern was introduced in the 1930s.

Cat. No.	Shape	U.S. $	Can. $	U.K. £
PrR-17	Bowl, lily 12″	100.00	75.00	65.00
PrR-22	Bowl, octagonal, 7″	250.00	125.00	175.00
PrR-24	Bowl, octagonal, 8″	300.00	145.00	200.00
PrR-53	Coffee pot, 3 cup	550.00	300.00	350.00
PrR-65	Condiment set	165.00	85.00	100.00
PrR-70	Cream and sugar	115.00	75.00	75.00
PrR-75	Demi-tasse	65.00	45.00	40.00
PrR-85	Jam pot	100.00	65.00	65.00
PrR-95	Jug, 5″	200.00	95.00	125.00
PrR-96	Jug, 7″	225.00	125.00	150.00

Cat. No.	Shape	U.S. $	Can. $	U.K. £
PrR-402	Plate, octagonal, 5″	65.00	30.00	40.00
PrR-406	Plate, octagonal, 9″	100.00	50.00	65.00
PrR-407	Plate, octagonal, 10″	125.00	65.00	75.00
PrR-130	Teacup and saucer	75.00	45.00	45.00
PrR-135	Teapot, 2 cup	375.00	200.00	250.00
PrR-136	Teapot, 4 cup	475.00	275.00	300.00
PrR-160	Vase, bud	100.00	65.00	65.00
PrR-163	Vase, spill, 8″	165.00	95.00	100.00
PrR-162	Vase, trumpet 6″	135.00	75.00	85.00
PrR-165	Vase, 9″	225.00	125.00	150.00

PRISCILLA

This chintz pattern was introduced in 1940 and it is favorably mentioned in the *Pottery Gazette* in April, 1941 and described as "an all-over chintz in pink apple blossom applied to a delicate buff ground, and broken up by small white speedwell flower heads."

Cat. No.	Shape	U.S. $	Can. $	U.K. £
Ps-17	Bowl, lily 12"	90.00	75.00	65.00
Ps-22	Bowl, octagonal, 7"	200.00	125.00	150.00
Ps-24	Bowl, octagonal, 8"	225.00	145.00	175.00
Ps-53	Coffee pot, 3 cup	425.00	300.00	300.00
Ps-65	Condiment set	150.00	95.00	90.00
Ps-70	Cream and sugar	90.00	75.00	60.00
Ps-75	Demi-tasse	45.00	45.00	35.00
Ps-85	Jam pot	90.00	65.00	65.00
Ps-95	Jug, 5"	125.00	95.00	75.00
Ps-96	Jug, 7"	150.00	125.00	90.00

Cat. No.	Shape	U.S. $	Can. $	U.K. £
Ps-402	Plate, octagonal, 5"	45.00	30.00	35.00
Ps-406	Plate, octagonal, 9"	75.00	50.00	65.00
Ps-407	Plate, octagonal, 10"	95.00	75.00	65.00
Ps-130	Teacup and saucer	55.00	40.00	40.00
Ps-135	Teapot, 2 cup	295.00	200.00	225.00
Ps-136	Teapot, 4 cup	350.00	275.00	250.00
Ps-160	Vase, bud	90.00	65.00	65.00
Ps-163	Vase, spill, 8"	135.00	95.00	90.00
Ps-162	Vase, trumpet 6"	115.00	75.00	75.00
Ps-165	Vase, 9"	175.00	125.00	150.00

"PURPLE CHINTZ"

This is one of the most popular Crown Ducal chintzes in the United States.

Cat. No.	Shape	U.S. $	Can. $	U.K. £
PuC-17	Bowl, lily 12"	150.00	135.00	85.00
PuC-22	Bowl, octagonal, 7"	375.00	250.00	250.00
PuC-24	Bowl, octagonal, 8"	425.00	300.00	275.00
PuC-53	Coffee pot, 3 cup	800.00	550.00	500.00
PuC-65	Condiment set	250.00	165.00	175.00
PuC-70	Cream and sugar	165.00	125.00	100.00
PuC-75	Demi-tasse	100.00	75.00	65.00
PuC-85	Jam pot	150.00	115.00	85.00
PuC-95	Jug, 5"	325.00	225.00	175.00
PuC-96	Jug, 7"	375.00	275.00	225.00

Cat. No.	Shape	U.S. $	Can. $	U.K. £
PuC-402	Plate, octagonal, 5"	100.00	65.00	65.00
PuC-406	Plate, octagonal, 9"	150.00	95.00	85.00
PuC-407	Plate, octagonal, 10"	175.00	125.00	125.00
PuC-130	Teacup and saucer	110.00	75.00	65.00
PuC-135	Teapot, 2 cup	550.00	325.00	350.00
PuC-136	Teapot, 4 cup	675.00	425.00	450.00
PuC-160	Vase, bud	150.00	135.00	90.00
PuC-163	Vase, spill, 8"	250.00	175.00	175.00
PuC-162	Vase, trumpet 6"	200.00	150.00	125.00
PuC-165	Vase, 9"	350.00	225.00	225.00

ROSE & MOTIFS

This was one of the earliest Crown Ducal chintzes and was introduced in 1918. It has been found on vases and toiletware only.

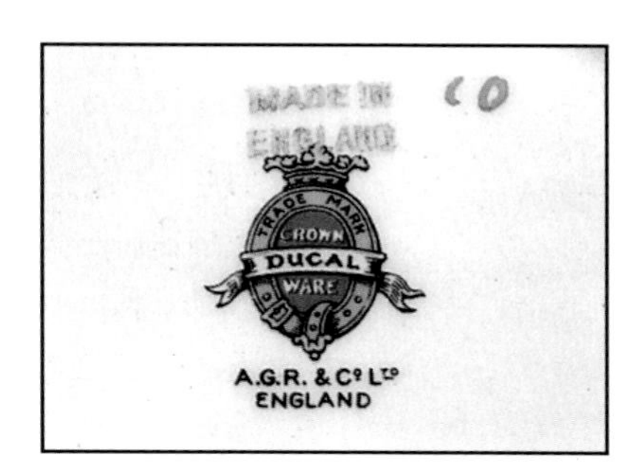

Cat. No.	Shape	U.S. $	Can. $	U.K. £
RM-95	Jug, 5″	275.00	175.00	175.00
RM-96	Jug, 7″	325.00	200.00	225.00
RM-160	Vase, bud	150.00	125.00	85.00

Cat. No.	Shape	U.S. $	Can. $	U.K. £
RM-163	Vase, spill, 8″	250.00	145.00	175.00
RM-162	Vase, trumpet 6″	200.00	125.00	150.00
RM-165	Vase, 9″	350.00	175.00	250.00

"SPRING BLOSSOM"

This pattern is in the recently discovered A.G. Richardson pattern books as pattern number 3271 with a note to see 1185 (**Blue Chintz**). Looking at the sequence of pattern numbers would suggest that this pattern was produced around 1933. We have named this pattern without the bird "**Spring Blossom**." It tends to sell for less than the **Blue Chintz** (see page 139)**.** This pattern was also used by other manufacturers including Elijah Cotton.

Cat. No.	Shape	U.S. $	Can. $	U.K. £
SB-17	Bowl, lily 12″	105.00	110.00	65.00
SB-22	Bowl, octagonal, 7″	250.00	195.00	175.00
SB-24	Bowl, octagonal, 8″	300.00	245.00	200.00
SB-53	Coffee pot, 3 cup	550.00	425.00	325.00
SB-65	Condiment set	175.00	135.00	100.00
SB-70	Cream and sugar	115.00	95.00	75.00
SB-75	Demi-tasse	65.00	60.00	35.00
SB-85	Jam pot	110.00	85.00	65.00
SB-95	Jug, 5″	225.00	175.00	125.00
SB-96	Jug, 7″	300.00	200.00	145.00

Cat. No.	Shape	U.S. $	Can. $	U.K. £
SB-402	Plate, octagonal, 5″	65.00	40.00	35.00
SB-406	Plate, octagonal, 9″	105.00	70.00	65.00
SB-407	Plate, octagonal, 10″	125.00	80.00	70.00
SB-	Reamer	EXTREMELY RARE		
SB-130	Teacup and saucer	70.00	50.00	40.00
SB-135	Teapot, 2 cup	375.00	250.00	225.00
SB-136	Teapot, 4 cup	475.00	350.00	300.00
SB-160	Vase, bud	105.00	115.00	65.00
SB-163	Vase, spill, 8″	175.00	145.00	100.00
SB-162	Vase, trumpet 6″	140.00	125.00	90.00
SB-165	Vase, 9″	235.00	175.00	135.00

RIDGWAY POTTERIES LTD.

The firm was founded in 1866 at the Bedford Works in Shelton by Edward John Ridgway and produced both fine and utility earthenwares. The firm had a variety of names and partnerships through the first half of the twentieth century and by 1955 the firm had eight different works in Staffordshire, including Colcloughs and Booths. Ridgway Potteries Ltd. now operates under the Royal Doulton umbrella.

UNKNOWN

Little is known about the range of pieces produced.

Cat. No.	Shape	U.S. $	Can. $	U.K. £
RP-78	Egg cup, large	65.00	75.00	40.00
RP-93	Jug, 6″	250.00	300.00	175.00
RP-106	Plate, 9″	125.00	150.00	75.00

ROYAL DOULTON LTD.

Doulton & Company manufactured drainpipes in the mid-nineteenth century, and from that beginning a huge company has grown which today encompasses Royal Crown Derby, Minton, Shelley, Beswick, Royal Albert and many more. The firm opened their present-day works on Nile Street in Burslem in 1882. The only all-over transfer which might be of interest to chintz collectors was produced in several versions by Doulton around 1913 and was called **Persian**. It was a forerunner of the patterns produced by A.G. Richardson some five years later. The pattern was used on a wide variety of pieces including candle sticks, octagon shape tea set and jardinaire, rack plates and cabinet pieces. The pattern continued in production until approximately 1940.

PERSIAN

This is an early chintz-type pattern and not yet collected by enough chintz collectors to establish a market. This pattern also came in another colourway called **Blue Persian**.

Cat. No.	Shape	U.S. $	Can. $	U.K. £
Per-107	Plate, 10"	125.00	115.00	75.00

Cat. No.	Shape	U.S. $	Can. $	U.K. £
Per-145	Tennis Set	125.00	95.00	85.00

SHELLEY POTTERIES LTD.

In 1853 Henry Wileman became a partner in Foley Potteries and three years later built Foley China Works. Joseph Shelley became a partner in 1872, and the name changed to Wileman & Co. By 1884 Wileman had gone and the firm became a Shelley family business. Although the Shelley backstamp was introduced as early as 1910 it was not until 1925 that Wileman & Co. became Shelley Potteries.

Shelley produced an extraordinary range of teawares in a range of shapes and decorative techniques. According to Susan Hill's book, some of the all-over transfers such as **Cloisonne** were used by Shelley as "seconds" patterns and applied to ware which did not meet the factory's high standards. Patterns like **Maytime** and **Melody** however, were offered on a wide range of wares and were advertised first in the 1930s. These patterns were produced on earthenware before the second world war and on bone china following the war. Shelley stopped producing earthenware after the war and as a result the other Shelley chintz patterns appear only on bone china. The pattern numbers for most of these chintzes range from 13300 to 14300 which means they were sold from about 1942 until 1962. Chris Davenport, a researcher on post-war Shelley, told us that the last chintz pattern was 14341 and was produced on the 18th of May,1964. The chintz patterns were used particularly on teacups and the variations of pattern are endless. Some cups have pattern inside, some outside, some have pattern only on the center of the saucer, some just around the outside. Shelley chintz collectors sometimes specialize in different shapes of cup and variations of pattern. There is page after page of chintz in the Shelley pattern books and it is amazing that so little has been written about them. Although two books have been written on Shelley Potteries only a couple of lines have been devoted to the all-over florals that they produced. The rarest of the Shelley chintzes is the black or multi chintz and closely resembles the Royal Winton black background chintzes.

The Shelley family remained in the business until 1966, when the company was taken over by Allied English Potteries. The owners of Allied acquired Doulton & Company in 1971, and the companies merged to form Royal Doulton Tableware Ltd.

BLUE DAISY

This pattern is one of the most common of the Shelley chintzes and was also produced with a green background. See **Green Daisy** (page 165).

Cat. No.	Shape	U.S. $	Can. $	U.K. £
BD-01	Ashtray, small	55.00	50.00	35.00
BD-02	Ashtray, large	80.00	65.00	50.00
BD-04	Bonbon dish	50.00	45.00	30.00
BD-05	Bonbon dish, tab handles	50.00	45.00	30.00
BD-36	Cake plate	150.00	145.00	100.00
BD-55	Coffee pot, 6 cup	200.00	250.00	125.00
BD-70	Cream and sugar	100.00	125.00	50.00
BD-98	Pin tray, small	60.00	50.00	35.00
BD-104	Plate, 8"	65.00	60.00	40.00
BD-130	Teacup and saucer	85.00	65.00	50.00
BD-130	Teacup/saucer, Oleander	100.00	85.00	50.00
BD-137	Teapot, 6 cup	300.00	325.00	175.00

CLOISONNE

According to Susan Hill's book on Shelley, **Cloisonne** was a seconds pattern, used to disguise imperfect china but Shelley collectors say they have seen it on Shelley Ideal china as well. This pattern also comes with a bright blue background. This litho was used by other companies including John Shaw & Sons "Burlington Ware."

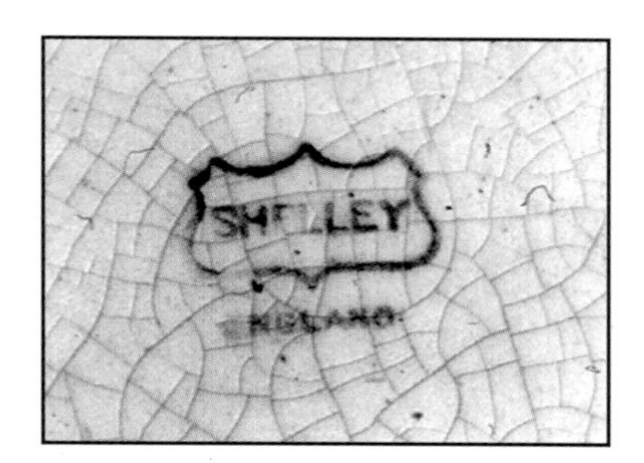

Cat. No.	Shape	U.S. $	Can. $	U.K. £
Clo-01	Ashtray, small	55.00	40.00	35.00
Clo-02	Ashtray, large	80.00	60.00	50.00
Clo-04	Bonbon dish	50.00	35.00	30.00
Clo-05	Bonbon dish, tab handles	50.00	35.00	30.00
Clo-36	Cake plate	145.00	85.00	100.00
Clo-55	Coffee pot, 6 cup	200.00	175.00	125.00

Cat. No.	Shape	U.S. $	Can. $	U.K. £
Clo-70	Cream and sugar	95.00	75.00	50.00
Clo-98	Pin tray, small	60.00	35.00	35.00
Clo-104	Plate, 8"	65.00	45.00	40.00
Clo-130	Teacup and saucer	75.00	45.00	45.00
Clo-137	Teapot, 6 cup	300.00	275.00	175.00

COUNTRYSIDE

This pattern is listed as produced on four different Shelley shapes but it is rare in North America.

Cat. No.	Shape	U.S. $	Can. $	U.K. £
Cs-01	Ashtray, small	90.00	65.00	50.00
Cs-02	Ashtray, large	100.00	95.00	55.00
Cs-04	Bonbon dish	75.00	65.00	50.00
Cs-05	Bonbon dish, tab handles	75.00	65.00	50.00
Cs-36	Cake plate	200.00	175.00	125.00
Cs-55	Coffee pot, 6 cup	425.00	300.00	300.00
Cs-70	Cream and sugar	145.00	135.00	90.00
Cs-98	Pin tray, small	85.00	65.00	60.00
Cs-104	Plate, 8"	90.00	75.00	50.00
Cs-130	Teacup and saucer	115.00	70.00	75.00
Cs-130	Teacup/saucer, Oleander	140.00	95.00	100.00
Cs-137	Teapot, 6 cup	450.00	350.00	300.00

GREEN DAISY

This pattern does not appear as often in North America as the other colourway **Blue Daisy** and it is sometimes confused with **Marguerite**.

Cat. No.	Shape	U.S. $	Can. $	U.K. £
GD-01	Ashtray, small	55.00	50.00	35.00
GD-02	Ashtray, large	80.00	65.00	50.00
GD-04	Bonbon dish	50.00	45.00	30.00
GD-05	Bonbon dish, tab handles	50.00	45.00	30.00
GD-36	Cake plate	150.00	145.00	100.00
GD-55	Coffee pot, 6 cup	200.00	250.00	125.00

Cat. No.	Shape	U.S. $	Can. $	U.K. £
GD-70	Cream and sugar	100.00	125.00	50.00
GD-98	Pin tray, small	60.00	50.00	35.00
GD-104	Plate, 8"	65.00	60.00	40.00
GD-130	Teacup and saucer	85.00	65.00	50.00
GD-130	Teacup/saucer, Oleander	100.00	85.00	50.00
GD-137	Teapot, 6 cup	300.00	325.00	175.00

MARGUERITE

This pattern was available on five different shapes but it is still difficult to find in North America.

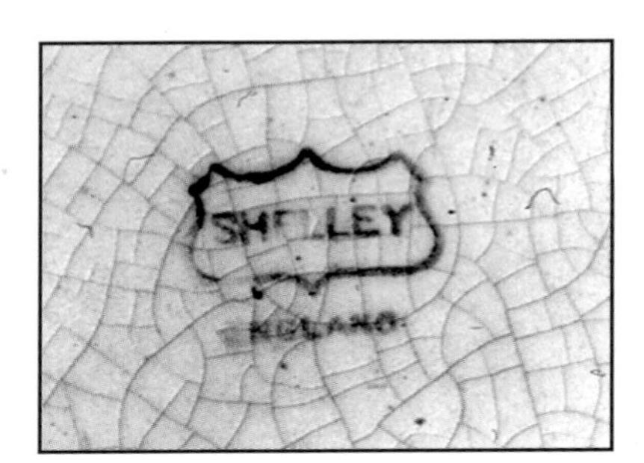

Cat. No.	Shape	U.S. $	Can. $	U.K. £
MS-01	Ashtray, small	60.00	55.00	35.00
MS-02	Ashtray, large	85.00	70.00	500.00
MS-04	Bonbon dish	55.00	50.00	35.00
MS-05	Bonbon dish, tab handles	55.00	50.00	35.00
MS-36	Cake plate	160.00	150.00	125.00
MS-55	Coffee pot, 6 cup	275.00	260.00	200.00
MS-70	Cream and sugar	110.00	135.00	60.00
MS-98	Pin tray, small	65.00	55.00	45.00
MS-104	Plate, 8"	70.00	65.00	35.00
MS-130	Teacup and saucer	90.00	65.00	50.00
MS-130	Teacup/saucer, Oleander	100.00	90.00	60.00
MS-137	Teapot, 6 cup	350.00	325.00	225.00

MAYTIME

This pattern was very popular and appears on a great variety of shapes produced in earthenware prior to the Second World War. **Maytime** was produced only in bone china following the war.

Cat. No.	Shape	U.S. $	Can. $	U.K. £
Mat-01	Ashtray, small	85.00	60.00	50.00
Mat-02	Ashtray, large	95.00	85.00	60.00
Mat-04	Bonbon dish	70.00	60.00	40.00
Mat-05	Bonbon dish, tab handles	70.00	60.00	40.00
Mat-36	Cake plate	200.00	165.00	125.00
Mat-55	Coffee pot, 6 cup	450.00	300.00	300.00
Mat-70	Cream and sugar	140.00	125.00	80.00
Mat-98	Pin tray, small	80.00	60.00	60.00
Mat-104	Plate, 8"	90.00	70.00	60.00
Mat-130	Teacup and saucer	115.00	65.00	75.00
Mat-130	Teacup/saucer, Oleander	135.00	95.00	75.00
Mat-137	Teapot, 6 cup	400.00	350.00	250.00

MELODY

"Its colouring and pattern makes an instant appeal and gives a pleasure that increases on its daily appearance"(*Pottery Gazette*, 1940). This pattern appears on more shapes than any other Shelley chintz and it is the most popular in North America. **Melody** was produced in earthenware prior to the Second World War and in bone china following the war.

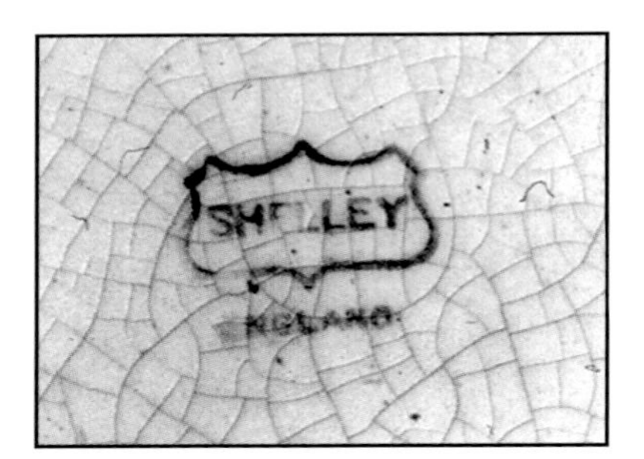

Cat. No.	Shape	U.S. $	Can. $	U.K. £
Me-01	Ashtray, small	100.00	70.00	60.00
Me-02	Ashtray, large	110.00	100.00	65.00
Me-04	Bonbon dish	75.00	70.00	40.00
Me-05	Bonbon dish, tab handles	75.00	70.00	40.00
Me-36	Cake plate	200.00	195.00	125.00
Me-	Cigarette Set	EXTREMELY RARE		
Me-55	Coffee pot, 6 cup	450.00	375.00	350.00
Me-70	Cream and sugar	150.00	145.00	100.00
Me-98	Pin tray, small	90.00	70.00	50.00
Me-180	Lamp Base	EXTREMELY RARE		
Me-104	Plate, 8"	100.00	80.00	60.00
Me-130	Teacup and saucer	125.00	75.00	75.00
Me-130	Teacup/ saucer, Oleander	150.00	95.00	100.00
Me-137	Teapot, 6 cup	500.00	400.00	350.00

PINK CLOVER

Although this pattern is the pink colourway of **Summer Glory** and is found with that back stamp, the American Shelley Group are using this name which was found in a 1964 Edward Walker Company sales catalogue. This is one of the most popular Shelley chintzes in North America and found more often than the other colourway. See **Summer Glory** (page 172).

Cat. No.	Shape	U.S. $	Can. $	U.K. £
PiC-01	Ashtray, small	95.00	65.00	60.00
PiC-02	Ashtray, large	100.00	90.00	60.00
PiC-04	Bonbon dish	75.00	65.00	50.00
PiC-05	Bonbon dish, tab handles	75.00	65.00	50.00
PiC-36	Cake plate	225.00	175.00	150.00
PiC-55	Coffee pot, 6 cup	500.00	350.00	350.00
PiC-70	Cream and sugar	150.00	125.00	100.00
PiC-98	Pin tray, small	95.00	65.00	60.00
PiC-104	Plate, 8"	100.00	65.00	60.00
PiC-130	Teacup and saucer	125.00	70.00	85.00
PiC-130	Teacup/saucer, Oleander	150.00	85.00	100.00
PiC-137	Teapot, 6 cup	500.00	375.00	350.00

PRIMROSE

This pattern appears on more cup shapes than any other Shelley chintz but is not particularly popular with American collectors. The cup typically has a pink handle and a light yellow interior.

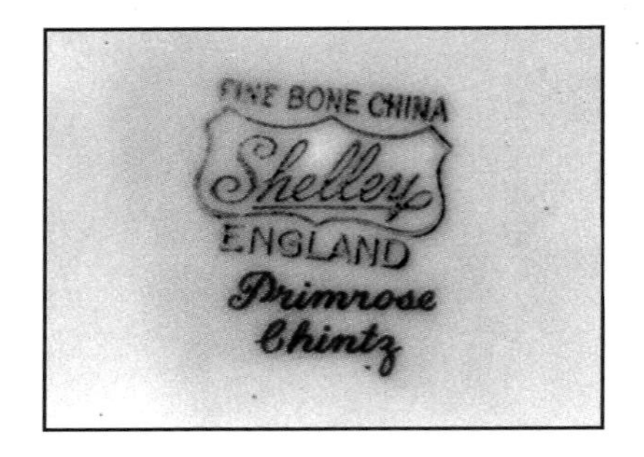

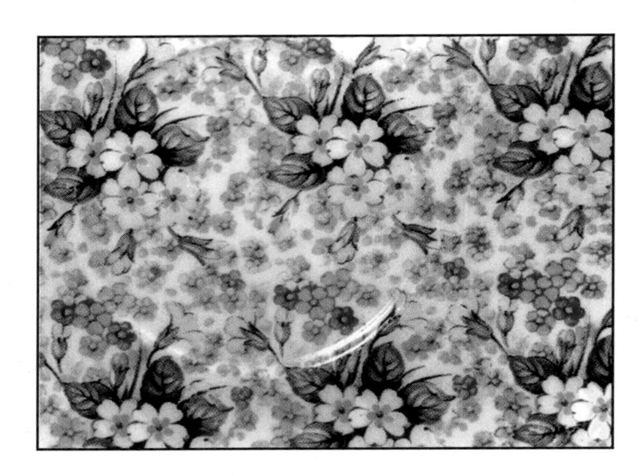

Cat. No.	Shape	U.S. $	Can. $	U.K. £
Pri-01	Ashtray, small	65.00	55.00	40.00
Pri-02	Ashtray, large	85.00	70.00	60.00
Pri-04	Bonbon dish	60.00	50.00	40.00
Pri-05	Bonbon dish, tab handles	60.00	50.00	40.00
Pri-36	Cake plate	165.00	160.00	100.00
Pri-55	Coffee pot, 6 cup	325.00	275.00	250.00
Pri-70	Cream and sugar	125.00	135.00	75.00
Pri-98	Pin tray, small	75.00	60.00	45.00
Pri-104	Plate, 8"	75.00	65.00	45.00
Pri-130	Teacup and saucer	95.00	65.00	50.00
Pri-130	Teacup/ saucer, Oleander	115.00	95.00	65.00
Pri-137	Teapot, 6 cup	375.00	325.00	225.00

ROCK GARDEN

This pattern is difficult to find in England and it is considered one of the most desirable chintz patterns to Shelley collectors.

Cat. No.	Shape	U.S. $	Can. $	U.K. £
RG-01	Ashtray, small	100.00	70.00	60.00
RG-02	Ashtray, large	120.00	95.00	70.00
RG-04	Bonbon dish	80.00	65.00	45.00
RG-05	Bonbon dish, tab handles	80.00	65.00	45.00
RG-36	Cake plate	200.00	175.00	125.00
RG-55	Coffee pot, 6 cup	450.00	325.00	300.00
RG-70	Cream and sugar	150.00	145.00	100.00
RG-98	Pin tray, small	100.00	75.00	75.00
RG-104	Plate, 8″	110.00	75.00	75.00
RG-130	Teacup and saucer	125.00	85.00	85.00
RG-130	Teacup/saucer, Oleander	150.00	115.00	100.00
RG-137	Teapot, 6 cup	500.00	375.00	350.00

SUMMER GLORY

This pattern is very popular with North American Shelley chintz collectors. See **Pink Clover** (page 169) for the alternate colourway.

Cat. No.	Shape	U.S. $	Can. $	U.K. £
SuG-01	Ashtray, small	85.00	65.00	45.00
SuG-02	Ashtray, large	95.00	95.00	50.00
SuG-04	Bonbon dish	70.00	65.00	40.00
SuG-05	Bonbon dish, tab handles	70.00	65.00	40.00
SuG-36	Cake plate	185.00	175.00	125.00
SuG-55	Coffee pot, 6 cup	450.00	325.00	300.00

Cat. No.	Shape	U.S. $	Can. $	U.K. £
SuG-70	Cream and sugar	140.00	145.00	75.00
SuG-98	Pin tray, small	85.00	75.00	50.00
SuG-104	Plate, 8"	90.00	75.00	50.00
SuG-130	Teacup and saucer	115.00	85.00	70.00
SuG-130	Teacup/saucer, Oleander	145.00	115.00	75.00
SuG-137	Teapot, 6 cup	450.00	350.00	350.00

TAPESTRY ROSE

This pattern is one of the later Shelley chintzes and does not appear to have been widely used on different shapes. The pattern came in two colourways, burgundy and yellow.

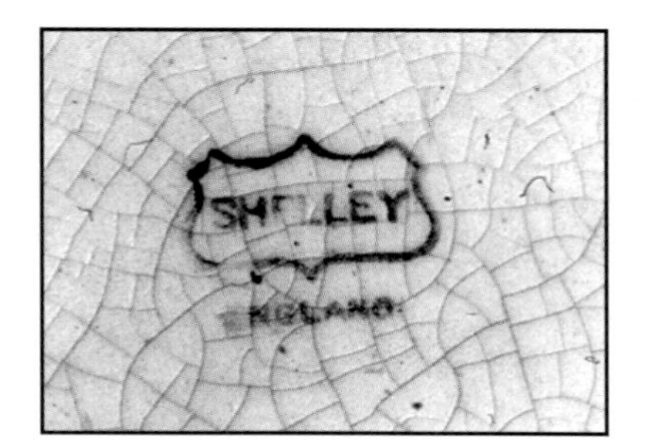

Cat. No.	Shape	U.S. $	Can. $	U.K. £
TR-01	Ashtray, small	55.00	40.00	30.00
TR-02	Ashtray, large	80.00	65.00	50.00
TR-04	Bonbon dish	50.00	45.00	40.00
TR-05	Bonbon dish, tab handles	50.00	45.00	40.00
TR-36	Cake plate	150.00	125.00	100.00
TR-55	Coffee pot, 6 cup	200.00	175.00	125.00
TR-70	Cream and sugar	100.00	75.00	60.00
TR-98	Pin tray, small	75.00	50.00	50.00
TR-104	Plate, 8"	65.00	50.00	40.00
TR-130	Teacup and saucer	75.00	60.00	50.00
TR-130	Teacup/ saucer, Oleander	100.00	85.00	60.00
TR-137	Teapot, 6 cup	300.00	225.00	175.00

Looking forward to the day when the present limitations on coloured china will be lifted, we have prepared many attractive and colourful designs in keeping with our high traditions. Maytime ware illustrated above is one of the very wide range which will be offered to bring colour, grace and harmony to the post-war table.

Shelley
FINE BONE
CHINA

SHELLEY POTTERIES LTD., LONGTON, STOKE-ON-TRENT

Stockists: British Ceramics and Crystal Limited, 7 Wellington Street West, Toronto

WADE CERAMICS LTD.

The original company was founded in 1810 and made pottery fittings for shuttles and textile machinery. The firm was bought by George Wade just after the turn of the century. The Wade Group of Potteries came into existence in the mid 1950s; prior to that time there were a number of individually owned companies with members of the Wade family or their friends in control. The only all-over pattern that Wade appears to have done in the 1920s was the open stock **Paisley** pattern used by many other companies, including Grimwades. In the 1950s the Wade Group offered two chintz patterns among a group of 18 transfer-type patterns available in tea ware and dinner ware on the Orb shape.

The Wade Group's combination of giftwares and industrial products, such as gas refactories and high alumina bodies used in micro-electronic and nuclear fields, have helped them to survive through several recessions in the pottery industry.

"BUTTERFLY CHINTZ"

This pattern was one of two chintz patterns available on a complete range of tablewares in the mid 1950s.

Cat. No.	Shape	U.S. $	Can. $	U.K. £
Bu-103	Plate, 6"	60.00	40.00	35.00
Bu-104	Plate, 7"	75.00	60.00	45.00

Cat. No.	Shape	U.S. $	Can. $	U.K. £
Bu-130	Teacup and saucer	75.00	50.00	45.00

PAISLEY

This pattern was also produced by Grimwades Ltd. **Paisley** is often sought after by Wade collectors rather than Chintz collectors.

Cat. No.	Shape	U.S. $	Can. $	U.K. £
Pai-103	Plate, 6"	60.00	35.00	35.00
Pai-104	Plate, 7"	75.00	55.00	45.00

Cat. No.	Shape	U.S. $	Can. $	U.K. £
Pai-130	Teacup and saucer	75.00	45.00	45.00

THISTLE CHINTZ

This pattern was one of two chintz patterns available on a complete range of tablewares in the mid 1950s.

Cat. No.	Shape	U.S. $	Can. $	U.K. £
Th-103	Plate, 6"	60.00	35.00	35.00
Th-104	Plate, 7"	75.00	55.00	45.00

Cat. No.	Shape	U.S. $	Can. $	U.K. £
Th-130	Teacup and saucer	75.00	45.00	45.00

WEDGWOOD & COMPANY LTD.

The firm was formerly Podmore, Walker & Co. but renamed Wedgwood & Company in 1860. They were housed at the Unicorn and Pinnox Works in Tunstall and as a result, a number of the backstamps over the years have included a unicorn. They were an undistinguished firm who produced a broad range of domestic earthenware. In 1932 they launched a new shape called Farnol which was almost an exact copy of Shelley's Eve shape. In similar fashion they produced several chintzes in the thirties, several years after the leading firms had established the market. The firm was renamed Enoch Wedgwood (Tunstall) Ltd. in 1965. Ironically they acquired A.G. Richardson & Company in 1974 only to be taken over in their turn by the Wedgwood Group in 1980 and renamed the Unicorn Pottery.

UNKNOWN

This pattern probably dates to about 1936 since both the Wedgwood chintzes were found on the same page in the Capper Rataud pattern books along with several of the Royal Winton chintzes dating to the middle of the 1930s.

Backstamp not available
at
press time

Cat. No.	Shape	U.S. $	Can. $	U.K. £
WC1-120	Sandwich Tray	150.00	95.00	100.00
WC1-130	Teacup and saucer	60.00	45.00	40.00

Cat. No.	Shape	U.S. $	Can. $	U.K. £
WC1-205	Plate, 8″	100.00	50.00	65.00

UNKNOWN

This pattern probably dates to about 1936 since both the Wedgwood chintzes were found on the same page in the Capper Rataud pattern books along with several of the Royal Winton chintzes dating to the middle of the 1930s.

Backstamp not available
at
press time

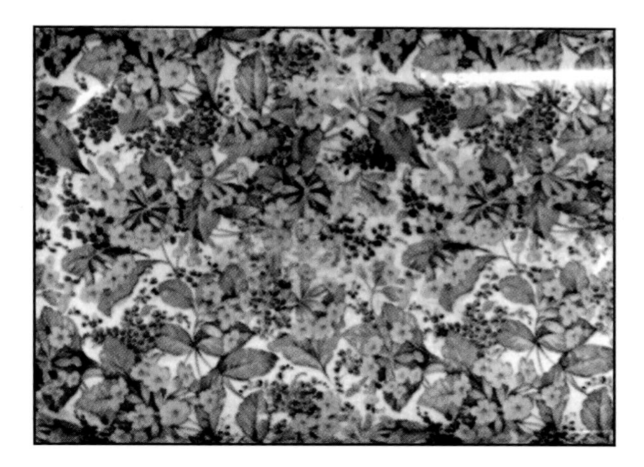

Cat. No.	Shape	U.S. $	Can. $	U.K. £
WC2-120	Sandwich Tray	145.00	95.00	100.00
WC2-130	Teacup and saucer	55.00	45.00	40.00

Cat. No.	Shape	U.S. $	Can. $	U.K. £
WC2-205	Plate, 8″	95.00	50.00	60.00

A. J. WILKINSON, LTD.

Arthur J. Wilkinson set up his earthenware factory in Burslem in 1885. His brother-in-law Arthur Shorter had some years before started a factory in Stoke-upon-Trent. When, six years later, Wilkinson fell to his death while on holiday in Switzerland, Shorter was appointed to manage the Burslem factory. Three years later he bought the firm of A. J. Wilkinson. Around the turn of the century, his son Colley was sent to Wilkinson's and shortly thereafter his second son Guy went to Shorter & Sons. Wilkinsons became known for medium priced earthenwares which were marketed under the name of Royal Staffordshire and included a full range of tablewares, toilet ware and ornamental lines. An early mention of the firm in *The Pottery Gazette* April 2, 1917 commended them for their enterprise and concluded that "A.J. Wilkinson have been successful in securing some superior specimens of litho work for their dinnerware." They show several pictures of an early chintz called **Rose and Trellis** which is very like the A.G. Richardson and Grimwades chintzes of the same period. In 1919 Wilkinson are mentioned in the *Glass Trade Review* as "makers of a grade of earthenware which plays a very definite part in the middle-class trade, not only of our own country merely, but in the majority of the leading export markets of the world."

In 1926 Wilkinson were reported to claim "to have one of the most representative ranges in the trade of useful and decorative earthenware." At the same time as Clarice Cliff was beginning to handpaint visible brush strokes of orange and blue paint on a warehouse full of abandoned ware at the Newport Pottery (bought by Wilkinson in 1920), *The Gazette* was commending the firm for the **Mayflower** chintz which "we should regard as a good provincial or suburban line. We do not suggest that it will sell briskly in the city, though one never knows." As the twenties continued and Clarice's work was eagerly sought around the country, more and more of the resources of the firm went in the direction of handpainted deco ceramics. Whenever one thinks of Wilkinson's today it is immediately Clarice Cliff who comes to mind, although they produced a number of interesting chintzes as part of their overall line.

The strangest designs are the combination of the very modern Clarice shape — like the cup on the artist's palette tray — with a traditional chintz although "**Modern Mayflower**" is clearly an attempt to update the 1920s **Mayflower.** The 1950s versions of some of the chintzes are a startling attempt to find a new way to attract buyers once it became clear that post-war housewives were looking for something different.

In 1964 Clarice Cliff sold A.J. Wilkinson and Newport Pottery to W.R. Midwinter. and in 1970 the combined firm was taken over by the Wedgwood Group.

MAYFLOWER

The first appearance of this pattern was numbered 7929. The September 1, 1926 Gazette reported that, "one of the finest lithographic patterns which has been put on the market for some time as regards effect and colouring is probably the "Mayflower" pattern, which the firm under notice brought out last spring . . . the effect of the lithograph itself is to portray a feeling of brushwork and extension, the design being intended to create an impression of a meadow in Maytime."

Cat. No.	Shape	U.S. $	Can. $	U.K. £
Maf-405	Plate, 8" octagonal	75.00	65.00	40.00
Maf-120	Sandwich Tray	125.00	95.00	75.00

Cat. No.	Shape	U.S. $	Can. $	U.K. £
Maf-145	Tennis Set	85.00	75.00	50.00

"MODERN MAYFLOWER"

Although little is known about this pattern to date, it seems to be an updated version of **Mayflower** and it appears on modern 1950s shapes and has a Royal Staffordshire Ceramics backstamp associated with the 1950s. The bright oranges and modern look make it unpopular with traditional chintz collectors.

Backstamp not available
at
press time

Cat. No.	Shape	U.S. $	Can. $	U.K. £
MM-405	Plate, 8" octagonal	60.00	50.00	35.00
MM-120	Sandwich Tray	95.00	75.00	65.00

Cat. No.	Shape	U.S. $	Can. $	U.K. £
MM-145	Tennis Set	75.00	65.00	40.00

060. TEAPOT "HASTINGS"
061. SUGAR "HASTINGS"
062. CREAM "HASTINGS"
063. TEA & SAUCER "HASTINGS"
064. TEA PLATE "ASCOT"
066. BRIDGE CREAM "STUART"
065. BRIDGE SUGAR "STUART"
068. BRIDGE SUGAR "COUNTESS"
067. TEAPOT "COUNTESS"
069. BRIDGE CREAM COUNTESS
070. BRIDGE SUGAR "GRECIAN"
071. BRIDGE CREAM "GRECIAN"
BRIDGE
NORMAN
077. BR
CREAM
"HECTOR"
073. BRIDGE SUGAR "NORMAN"
074. BRIDGE SUGAR "ASCOT"
076. TEAPOT "ASCOT"
075. BRIDGE CREAM "ASCOT"
078. BRIDGE SUGAR "HECTOR"
079. TEAPOT STAND "ASCOT"
081 EGGCUP FAST STAND PLAIN
082 EGGCUP FOOTED PLAIN
083. EGGCUP FAST STAND "ASCOT"
080. TEAPOT STAND ROUND
084. TEA & SAUCER TALL "ASCOT"
085 COVERED JUG "SEXTA"
086. TOAST RACK 3 BAR "QUEEN"
087. COVERED JUG "COUNTESS"
088. TEA & SAUCER "KING"
089. COFFEE & SAUCER "CAN"
090. COFFEE & SAUCER "ASCOT"
091 BEAKER HANDLED "STRAIGHT"
093 BON-BON HANDLED "OCTAGON"
095. COVERED MUFFIN "COUNTESS"
094 BON-BON UNHANDLED "OCTAGON"
092. BEAKER UNHANDLED "STRAIGHT"

WOOD & SONS LTD.

The name of Wood stretches back seven generations in the pottery industry in Staffordshire. In 1865 Thomas Wood established the present firm of Wood and Sons and he built it into one of the largest manufacturers of earthenwares and ironstones in the area. H.J. Wood joined the firm in 1889 and he was an outstanding businessman. He had working relationships with many of the leading designers of the day. He brought Frederick Rhead into the firm in 1912 as art director and Rhead's daughter Charlotte joined him and worked for Wood and Sons until the mid twenties. The company produced such good quality whiteware that a number of firms including A.E. Gray and subsequently Susie Cooper bought in their wares.

As early as 1931 the firm was experimenting with colourful lithograph patterns for their Ivory Ware and may have produced several all-over florals around this time. The association with Susie Cooper and her very different approach to the use of lithos probably steered Wood & Sons away from any involvement in the production of chintz ware. The factory finally passed out of the family in the early 1980s but the name was retained.

UNKNOWN

This pattern is rarely found in North America and eagerly sought by collectors.

Cat. No.	Shape	U.S. $	Can. $	U.K. £
WS-103	Plate, 6″	75.00	50.00	45.00

Cat. No.	Shape	U.S. $	Can. $	U.K. £
WS-130	Teacup and saucer	125.00	75.00	75.00

SHAPES

Word descriptions of shapes are very difficult for most people to visualize so we have gathered as many different shapes as possible to demonstrate the various styles available. Whenever we think we have seen just about every shape, someone sends us a picture of something we have never seen before—the "Ash Box" ashtray covered in **Old Cottage Chintz**, the Rustic Hot Water Pot, the unknown **Hazel** toast rack, and the list goes on. Toni Cardwell's discovery of the 1936 Grimwades' Export Catalogue from Australia was of great value in identifying a number of unknown shapes and we have reproduced some of the more interesting pages. If the piece was large enough Grimwades usually impressed the shape name into the ceramic body. In many cases, however, the pieces were simply too small for this to be possible.

There were two versions made of the Athena shape. The second version, without the little piece on the handle, we have named Later Athena. These pieces were produced after the Second World War as an economy measure. The increasing use of the internet with accompanying pictures has made buying easier. If you are buying over the phone and are unsure about a shape, you may be wise to ask for a photograph. It is very easy to make mistakes.

Shape identification of pieces other than Royal Winton is a little more difficult. Although we have been able to identify a number of James Kent and Crown Ducal shapes, we have found nothing for most of the other companies. We have tried to include some of the more common shapes and we hope you will continue to send us clear photographs of pieces we have not illustrated, for use in the third edition. If you know the shape names for any of the shapes we have illustrated but not named, please let us know and we will be sure to include it in the next edition.

ELIJAH COTTON (LORD NELSON), MIDWINTER AND A.J. WILKINSON

Lord Nelson: Stacking Teapot, Demitasse (Royal Brocade), Stacking Teapot (Green Tulip), Jug (Green Tulip), Jug (Heather), Jug (Marina), Jug (Rosetime), Sauce Boat (Black Beauty)

Lord Nelson: Bud Vases (Marina, Heather, Rosetime, Marina), Tennis Set (Black Beauty), Relish Dish (Marina)

Midwinter: Biscuit Barrel (Springtime), Sugar Shaker (Lorna Doone), Vase (Lorna Doone), Covered Box (Springtime)

Midwinter: Coffee Pot (Springtime), Candlestick (Lorna Doone), Sardine Box (Springtime),
A.J. Wilkinson: Tennis Set ("Modern Mayflower")

ROYAL WINTON BASKETS AND COVERED BOXES

Dudley (Marion), Hampton (Hazel), Kew (Cotswold), Rosebud (Marion)

Rowsley (Shrewsbury), Rowsley (Morning Glory), Unknown (Somerset), Unknown (Somerset)

Candy Box (Joyce-Lynn), Candy Box (Hazel), Candy Box (Marion), Candy Box (English Rose), Lotus (Welbeck), Rosebud (Welbeck), Petunia (Triumph)

Chinese Jar Potpourri (Hazel), Gordon (Royalty), Olympic (Florence), Unknown (Summertime)

ROYAL WINTON BEDSIDE, BREAKFAST AND TENNIS SETS, CUPS

Ascot Bedside Set (Bedale), Countess Bedside Set (Stratford), Honeymoon Bedside Set (Julia), Lily Bedside Set (Welbeck),

York Bedside Set (June Roses), Unknown (Old Cottage Chintz), Honeymoon Set (Cheadle), Tennis Set (Old Cottage Chintz)

Tennis Set (Shrewsbury), Raleigh Teacup (English Rose), Tennis Set (Evesham), Irish Breakfast Cup (Crocus),
Raleigh Teacup (Somerset), Raleigh Breakfast Cup (Estelle)

1950s Raleigh Variation (Cotswold), Teacup (Cotswold), Teacup (Sweet Pea), Beaker (Hazel), Unhandled Beaker (Sweet Pea)

ROYAL WINTON BISCUIT BARRELS, CAKE PLATES AND SAUCE BOATS

Athena (Queen Anne), Rheims (OCC), Rheims (Marion), Rheims (Royalty), Unknown (Somerset)

Unknown (OCC), Unknown (OCC), Unknown (Royalty), Unknown (Hazel)

Ascot high (Hazel), Ascot low (Somerset), Two-Tier Cake Plate (Florence), Two-Tier Cake Plate (Sweet Pea)

Duchess (Sunshine), Era (Old Cottage Chintz), Later Athena Gravy Boat (OCC), Rosebud (Welbeck)

ROYAL WINTON BUTTER DISHES, CHEESE KEEPS, JAM POTS

Ascot Square Butter (Hazel), Ascot Rectangular Butter (Welbeck), Unknown (OCC), Dane Cheese Large (Delphinium Chintz), Dane Cheese Small (Evesham), Marvel Cheese (Old Cottage Chintz), Rex Cheese (Spring)

Ascot (Florence), Ascot (Julia), Athena (Julia), Chelsea (Balmoral), Chelsea [missing underplate] (Mayfair)

Chelsea [with attached stand] (Royalty), Ninevah (Kinver), Norman (Hazel), Rheims [missing underplate] (Old Cottage Chintz), Rheims Tall (Old Cottage Chintz)

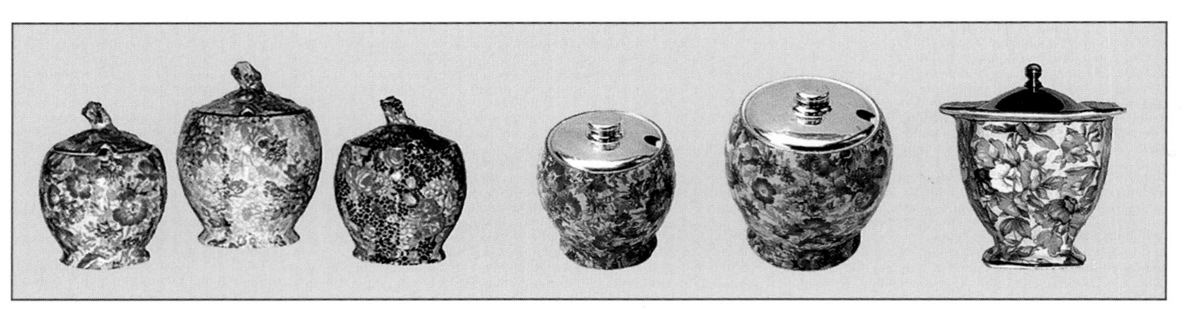

Rosebud (Royalty), (Welbeck), (Hazel), Rosebud base with plated lid (Royalty), (Royalty), Unknown (Sweet Pea)

ROYAL WINTON BOWLS AND DISHES

Crown (Marguerite), Ely (Marion), Fife (Somerset), King (Summertime), Unknown (Cheadle)

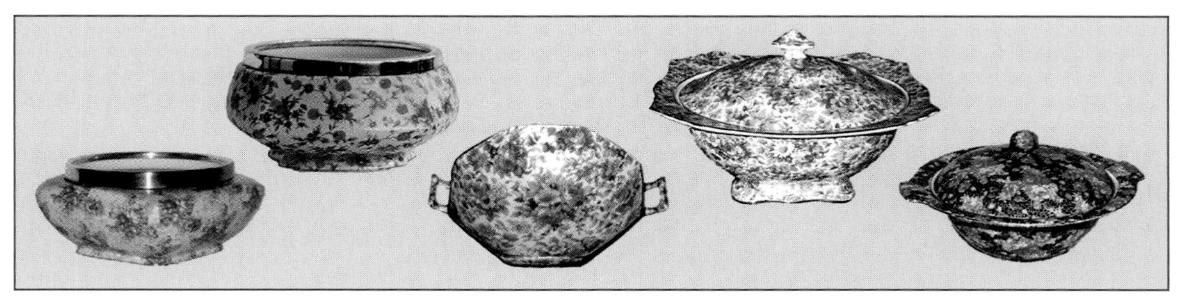

Rheims (Welbeck), Unknown (Old Cottage Chintz), Octagon (Summertime), Ascot (Summertime), Unknown (Hazel)

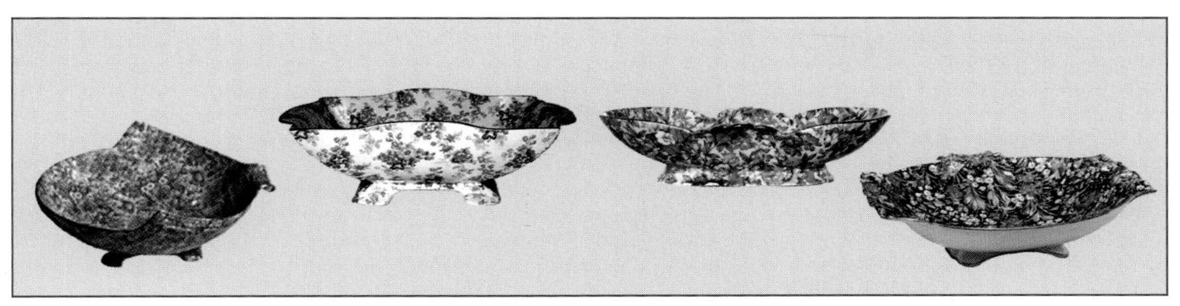

Bude (Sunshine), Corfe (Cotswold), Unknown (Sweet Pea), Unknown (Triumph)

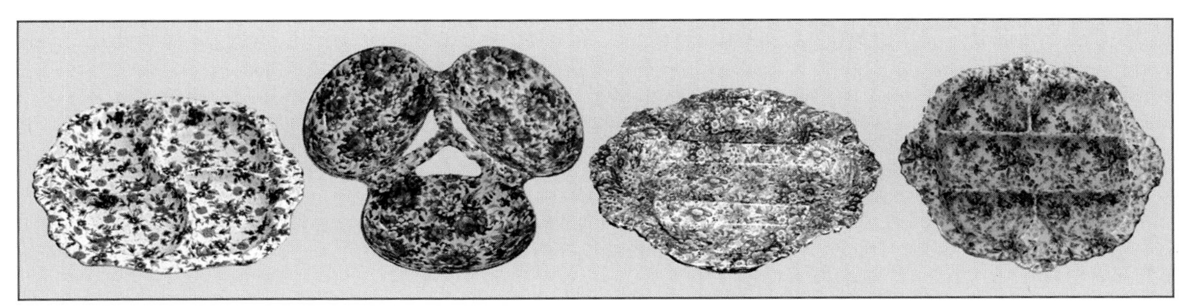

Ascot 4-part (Old Cottage Chintz), Gem (Summertime), Marina 3-part (Sunshine), Marina 5-part (Floral Feast)

ROYAL WINTON DISHES AND PLATES

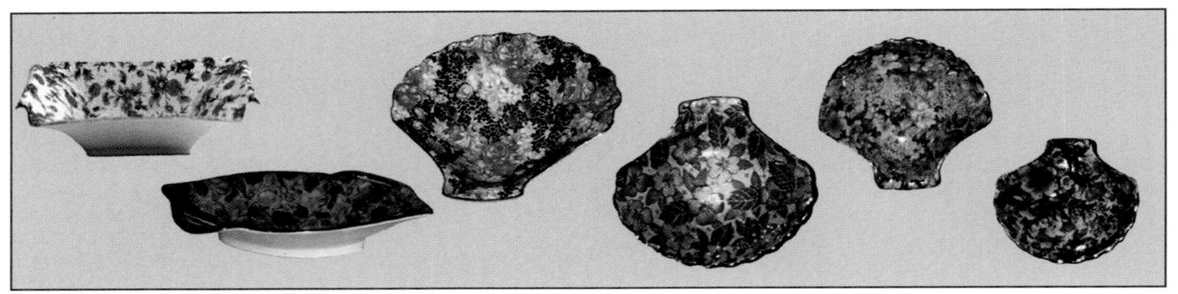

Kipling (Old Cottage Chintz), Unknown (Stratford), Shell (Hazel), Shell 4 1/2" (Clyde), Shell 4" (Marion), Shell 3" (Sunshine)

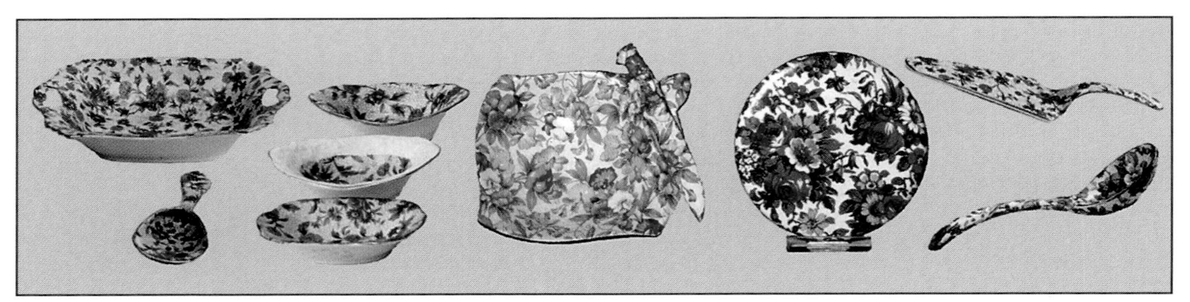

Large Nut Dish and Scoop, Nut Dishes (Old Cottage Chintz), Rosebud Scone Set (Sweet Pea), Coaster (Summertime), Mayonnaise Set Spoon (Summertime), Pie Server (Old Cottage Chintz)

Unknown (Royalty), Unknown (Evesham), Saville (Triumph), Unknown (Triumph), Unknown (Hazel)

Wedgwood Border (Bedale), Wedgwood Border (Beeston), Ascot (June Roses), Athena (Bedale), Athena (Summertime)

ROYAL WINTON BUD VASES, VASES AND CANDLESTICKS

Neme (Julia), Unknown (Peony), Clywd (Sweet Nancy), Etona (Spring), (Sunshine), (Floral Feast), (Welbeck), (Victorian)

Gem (Majestic), (Evesham), (OCC), (Floral Garden), Tudor (Cotswold), (OCC), (Summertime), Lune (Peony)

Savoy (Welbeck), Avon (Welbeck), Capri (Summertime), Melbourne (Hazel), Ming (Hazel),
Snowdrop (Sweet Pea), (Hazel), (Royalty)

Greek Candlesticks (Hazel), Octron Candlesticks (Summertime), Candlesticks (Julia)

ROYAL WINTON COFFEE POTS AND TEAPOTS

Ascot (Hazel), Albans (Julia), Greek (June Roses), Norman (Rutland), Perth (Hazel)

Ajax (Spring), Albans (Evesham), Ascot (Stratford), Ascot (Joyce-Lynn), Countess (Sweet Pea)

Delamere (Julia), Elite (June Roses), Hastings (Rose du Barry), Later Athena (Sunshine), Rosebud (Welbeck)

Sexta (Sweet Pea), Sylva (Old Cottage Chintz), Unknown (Hazel), Unknown (Hazel), Unknown (Triumph)

ROYAL WINTON CREAM & SUGAR AND HOT WATER POTS

Albans (Florence), Ascot (Majestic), Athena (Hazel), Hector (Somerset)

Countess (Sweet Pea), Elite (Old Cottage Chintz), Grecian (Hazel), Jacobean (June Roses)

Later Athena (Old Cottage Chintz), Royalty (Norman), Stuart (Victorian), Ventnor (Peony)

Albans (Mayfair), Countess (Summertime), Rustic (Old Cottage Chintz), Sexta (Hazel), Sexta Variation (Old Cottage Chintz)

ROYAL WINTON EGGCUPS, SALT & PEPPER AND TOAST RACKS

Bucket Eggcup (Welbeck), Double Eggcup (Summertime), Footed Square Eggcup (Hazel), Plain Eggcup (Julia), Ascot Egg Cruet Set (Wildflowers)

Athena Set (Spring), Saville Eggset (Welbeck), Acme Cruet Set (Hazel), Fife Cruet Set (Stratford)

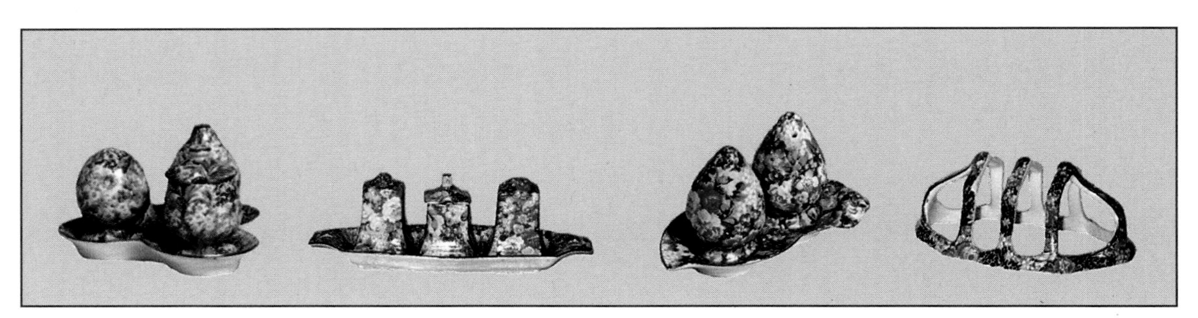

Clover Leaf Cruet Set (Crocus), Fife Cruet Set (Julia), Lily Cruet Set (Julia), Toast Rack (Hazel)

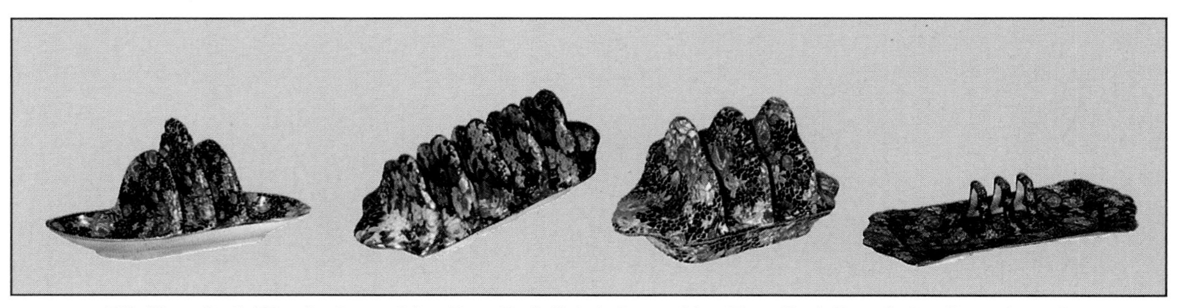

Lily Toast Rack (Hazel), Queen 5-bar Toast Rack (Julia), Queen 3-bar Toast Rack (Hazel), Saville Set (Hazel)

ROYAL WINTON JUGS

Albans (Kew), Albans (Evesham), Albans (Nantwich), Albans (Julia), Cambridge (Welbeck), Delius (Wild Flowers)

Dutch (Cranstone), Dutch (Summertime), Dutch (Fireglow), Duval (Hazel), Diamond (Florence)

Globe (English Rose), Globe (Sweet Pea), Isis (Welbeck), Later Athena (Estelle), Lily (Sweet Pea)

Raleigh (Marion), Rosebud (Royalty), Shetland (Julia), Ventnor (Majestic), Unknown (Old Cottage Chintz)

ROYAL WINTON RARE SHAPES

Lamp Bases: (Cotswold), (Esther), (Pekin), Eden (Summertime)

Lamp Base (Summertime), Lavebo (Victorian Rose), Dora Wall Pocket (Marion), Nita Wall Pocket (May Festival)

Clock (Summertime), Pyramid Ash Box (Old Cottage Chintz), Lighter (Cheadle), Lily Comport with tray (Summertime)

Bell (Old Cottage Chintz), Fife Sugar Shaker (Somerset), Sugar Shaker (OCC), Rosebud Sugar Shaker (Welbeck)

JAMES KENT

Cream and Sugar (Apple Blossom), Kent Cream and Sugar (Mille Fleurs), Cream and Sugar on Tray (Du Barry), Granville Jug (Du Barry), York Jug (Primula)

Teapot (Apple Blossom), Toast Rack (Hydrangea), Diamond Teapot (Du Barry), Granville Cocoa Pot (Du Barry), Melville Teapot (Du Barry), Tudor Teapot (Apple Blossom)

Breakfast Set, Diamond Cruet Set, Diamond Honey Pot, Granville Honey Pot with Fast Stand, Granville Butter Dish, Kent Cheese Keep (All Du Barry)

Eggcup Set (Du Barry), Cup and Saucer (Du Barry, Hydrangea Black), Bud Vase (Rapture), Vase (Hydrangea Black), Bud Vase (Hydrangea), Dish (Hydrangea), Dish (Du Barry)

A.G. RICHARDSON (CROWN DUCAL)

Candlesticks (Blue Chintz), Candlesticks (Marigold), Vase (Pink Chintz), Rose Bowl # 4 (Festival)

Vases: (Blue Chintz), (Florida), (Rose & Motifs), (Ivory Chintz), (Ivory Chintz)

Vase (Festival), Vase (Purple Chintz), Bud Vase (Blue Chintz), Vase (Florida), Fan Vase (Festival)

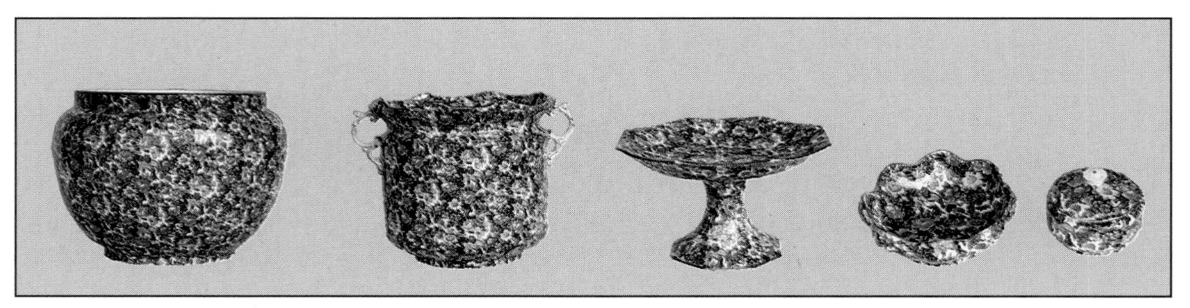

Rounded Jardinere, Jardinere, Footed Compote, Bowl, Covered Bowl (All Ivory Chintz),

A.G. RICHARDSON (CROWN DUCAL)

Jug (Peony), Jug (Blue Chintz), Biscuit Barrel (Florida), Biscuit Barrel (Florida)

Teapot (Blue Chintz), Chocolate Pot (Florida), Teapot (Primula), Victorian Coffee Pot (Pink Chintz), Victorian Teapot (Ascot)

Lily Bowl (Blue Chintz), Cedric Salad Bowl (Roseland), Bowl (Florida), Bowl (Blue Chintz), Salad Bowl and Servers (Peony)

Cup and Saucer, Demi Tasse, Tennis Set (Florida), Victory Cup and Saucer (Peony), Victorian Cream and Sugar (Ascot)

A.G. RICHARDSON (CROWN DUCAL)

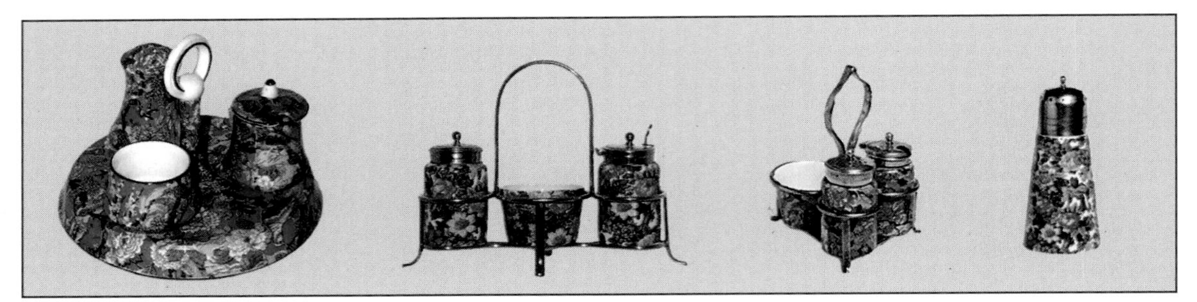

Cruet (Blue Chintz), Cruet (Ivory Chintz), Cruet (Blue Chintz), Sugar Shaker (Ivory Chintz)

Eggcup Set (Pink Chintz), Jam Pot (Blue Chintz), Jam Pot (Florida), Jam Pot (Florida), Butter Dish (Florida)

Reamer (Spring Blossom), Breakfast Set (Peony), Mayonnaise Bowl (Florida), Ladle (Peony)

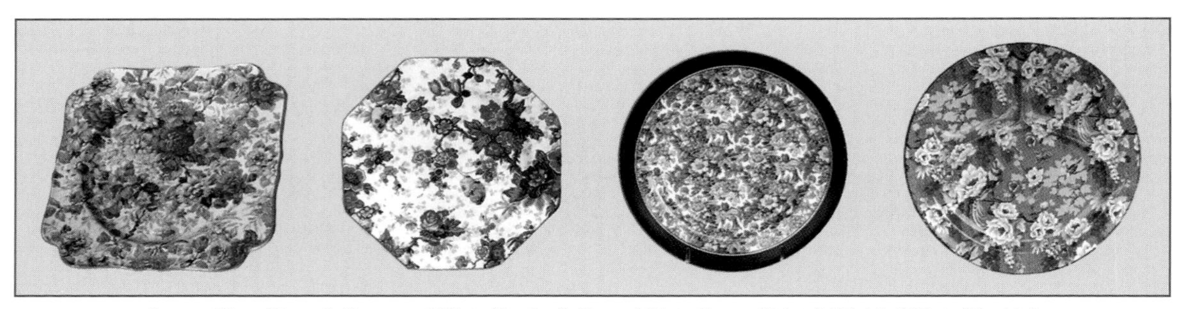

Square Plate (Peony), Octagonal Plate (Festival), Round Plate (Ivory Chintz), Divided Plate (Florida)

SHELLEY

Richmond Teapot (Rock Garden), Richmond Cream and Sugar (Rock Garden), Teapot (Maytime)

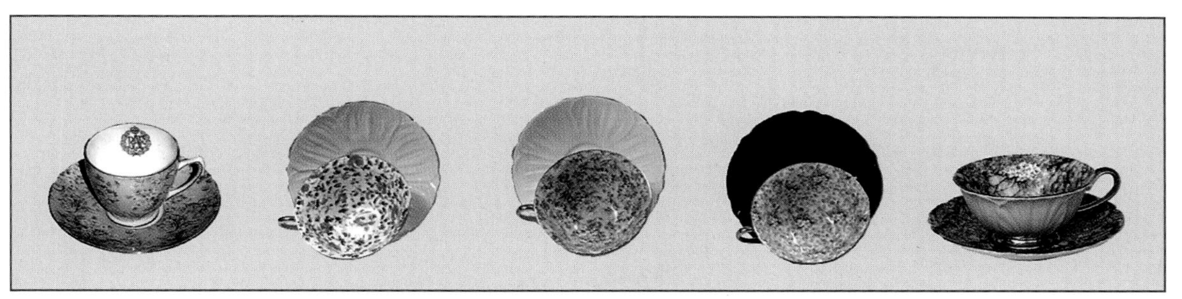

Cup and Saucer (Melody), Oleander Cups and Saucers: (Briar Rose, Marguerite, Primrose), Reverse Pattern Oleander Cup and Saucer (Rock Garden)

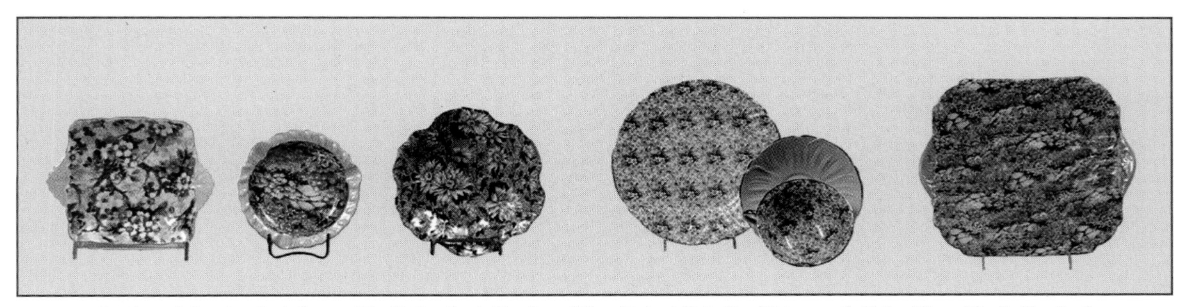

Bonbon (Maytime), Ashtray (Rock Garden), Bonbon (Blue Daisy) Trio Set (Primrose), Cake Plate (Rock Garden)

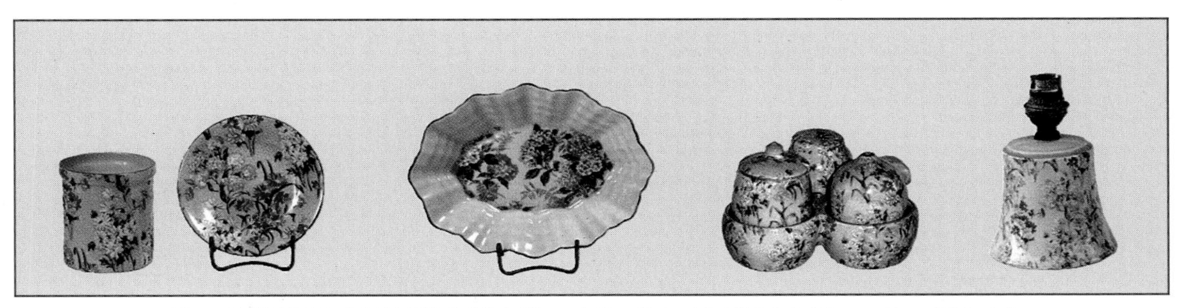

Cigarette Set (Melody), Nut Dish (Pink Clover), Condiment Set (Melody), Lamp Base (Melody)

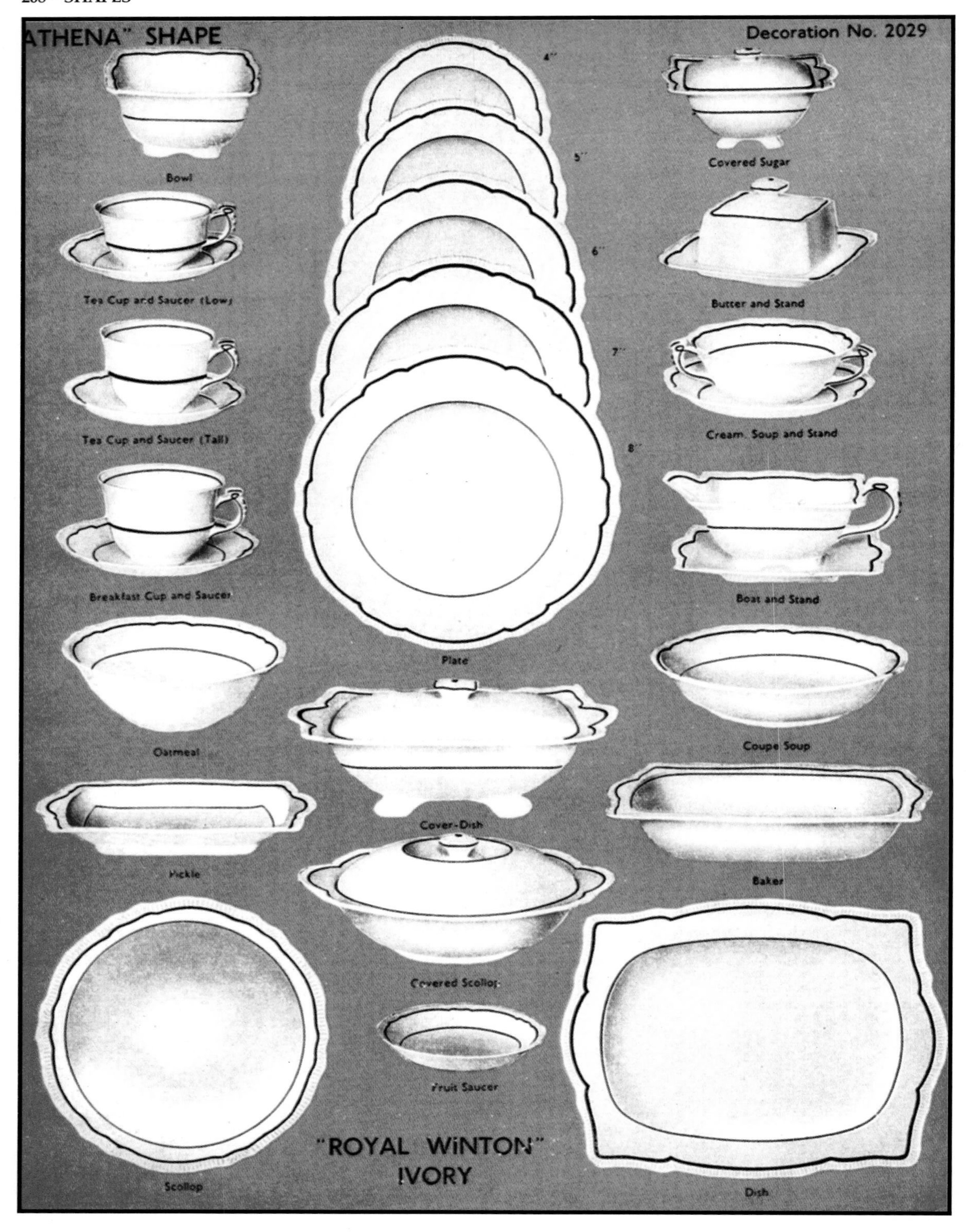
ATHENA" SHAPE
Decoration No. 2029
Bowl
4"
5"
6"
7"
8"
Covered Sugar
Butter and Stand
Tea Cup and Saucer (Low)
Tea Cup and Saucer (Tall)
Cream Soup and Stand
Breakfast Cup and Saucer
Boat and Stand
Plate
Oatmeal
Coupe Soup
Cover-Dish
Pickle
Baker
Covered Scollop
Fruit Saucer
"ROYAL WiNTON"
IVORY
Scollop
Dish

"ASCOT" SHAPE (Reg. No. 768985).
Decoration 3459.
Covered Sugar
Fruit Saucer
Individual Butter Pad
Cream
3"
4"
5"
6"
7"
8"
Bowl
Coupe Soup
Cream, Soup & Stand
Teacup and Saucer (Tall)
Plate
Sauce Boat
Oatmeal
Pickle or Boat Stand
Covered Vegetable Dish
Low Comport
Dish
"ROYAL WINTON" IVORY.
Scollop

GRIMWADES LTD., Winton Pottery, Stoke-on-Trent.
DUCHESS 9988.
ETON 9969.
HECTOR 9737.
HECTOR 9749.
ASCOT 1080.
ASCOT 1094.
London Show Rooms—Atlantic House (3rd floor by lift), 45 to 50, Holborn Viaduct, E.C. 1.

040. SWEET "HOLBORN"
041. SWEET "BOW"
042. OATMEAL
043. MINT BOAT & STAND "ERA"
044. LOW COMPORT "ASCOT"
045. CHOCOLATE COMPORT "LILY"
046. FOOTED NUT "BOW"
047. JUG "CAMBRIDGE"
048. JUG "GLOBE"
049. COFFEEPOT "PERTH"
050. CHOCOLATE COMPORT "GREEK"
051. CHOCOLATE COMPORT "ETON"
052. JUG "DUVAL"
053. JUG "GRAFTON"
054. CAKE PLATE HANDLED "ASCOT"
055. COFFEEPOT "NORMAN"
056. COFFEEPOT "GREEK"
057. BOWL "FIFE"
058. PLATE "ASCOT"
059. BOWL "KING"

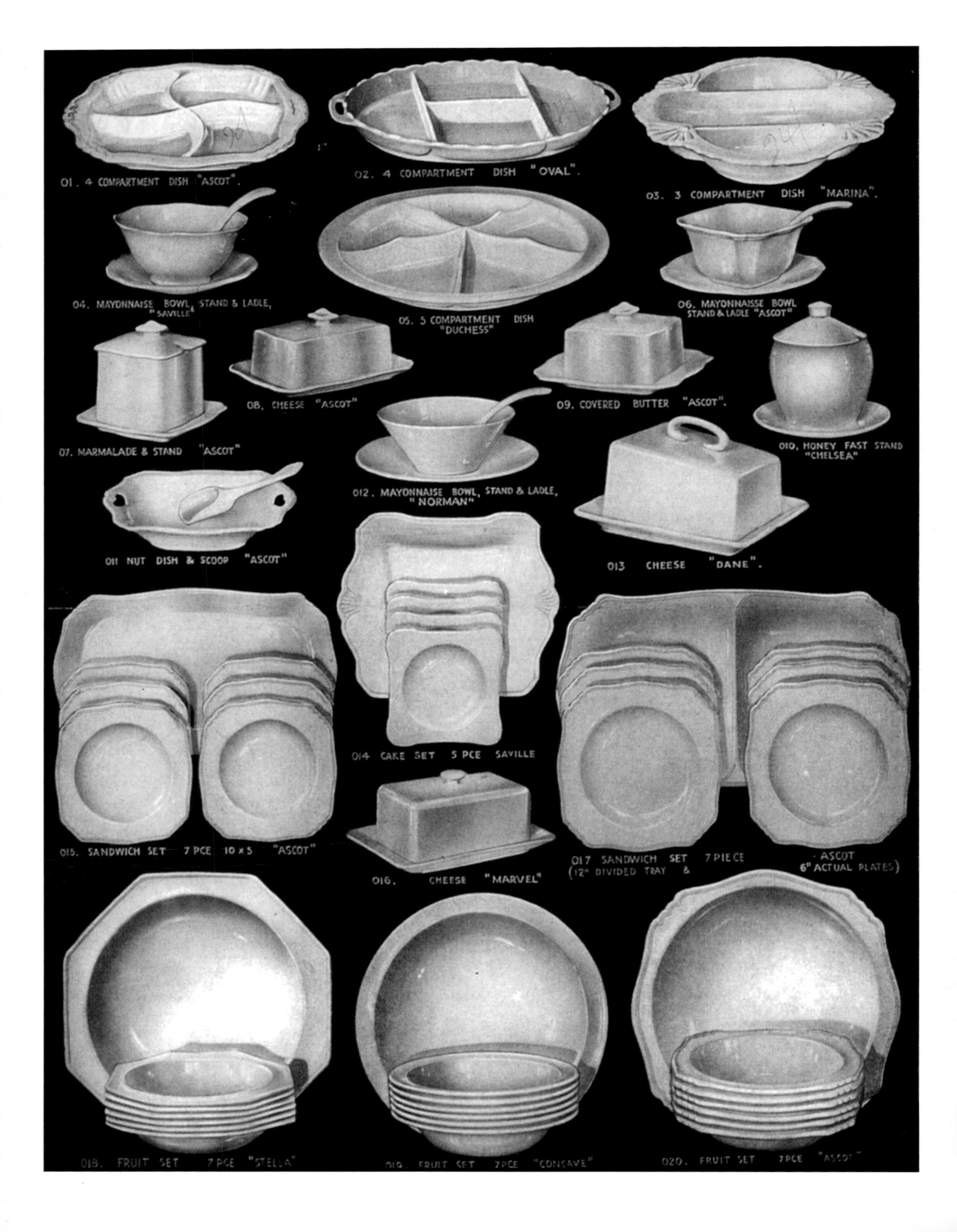

O1. 4 COMPARTMENT DISH "ASCOT".
O2. 4 COMPARTMENT DISH "OVAL".
O3. 3 COMPARTMENT DISH "MARINA".
O4. MAYONNAISE BOWL, STAND & LADLE, "SAVILLE"
O5. 5 COMPARTMENT DISH "DUCHESS"
O6. MAYONNAISSE BOWL STAND & LADLE "ASCOT"
O7. MARMALADE & STAND "ASCOT"
O8. CHEESE "ASCOT"
O9. COVERED BUTTER "ASCOT".
O10, HONEY FAST STAND "CHELSEA"
O11 NUT DISH & SCOOP "ASCOT"
O12. MAYONNAISE BOWL, STAND & LADLE, "NORMAN"
O13 CHEESE "DANE".
O14 CAKE SET 5 PCE SAVILLE
O15. SANDWICH SET 7 PCE 10 x 5 "ASCOT"
O16. CHEESE "MARVEL"
O17 SANDWICH SET 7 PIECE ASCOT (12" DIVIDED TRAY & 6" ACTUAL PLATES)
O18. FRUIT SET 7 PCE "STELLA"
O19. FRUIT SET 7 PCE "CONCAVE"
O20. FRUIT SET 7 PCE "ASCOT"

Pattern Index

Shape Index

LOOKING FOR CHINTZ?

We have the Largest Inventory in the United States

All Our Merchandise Is Guaranteed
Highest Prices Paid For Collections And Individual Pieces

OUR STOCK INCLUDES:

Bowls, Breakfast Sets, Butter Dishes, Cake Plates, Coffee Pots, Cream and Sugar, Jam Pots, Jugs, Nut Dishes,

No Lists Available

Specific Requests Please

If you're in the chintz market, you know its A Time For Antiques!

Whether you are looking to buy or sell Royal Winton, Shelley, James Kent, Lord Nelson or Crown Ducal,
you can be assured that you will find no selection larger than ours.

A Time For Antiques, Ltd.

P.O.Box7083, Buffalo, NY 14240

(716)885-2600